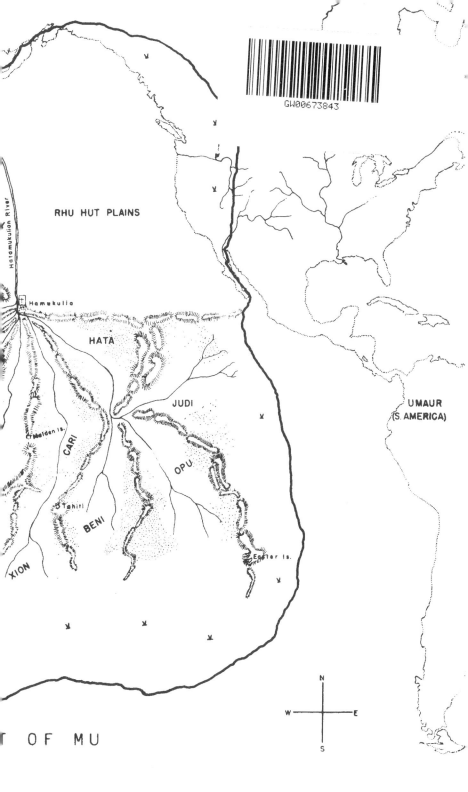

RHU HUT PLAINS

Hatamukulian River

† Hamakulia

HATA

JUDI

CARI

Malden Is.

Tahiti

OPU

BENI

Easter Is.

XION

UMAUR
(S. AMERICA)

N
W — E
S

OF MU

The story of the formation
of the first and greatest
civilization on this earth
as it actually occurred
78,000 years ago.

THE SUN RISES

by Dr. Robert D. Stelle

Illustrations by the author

Lemurian Fellowship
Ramona, California

Fourth Printing

Library of Congress Classification:

BF1999.S722   133   52-12452

Printed in the United States of America

CONTENTS

ILLUSTRATIONS

Chapter One

LORD LITHARGOS

AS SILENT as the fading night, a shadowy form crept through the brush, its nose close to the ground as it followed a faint trail made fainter by the heavy dew. Presently it crouched; then, as if released by a mighty spring, soared upward to light softly and with sinuous grace upon a granite boulder. Here it paused, its sensitive nostrils testing the air, its greenish eyes glowing even in that dim dawn light.

Some sixty paces to the southeast and down wind from it, with equal silence, a bronzed hand reached from beneath its furry covering, grasped a six-foot bow and drew it under the covers. Deft and powerful fingers slipped the bowstring into place, then slid the three-foot arrow from its quiver with the skill of long practice, notching it even as their owner's eyes strove to pierce the gloom and locate the beast whose odor alone had awakened him from his slumber.

With infinite care, the archer fairly oozed from beneath the cover lest any movement betray him to the great cat-like creature which might even then be preparing to launch itself upon him, for the scent was strong and the breeze light.

At this moment, the beast, an ancestor of our modern jaguar, raised its head and as it got to its feet the better to peer into the north, stood silhouetted against the graying sky. A split second later, it shot high into the air, its screeches starting echoes that intensified their agonized bestiality while the animal clawed frantically at the arrow transfixing its heart . . . . then crashed to the ground to thrash out its fading life.

With a sweep of his arm, the youth beside the archer tossed

aside his covering and was on his feet, an eighteen-inch obsidian knife held ready for any emergency.

"I got him, Hut," chuckled the archer striving to hold back the tremor in his voice and to appear far calmer than he really felt.

"Phew!" half-whistled Hut. "Judging from the noise, it must be full grown. Are you sure, Rhu, that it isn't simply wounded and stalking us?"

"The arrow pierced its heart!" Rhu could not quite restrain the note of pride in his voice. "It lies beside our rock," he added. "You should have seen it clawing at that arrow!"

"Probably spoiled it," the other grunted. "Come. Let's see what he looks like." As the two started forward, Hut abruptly hesitated when he observed Rhu notching another arrow. "Thought you said it was dead!" he grumbled.

"I think it is, but hoogwars die hard, and I take no chances."

"Hoogwar!" exclaimed Hut. "I'll bet that's what has been killing our sheep! I saw tracks, two suns back, that my two hands could not cover!"

By now the two were cautiously nearing the shadowy and still twitching body. "Don't get too close," cautioned Rhu. "That's how I got clawed up last year. My arrows weren't as good as these."

But their wariness proved unnecessary, for the great, spotted brute was dead and seizing it by the tail, with a prodigious jerk, Rhu dragged it out into the growing light.

As he straightened up, the contrast between the two young fellows became more marked, for Rhu was rather short, wide of shoulder and deep of chest, while Hut was a good head taller, slender and wiry. Like Rhu, his long black hair reached to his shoulders. Both were hairy of chest, shoulder, and back, much more so than men of today. Yet, contrary to the age-old misconception of man at this period, they could not be classed even remotely as ape-like.

"It took courage to do that," Hut praised, his keen gray eyes glowing rather pridefully at his companion. "It must be twice my height from tip to tip, a good four steps (twelve feet) and every hair of it a fighting devil."

"Oh, I was scared enough," disclaimed Rhu. "In fact, I was

too scared *not* to shoot because it would have attacked us as soon as it saw us."

"Y-e-s-s?" drawled Hut skeptically. "Well, all I can say is that I like your brand of fear. Huh! I'll bet I shrank a good span between the time I heard those screams and when you said you'd shot him."

"Maybe so," grunted his friend, "but I notice that you came out of your bed with your knife ready, and I've seen you wield that knife at close quarters. Well, I must notch my moonstick. Do you realize that it is but five suns short of the fifth full moon since the Short Day?" (Approximately May 10, according to our modern calendar.)

"So it is," agreed Hut, at the same time notching his own moonstick, except that on *his* notch he made certain fine marks to indicate an unusual event. "I shan't forget this day," he remarked, and though neither of them suspected it, it was destined to prove to be even more important than either realized.

"Hold that corner of the skin, Hut," Rhu requested as he proceeded with the skinning of the beast, a task for which Hut displayed no enthusiasm whatsoever. Rather gingerly he complied.

"It's funny," Rhu commented, "that you like skins so well, and yet, I've never known you to kill unless you were attacked. I can't say I relish this job much myself, but I don't mind slaying anything that lives by killing, and hoogwars kill for the sheer joy of killing."

"I don't quite understand it myself, Rhu, but I have an ingrained feeling that if I kill, except in self-defense, I make myself liable to being killed."

For a time, Rhu worked at his disagreeable task in silence, finally taking the heavy skin from Hut's hands and with a savage yank, jerked it clear of the clublike tail. Walking over to the great boulder upon which the animal had stood when shot, he spread the dripping skin over it and stepped back to view his prize. Indeed, it was a splendid trophy—one of rare beauty, soft and velvety, a melody in tan and black, and a perfect pelt.

Reluctantly, he went back to the carcass, dragging it to the edge of the cliff and tossing it over. After washing off the gory stains and the arrow which he had carefully retrieved, he returned to Hut who still stood admiring the beautifully rosetted skin. Glancing at the sun, Rhu remarked, "N'Kul is now a quarter across the sky. Let us take the skin to our huts and have it prepared and dressed."

For a moment, his friend hesitated. "I have in mind that we should repair to our retreat, Rhu. It comes to me that we may learn something of importance there."

"Uh huh," grunted Rhu absent-mindedly, his attention focused upon a vulture which was swooping toward the yawning abyss into which he had thrown the victim of his prowess. "Say, Hut, did you ever notice how the feathers in a bird's tail seem to guide it? H-m-m. Now I just wonder. . . ." His voice trailed off, and he became lost in thought.

Hut eyed him questioningly. "You wonder what?" he finally demanded.

"Oh, nothing. . . . Just an idea." Rhu spoke slowly as if loath to be thus disturbed. Then shrugging his shoulders as if shaking off his ponderings, he said briskly, "If we're going to our cave, I'm going to roll up this skin and we'll carry it with us. Otherwise, between the vultures and other scavengers, there won't be much of it left by the time we return."

With the heavy skin wrapped about a sagging pole, the front end supported by Hut's shoulder and the other by Rhu's, they approached the well-hidden and little known cave where they had been coming since boyhood whenever their flocks and herds were in that vicinity—usually during the spring and early summer while the grazing was ample for the family herds.

"It's good to be a Mu Yan," grunted Rhu as they stopped and laid down their burden.

"Yes," agreed Hut, his eyes twinkling, "but some of the Cari Yans are not so bad."

"You should know," Rhu grinned back at him, and the ears of both burned while their faces grew warm as the blood mounted. "It's warm for this season," he finished, and both laughed self-consciously.

"Yes, it is the season of youth," a soft, deep voice announced.

Startled, both wheeled to stare at the tall, bearded, auburn-haired man whose kindly blue eyes were warm and friendly. Rather by instinct than intention, Rhu started to shift his long bow, while Hut's hand dropped to the stone knife in the skin girdle that held his soft hoogwarskin garment at the waist.

"Fear not. I am a friend," the tall stranger reassured them, his eyes twinkling as the chins of both his listeners indignantly tilted upward. "I am of the ones come to help you. It is to your credit that you resent the word fear, for to fear a thing, my sons, is to give it power. As you well know, all creatures will attack whatever fears them."

Hut was the first to regain his composure, his long hair covering his face as he bowed low. "Are you of the Lords of Venus?" he asked hesitantly, and Rhu's dark eyes opened wide as he, too, bowed somewhat stiffly.

"I am of the Mercurians," the stranger answered.

Rhu's face lit up with unaffected admiration and respect. "By what title shall we address you?" he asked. "We would do as is befitting, yet our knowledge is limited to what we have been told by the Elders."

"You may call me Lithargos, although names are of little consequence save for identification, and titles meaningless."

"Lord Lithargos of the Lords of Mercury!" breathed Hut ecstatically, and beads of sweat stood out upon his high forehead.

"Even so," Lithargos agreed easily, "but to you, Hut Mai Dan, and to you, Rhu Sol Ku, I shall henceforth be simply Lithargos, and though we shall become close friends, it is best that none know of our association for the time being. Rhu, you did well to slay the hoogwar, though it was sent merely to test your alertness. Had you been less so, you would have perished, as well as failed a great opportunity. And you, Hut, shall one day be called upon to *repay* your friend's skilled alertness, for it is ever thus."

"Do you mean that I must kill?" asked Hut.

"Why not, if it be the lesser of two unavoidable ills? Would you let your friend die that a beast might live?"

"No, I would not, yet I like not killing."

"Whereof would you eat, and whence your clothing unless something die? Be it plant or beast, some must die that others may live. What matter whether the killing be at your own or another's hand?"

Hut was visibly embarrassed.

"Yet our Elders state that N'Kul forbids us to kill." Rhu hastened to Hut's defense.

"Ah, but you have only part of the command. You shall not kill another person except in defense of self or state,' it is in full. Yet, if you had accepted this rule of your Elders, why did you kill the hoogwar?"

It was Rhu's turn to feel the sweat bedeck his brow, and Hut lost no time in shielding his friend.

"Because he knew it was the beast or us," he said. "And besides, Rhu kills not for the pleasure of killing, but either for food, clothing, or defense!"

Lord Lithargos chuckled softly. "Lucky the man whose friend overrides his own scruples in his behalf. Let it ever be thus," He stated firmly, and His gentle face grew stern as He looked at Hut. "It is only thus that you both may best serve and carry out the Great Work later to be assigned to you. Let it ever be thus," He repeated, and was gone.

"What do you suppose He meant?" Rhu demanded as soon as he recovered from his astonishment.

"I wish I knew," Hut answered, shaking his head. "Rhu, why is it that almost every time we come up here, something unusual happens? It was here that we first met an Elder, and it was from the Elders we learned that these Great Ones are here in the Mu Valley, but I never expected to see one, let alone talk to Him."

"Well, we did! And for the past five moons have I intended that if ever given the opportunity of seeing one of the Lords of Mercury, I would ask Him what sort of weapons They use up there!" Rhu looked the disgust he felt for himself.

Hut laughed. "If I didn't know you so well, Rhu, I'd surely think you had some Forest Dweller blood in you! Why must you ever be thinking of such things when there are so many others of importance?"

"Humph!" Rhu snorted. "Saving one's own skin seems to me to be highly important. Only last week I discovered traces of where a good sized band of Forest Dwellers had hidden near our huts. Since they made no effort to trade, I think they were marauders. I don't like it," he growled.

WHAT with the weight of the hoogwar skin, the heat of that early May day, and the good fifteen miles of rough going, both Hut and Rhu welcomed the sight of their home camps.

"Did you notice the feet of Lord Lithargos?" Rhu asked as he sat before the door of his hut rubbing his own bare and tired ones.

From where he sat doing likewise, Hut looked up inquiringly at his friend and shook his head.

"He had something the shape of His feet, but slightly larger, strapped on them," Rhu explained. "I'm going to make us each a pair . . . . if you'd like them. I still have some of that heavy hide I traded for when the Forest Dwellers were last here. Wait till I get it," he finished.

Without waiting for Hut's reply, he rose and entered the thatched hut which was the only type of home either had ever known. Made of interwoven pliant willow poles and twigs, this one was better constructed than the average and was covered with well sewed buckskin, making it both water and wind proof. It was his own personal hut, and as unusual as was Rhu himself.

The average family of that dim past lived in rambling, thatched structures composed of coarsely interwoven limbs well plastered with clay or sod, or thatched with reedlike grasses, depending upon which was most easily secured, and sometimes divided into a semblance of rooms by hanging skins. At best, these were but temporary structures, for the Plains Dwellers moved from place to place as the grazing for their herds of sheep and small, deerlike cattle made necessary.

The Ku and Dan families had lived close together for as far back as they had any record, either legendary or as depicted upon their family totem poles, the poles of the Ku and Dan families dating back the equivalent of some eight hundred of our modern years.

Since they measured time by the full moon for their thirteen months, and used the shortest day of the year as a starting point, they had long since discovered that there was a discrepancy of some eighteen days, or "suns," as they designated them. In other words, their lunar year was some three hundred and eighty-three suns, whereas there were three hundred sixty-five suns from one Short Day (Winter Solstice) to another. For the last three hundred of these years, or "Great Suns," they had disposed of this problem by the simple expedient of devoting these extra days to feasting and such simple pleasures as they could devise.

That this resulted in some further discrepancies bothered them little. In fact, they were far more concerned about the condition of their flocks and herds and guarding themselves from the predatory raids by the Forest Dwellers who, also, were their best customers, for the Plains Dwellers were skilled dressers of leather. At the time this history starts, some 76,000 B. C., they had not developed the art of weaving, dressing in skins exclusively.

Living by the chase alone, the Forest Dwellers were too ignorant even to build huts for themselves, and when they were unable to trade or steal tanned skins for their clothing, were accustomed to wear skins as stripped from their prey. As may well be supposed, these soon began to rot, and as a consequence, the stench of carrion usually caused the Plains Dwellers to scurry into bands to repel approaching Forest Dwellers.

When Rhu returned with the piece of stiff and heavy leather, Hut was lying with his feet close to the fire, a trick Rhu had taught him for relieving tired and aching feet, and which Rhu, in turn, had learned from the Cave Dwellers who were as skilled in stone work as the Forest Dwellers were in hunting. In fact, Hut's knife was a present from Rhu who had secured it on his epic trip into the mountains the year before. Its companion was in Rhu's belt.

They were really beautiful bits of craftsmanship, well shaped, their finely chipped edges terminating in sharp, thin points. They were made of obsidian or volcanic glass and possessed the sharpest edges mankind had yet devised, and while brittle, still were much tougher and more durable than modern man-made glass. Hut had wrapped their handles with strips of green rawhide which, shrinking as it had dried, made fine, tough grips easily held and more than doubling their effectiveness.

"Get up, Hut, and stand on this leather," Rhu ordered. As Hut complied, he marked the outline of his feet upon it with a charred stick.

"Now let me mark yours," Hut offered.

When Rhu sat down with the marked leather before him, his brow puckered as he studied it. "H-m-m-m!" he ruminated reflectively. "It's not going to be as simple as it looked! If I try to sew straps on this stuff," kicking the hard, heavy leather, "I'll break every bone needle I have, and they are hard to make."

Hut sat down and began also to contemplate the problem. "Maybe, Rhu, we can soften it by soaking."

"That's an idea, and I have another one. We'll cut them a finger wider than our feet. I have a sharp bone spike that is flattened on one end. Maybe I can cut holes through which we can run soft leather thongs."

Without comment, Hut began hacking at the leather with his knife until, after much grunting, he managed to haggle off the piece upon which his feet were outlined.

"I'll cut off my piece," Rhu volunteered, Hut agreeing with suspicious alacrity that was not lost upon Rhu who manfully attacked the unwieldy leather. "Phew! That's hard work!" he snorted, eyeing balefully the outlines of his feet. Then he chuckled. "I'm glad my feet aren't as big as yours!" he announced, glancing at the frowning Hut, who took his piece and started for the Dan hut.

"I'll be back after we eat," he called over his shoulder.

Rhu's eyes followed the retreating form. "He's got an idea," he growled to himself. "He's not dumb, that fellow, and it's up to me to do something right now. H-m-m-m! I've got it!"

Hurrying into his hut, he returned with an earthen bowl such as was used for cooking stews—a good two feet wide and almost as deep. Filling this with water, he set it over his fire, resting it upon three stones as was their custom, then placing the leather in it, weighted it down with another stone. When the water began to steam, he removed the vessel from the fire and set it aside while he joined the family circle for supper.

Rhu's father glanced up from where he sat wolfing down great chunks of meat from the mutton leg he held in his greasy hands. Several of Rhu's unmarried brothers were emulating him with such bits of meat as they succeeded in grabbing from the steaming pot, juggling them from hand to hand because of the heat. Contrasted with these hulking fellows, Rhu looked rather small, but their movements were awkward and clumsy, while his were lithe and smooth. He did not appear to move swiftly, yet he had no difficulty whatever in securing the particular tidbit that took his fancy, although one brother was already reaching for it.

"Give!" the brother snarled.

"Take!" Rhu dared him, eyes alert, for these big fellows were short of temper and brutally strong. However, long and bitter experience had taught them that, notwithstanding his comparatively small stature, Rhu was as quick and deadly as an adder when attacked, and not one of them but bore scars attesting this.

Rhu's father growled into his greasy beard, and he glared at the brother who subsided meekly. Despite his crude appearance, old Sol Ku was a just man, and a shrewd brain lay beneath his shaggy hair. For all he said little, he had long ago recognized in Rhu an ability totally lacking in his brothers. Among other things, he was by far their best hunter, and his skill in locating good pasturage in dry seasons was uncanny.

IN THE meantime, Hut had placed *his* piece of leather in a vessel of melted fat, and while it was soaking, joined his own family circle.

Old Mai Dan looked not unlike Rhu's father in general appearance, though of slighter build. His hair was coarse and jet black, having a tendency to stand stiffly erect and looking not unlike a black mane as it hung down his back. There were but three of Hut's brothers eating, all as tall as he, but more powerful of build. As at Rhu's, they were seated around the vessel containing the customary stew, but mixed with it were dandelion leaves, acorns, and reed (tule) roots. With his knife, Hut scooped up some of these and placed them in the earthen bowl he had brought for that purpose.

"Weeds," growled one of his brothers.

"Sheep feed," sneered another.

Hut's father paused from gnawing upon the succulent joint he had just cracked open for its tender marrow. "Better a sheep than a wolf whelp," he growled, and no further sound, beyond the gnawing and belching of the eaters, disturbed the meal.

Like Sol Ku, Mai also recognized the worth of his odd son whose almost weird ability to foretell the weather and periods of drought had many times saved the Dan and Ku herds. Contrary to the usual custom of the Plains Dwellers, these were herded together, each identified by certain ear markings, also suggested by Hut. Furthermore, both Hut and Rhu seemed to possess a rare ability to get others to work together, so much so, in fact, that not for the past five years had the two families been molested by their neighbors. When all assembled, the two family groups presented an imposing front, and under the direction of Rhu and Hut made a formidable unit.

By the time he had finished eating, Hut found the leather to be much softer and far more easily cut, so he wiped it off on the grass, drew new outlines for his feet, and mindful of Rhu's admonition, cut them a bit larger. He then departed to rejoin Rhu, who, to his surprise, was already driving the flattened bone spike through his own pieces.

As Hut approached, Rhu looked up from his task and grinned. "I see you soaked yours, too," he remarked. "H-m-m! In grease!" he exclaimed as Hut handed over his pieces. "That's better than mine. I used water."

"I brought these, too," Hut announced, handing several long strips of tough deerhide to Rhu. "Mother had cut them for lacing," he explained.

"How'd you get them?" Rhu inquired, well knowing the value placed upon such laboriously made things.

"Traded her that decorated bowl I made," Hut replied. "She has long wanted it."

"Don't blame her," was the enthusiastic comment. "You surely make some pretty things with those long fingers of yours, Hut. I'm making us a couple of new bows. Will you decorate mine when I have finished them?"

"You know I will, Rhu, even without your making me a new one. Don't make mine too stiff, though. Remember, I'm not you."

"Aw," Rhu grumbled, "strength isn't everything, and I'm finding that more pliable bows are about as good. It's the arrows that count. If I could only make them perfectly straight, we could really do some shooting."

"I've noticed that wet twigs can be bent to any shape, and if held so until dry, stay that way. Maybe we could make them straight by the same method," Hut suggested.

"That's an idea, only how can we hold them that way? You know how much wood gets out of shape after being wet and drying; if we don't hold them, they'll get out of shape much worse."

Hut stretched and yawned prodigiously before he sat down, and Rhu's eyes suddenly widened. "I've got it!" he exclaimed enthusiastically. "We'll *stretch* them straight. We'll tie them to a limb and hang a heavy weight on them. I'll bet that will work!"

"What gave you the idea?" Hut asked.

"Watching you straighten up as you stretched. It's funny how many things Nature teaches a fellow who looks for them. Now, if we can get our arrows really straight, I think I have another idea that will make them almost perfect, but I'm not going to tell about it before I try it. Every time I talk too much, I lose out, just like the time we thought we had figured a way to carry stuff and made a mess of it only to get laughed out of camp."

"I still think it's a good idea," Hut insisted. "There must be some way to make something round but not as heavy as logs."

For a time, both sat thinking of how they had tried to use a log as a crude wheel after they had taken a hard fall while walking on one that rolled from under them.

At last, Rhu had four thongs in one of Hut's leathers. "Stick out your foot," he ordered, then proceeded to tie it to Hut's foot. Crude it was, and far from a good sandal, but by the time they went to sleep in Rhu's hut, they had one passable pair.

Daylight found the two working diligently upon a pair for Rhu. They discovered that by splitting one end of each thong and making extra holes, they could make them fit very well, and Rhu insisted upon fixing Hut's the same way. Then, slipping away from camp, the lads tied them on to see how they worked, and despite the blisters from improperly adjusted straps, they found them to be a great improvement over bare feet, especially upon stony ground.

They then proceeded to utilize their experience and made an extra pair for themselves, and there was still a large piece of leather left. Rhu looked at Hut, who returned the stare with interest, and each felt his ears begin to burn.

"The problem is how to get their foot sizes without their knowing about it." Hut went directly to the point.

Rhu chuckled. "How about leading them across that clay bank? Then, when they are gone, we can make a pattern."

With a grin, Hut left for his home, returning a few minutes later with his sleeping skin, war club, and a package of food, to find Rhu also ready.

"Shall we wear them?" he asked.

"Why not? When we cross that field of shining stones, they will come in handy . . . . and we can remove them before we meet the girls," Rhu completed, answering Hut's unspoken question.

It was characteristic of the pair that with this simple preparation, they were departing upon a journey of more than a hundred miles, there and back. More importantly, they were going into a section of the country populated by a different tribe well known for its fierce dislike of all strangers, and who were warlike even among themselves—the Cari Yans, who dwelt in the great Valley directly to the east of the Mu Valley.

Chapter Two

THE PLACE OF SHINING STONES

SINCE THE Ku and Dan families occupied the northern and richest end of the Mu Valley where it did not exceed twenty miles across, Rhu and Hut had covered less than five miles when they reached the first of the grass covered hills along the eastern side. They had passed one of the herds where their relatives on guard had hailed them. Despite their appearance of what we would term surliness, in their rough and uncouth way, they all liked and admired these odd brothers of theirs. However, becoming increasingly conscious of their sandals, the two gave them a wide berth, contenting themselves with waving their hands and shouting as they forged steadily onward.

At the top of the first hill of consequence, Hut remarked, "I think that hot grease was not such a good idea. These things are so slick that I keep sliding all the time."

Rhu chuckled as he squeezed the sweat from his forehead and snapped it aside with a hairy forefinger. "I thought it was because mine had dried out even harder because of the water," he grunted. "Huh! I slip back one step for every three I take. I'm taking mine off until we come to that stretch of sparkling stones." Sitting down, he proceeded to do so, closely seconded by Hut.

"Gee! Look at the shine on their bottoms," Rhu snorted, for the grass certainly had given the heavy leather a glossy polish.

"Feels good to get them off," Hut announced, wriggling his toes blissfully. "It's too bad we wasted that leather."

Rhu studied his pair thoughtfully. "I'm not so sure about that,

Hut. It's probably because we haven't placed the straps properly, and I have an idea that we must grow accustomed to them. Do you remember the first time we slid down that big mud bank as we had seen the water squirrels (beavers) do?" A chuckle rumbled in his deep chest, echoed by Hut's hearty laugh.

"Yes," Rhu continued, "we failed to take into consideration that we have no flat tails to make it smooth, and what an awakening when we hit those stones!" And their mirth increased.

Finally, wiping his eyes with a hairy hand, Hut stated emphatically, "But you found a way to do it safely, and we'll probably do the same with these things," holding up his sandals. "I can still see you the first time you scooted down that slide on a tree limb. *I'd* never have thought of that."

"Maybe not, but you thought out our slider from it," referring to the crude sled Hut had devised for hauling things during wet weather.

"There! That's better!" Hut exclaimed as they started forward.

Until almost evening, little more was said, largely because it took all their breath for the arduous climb up the rugged, towering mountains separating theirs from the Cari Valley.

"There it is," announced Rhu, who was in the lead, pointing to the glittering mesa stretching a good half mile ahead of them and forming an almost impassable barrier for those who would cross it, notwithstanding their hard and calloused feet.

At some prehistoric time, a long since inactive volcano had spewed forth a vast mass of volcanic glass which must have hardened in the air, then shattered as it landed upon the granite beneath. Nor had the passing of time appreciably dulled the razor sharpness of the jagged fragments so that the least incautious step invariably cut to the bone any careless foot. This, the two had discovered some two months past when, despite their hurts, they had first crossed it in their search for a pass through the mountains. Its beauty had been lost to them then, and on their return, they had no time to do more than seek the least rough spots, for a warlike band was on their trail.

This was their second trip, and donning the heavy sandals, they found they could travel with such comparative comfort that they began to take notice of the seemingly endless variety of coloring, not all of which, by any means, was due to the refracted light. The glittering crystals were of every hue and shade, from ruby, magenta, violet, blue, green, and those perfectly clear to those the blackness of coal . . . . a veritable galaxy of colors that would have sent a modern gem hunter into ecstacies.

Nor was the effect much less upon Hut and Rhu who soon began to search out especially bright bits, discarding about as many as they kept, for they were finding almost every variety of both color and shape. Indeed, it was almost dark before they could tear themselves away to hasten to a sheltered spot for the night.

At the very edge, Rhu discovered a small piece of such peculiar shade that he knocked it loose, then picked it up, amazed at its unexpected weight. About the girth of his thumb, though considerably longer, it was a reddish brown on one side and a rather dull, dark hue where it had been broken away when Rhu struck it with his flint-headed club. Not alone that, but a galaxy of sparks flew from it when he did so, a fact he catalogued in his inquisitive mind for future experiment. Because of its weight, he dropped it into his quiver; then, in the press of other matters, he forgot it completely.

Once across the field, they removed the sandals, both surprised to see how little the soles were worn despite the roughness of the area over which they had crossed. Again, they began to take on something of their old value in the eyes of Rhu and Hut. Hurrying ahead, the lads reached the small cave they had discovered on their former trip and where they had providently stored some sticks for a fire. In that altitude, the nights were cold.

Arrived at the cave, Hut took from his pack a heavy earthen jar in which he uncovered several still red coals. He it was who discovered that coals from a certain hard wood, if well embedded in ashes would keep for many hours, and merely by adding a little dry bark or a few light twigs, a fire could easily be started. Thus, he and Rhu usually enjoyed the comfort of fires wherever they were, whereas ordinarily, the Mu Yans had fires only in their home camps. These were kept constantly alive by the women, one of them taking over that task each day.

The fire in the Ku family was over two hundred years old, and one of the first any of the Mu tribe had ever had. Originally started by lightning before an approaching thunderstorm had broken, it ignited some grass and brush. When discovered, it had burned into the trunk of a fallen tree. Legend had it that prior to that time, it was only while such fires lasted of their own accord that any enjoyed their comfort. At this later period, however, some shaggy-haired genius had evolved in his slow-thinking mind the idea of placing more sticks on this particular fire before it was completely burned out. The results had been so gratifying as to be almost revolutionary so far as their mode of life was concerned.

It seems that among the sticks piled on this fire, were some pitch pine knots. One of the more venturesome of the family found that these kept burning even when removed from the main conflagration which gave him a startling idea. Running, he carried one of them as far toward the home camp as he could before it began to burn out. Recalling the "miracle" he had previously witnessed, he started a fresh fire by placing light twigs about the dying ember he had carried. From this, he and his companions carried more burning embers until finally, the first family fire mentioned on any of the totem poles was brought to their home. Having learned the great secret of renewing it, the fire became a permanent and treasured feature in their lives.

Gradually, other families came to see this wonderful innovation, and taking embers, painstakingly and laboriously carried fire to their own camps. Now, practically all Plains Dwellers had their family fires, but they guarded their secret so well that even at this time, only a few of the Forest Dwellers knew how it was done.

In fact, it was the awe this seeming miracle inspired that saved many of the Plains Dwellers from devastating attacks by these shaggy, woodland savages who still were of the Mu tribe.

Hut had made the next great step ahead by his own carefully guarded secret, participated in by only Rhu, for these two shared all their ideas and discoveries.

While Hut was starting the fire, Rhu brought some water with which to wash down their evening meal consisting of some of the inevitable stew which Rhu had carried in a goat-skin bag. That the stew might have proved a bit strong, greasy, and indigestible to us moderns bothered these two not at all. In fact, Hut commented gustfully upon its excellent quality and taste, when Rhu confided that he had slipped into it a small lump of some grayish, rocklike stuff he had recently discovered.

"It has a peculiar flavor," he said, "and when, instead of a rock, I rubbed it on a skin to remove the excess fat, I found the skin did not rot although I lost it for a full twenty-one suns. Then, just five suns ago, while hunting, I happened to drop a little piece of it in the only water I had for cooking. The stew tasted so good that I made a trip and got more of the stuff. Here is a small piece," and he handed Hut a lump of the gray, crystalline rock salt he had found.

"Has your mother ever used it?" Hut asked, licking it.

"I offered her some, but she flew into a rage, vowing that it was likely poison, and that if I brought any of it into our camp, she would tell my father. Isn't it queer how everybody is so afraid to try something new?"

"Yes, Rhu, and not only are they afraid of new things, but they will even fight anything or anybody who *offers* something strange or unusual. *I* like it," Hut asserted stoutly. "And you say it made the skin keep fresh?"

"It did, Hut, and almost without smell of rot, except around the edges where I didn't rub it well."

"Then it should be good for us to eat, shouldn't it?"

Rhu chuckled softly, his eyes full of devilment. "Break off a little chunk and try it. I did."

Hut looked at him closely. "Huh!" he snorted. "What happened?" Long experience had taught him caution when Rhu's eyes danced in this manner.

"Well, I didn't die, but had such a consuming thirst that I finally lay down close to the spring where I could drink by turning my head. Phew! I was so full of water that I looked like an overfed calf! But it didn't hurt me otherwise, so far as I could see, and I'm getting so I don't care for stew without it." He chuckled. "I dropped a good-sized lump in our stew last night, and mother was mad because there was hardly enough left for the women and children. I noticed her smacking her lips as she ate it, too, and the pot was wiped so clean it needed no washing when they were through!"

"Have you much with you?" Hut asked.

"Yes, plenty so we can give some to Haitee and Marda to try. I'll bet they never heard of it. I noticed that the deer have many trails leading to the place where I found this. That was how I found it in the first place, and I figured that if it didn't hurt them it couldn't hurt me."

IT WAS almost noon the following day, and they were just emerging from the pass overlooking the Cari Valley when Rhu stopped short and raised his hand. Both faded into the underbrush as silently as shadows, where Rhu strung his bow and notched an arrow, while Hut drew his knife and took a fresh grip on his flint-headed club.

Presently, two shaggy, beetle-browed, hook-nosed men stepped into the open, peering swiftly about them and conversing gutturally in the Cari Yan tongue which was sufficiently like the Mu Yan so that Rhu and Hut could understand most of what was said.

"Ugh," grunted the larger of the two, a red-headed giant, hairy of body and brutish of face, his receding forehead affording a scant finger's breadth between his hair and eyebrows. Pointing a gnarled and stubby finger to the trail, he growled, "Track."

"Where?" demanded the barrel-chested, hairy ape with him, the drool dripping upon his hair-matted chest from a pendulous underlip.

"Come. . . . Here," insisted the larger one, his sluggish brain evidently groping for something further to say. "See tracks," he finally grunted.

For a long moment, they stood silently, the shorter one's wide nostrils dilating as they tested the air like an animal. A leer of bestial cunning distorted his face, showing his heavy, yellow, broken, fanglike teeth, and slowly, the great corded muscles in his back writhed. Then, with the speed of a striking rattler, his heavy stone-headed war club swung and crashed through the skull of his erstwhile companion, splitting it like an eggshell.

"Good!" he snarled. "Mine!" and as he swung toward a heavy bush at his right, two frantic girls bounded to their feet and fled screaming directly toward the bush concealing Hut and Rhu.

"Ho!" the brute snarled, his face alight and eyes glistening. With a speed as surprising as was the slaying of his companion, he leaped in pursuit, but even as he started, Rhu arose and his arrow arm drew back. The muscles in his broad back knotted, but in his desire to gain the last ounce of power from his heavy bow, he overstrained it. With a crash, it splintered as the now roaring brute swung toward him.

With a yell of fury, Rhu closed in, his war club whirling down upon the upflung one of the berserk creature before him, and so great was the force that both clubs broke under the impact.

Savagely, the red-haired, slavering creature reached for his adversary, but Rhu evaded the great, hairy, clutching hand with a lightning twist of his body, at the same time whipping out his knife. With the speed of light, he ducked under his foe's outstretched arms and drove home the blade with such force that he could feel it grate upon the spine. Giving it a twist, he yanked it free and was out of the way as the man crumpled to earth.

Anxiously, Rhu examined his knife, then grinned. The point was still intact, and he heaved a sigh of relief.

Turning to retrieve his precious bowstring, he found himself face to face with the smaller of the two girls who, without even so much as a single glance at either of the dead men, stood with her arms half outstretched toward Rhu. Even by our present-day standards, she would have been considered fair to look upon. By their standards, she was truly beautiful even though many probably regarded her as rather frail. Her dark, auburn hair shone like burnished copper in the sun, her firm young breasts rising and falling swiftly from her emotions, while her deep-set, hazel eyes glowed with pride as she looked at Rhu.

"Haitee!" he exclaimed, taking her into his arms just as any modern youth would do.

"Oh, Rhu!" she breathed, trembling as the reaction set in. "Oh, Rhu!" she repeated, clinging to him. "Those two Forest Dwellers were hiding near the trail and followed us. Marda and I thought we had outrun them, but they are like the animals they hunt and followed by scent when they could not see. I—we—thought you had not come as agreed. But you did!"

"I guess it was seeing you flee that made me overstrain my bow," Rhu answered, holding her even closer and experiencing a keen delight in the warmth of her softly yielding body. "Well, they won't bother you any more."

"I'll say they won't!" agreed Hut, approaching with his arm about the slender waist of the taller of the two girls. Taller by half a head than Rhu, she still was shorter than Hut. Like Haitee, she was dressed in a soft deer skin that crossed her left shoulder, covering her breasts, and reaching almost to her knees. A bit of flowering vine from which most of the blossoms had now been torn away encircled her waist, thus holding her attire in place. Long, tawny hair, escaping from its restraining leather thong, cascaded well below her waist in luxuriant waves.

Although their faces were sufficiently unlike to show they were of different families, there was no question as to their being of the same tribe, notwithstanding that their features were much finer and more intelligent than those of the average women of their time. About Marda there was just a slight touch of hauteur—a trace of aloofness, while about Haitee there was an air of impulsiveness somewhat offset by a certain firmness in the set of her very determined little chin. Both had the open foreheads of thinkers, and there was no doubt but that they possessed plenty of courage. Even the most casual would have observed their fitness as mates for Rhu and Hut.

After Rhu and Hut had stripped the dead men of everything which had value in their eyes, Rhu taking the war club of the one slain by his companion, the two couples walked away to a secluded spot.

"We have been forbidden to come up this way since you were discovered before," Marda announced.

"And if we return now and they find that we have come up here anyhow, we shall be killed," Haitee added quickly. "I cannot understand why they are so bitter about people they have never seen."

"That is the general thing," Hut assured her. "The Mu Yans are little different. But if we are unwelcome at my father's hut, I shall take Marda and my share of animals and establish our own home."

"And so will I," Rhu agreed promptly. "In fact, both the Ku and the Dan families need new blood."

"No question about that, Rhu, but will they be content to let us alone?"

"They'd better." Rhu's voice was so soft that Hut glanced at him quickly. He knew that tone, and he loved peace, a thing for which Rhu seemed to care nothing, once thoroughly aroused.

"I know exactly the place for us," Rhu continued, "but first, I suggest that we take the girls to the Elders where they will be perfectly safe and comfortably cared for. We can then see what is the attitude of our fathers and decide upon our course."

"What do you think of that, Marda?" Hut asked.

Haitee smiled up into Rhu's face. "I knew you'd think of a way," she confided.

"I suppose it's all right if you say so, but who are these Elders you mention?" Marda wanted to know. "You have spoken of them before."

"They are those of our tribe who have devoted their lives to communion with the gods; they are the wise ones to whom those who know of them go for help in times of need. They live in a securely hidden place where only those who have earned their confidence may go, or even find them," Hut explained.

Marda frowned uncertainly while Haitee's eyes widened. "Do you know where to find them, Rhu?" she asked.

"Of course," he assured her. "Hut and I visit them every full moon. That is why we can. . . ."

"Er hum!" Hut interrupted.

Rhu grinned back at him impudently. "Don't worry, Hut. Besides, if we take the girls up there, they will learn much."

"But we don't know whether the Elders will admit them," Hut demurred uneasily. "You know how particular they are."

"Uh huh," Rhu grunted inelegantly, "but I've already spoken to them about it! They say they will be glad to do it for us if we will assume full responsibility for the girls' never divulging anything which the Elders prefer to have kept secret. I have agreed for Haitee."

"Isn't that quite a lot of confidence to have in someone whom you have seen but once and then for such a short time?" Marda asked.

"If I didn't trust her, I wouldn't want her," Rhu answered shortly, adding by way of explanation, "Besides, when we hid near your huts and you did not betray us, even agreeing to meet us today as you did, why shouldn't we trust you?"

Haitee nestled even closer in Rhu's encircling arm. "I'd die before I'd discredit you," she whispered, and he gave her a little appreciative squeeze.

"How about you, Marda?" Hut asked. "My trust in you is no less than Rhu's in Haitee."

"Of course I'll agree," she answered. "I'll admit this is all new to me, but Haitee can tell you that I don't talk."

Hut heaved a sigh of relief. That impulsive Rhu caused him many a breathless moment, even though he would trust him with his life and had never known him to betray the slightest confidence. Still, he had a way of acting so quickly at times that a more deliberate person could never be sure of what he might do next. For example, his nerve in broaching such a subject to an *Elder*, even before he knew for sure whether the girls would really come with them . . . . or did he? One could never be too certain about what Rhu knew or did not know, but no living man might justly doubt his sincerity, and he had pledged his word.

Suddenly, Hut's eyes brightened. "Let's get going," he announced, rising and starting up the trail. "They may be trailing you girls even now."

"You're right," Rhu agreed, "and I feel almost naked without my bow. Those of these fellows aren't worth taking," he grumbled. "You walk on ahead," he instructed Haitee. "I'll keep well behind so they can't sneak up on us. Travel fast," he called to Hut who nodded his assent and lengthened his stride until the girls were hard pressed to keep pace. Once they reached the top of the mountain, it was down grade, and they made swift progress, running much of the time.

As they emerged from the pass and reached "the place of shining stones," the westering sun turned it into a riot of blazing color difficult to face. Rhu called to Hut and handed him some soot from a small skin bag.

"Rub this on your cheeks and around your eyes. It will deaden the light as I discovered in the snow. We'll put some on the girls, too," and despite their objections because of the rather frightful appearance of Rhu and Hut, they were given no choice. Then, looking at one another, they broke into peals of carefree laughter.

Next, Rhu and Hut donned their sandals. "You'd never get across on your bare feet," Rhu explained.

"Then how shall we make it?" Haitee asked.

"Hut will carry you because you are lighter. I'll carry Marda," he explained, and though they all might have preferred it otherwise, none objected.

"What beautiful stones!" Marda exclaimed when they were about halfway across. "I'd like to get down and gather a few."

"No," answered Rhu shortly. "Even with these heavy things on my feet, one is already bleeding. These stones are sharper than Hut's knife!"

Silence ensued for a few minutes while Rhu plodded onward.

"I never saw anything like those foot things before. Did you and Hut have them when you first came?"

"No. And we had sore feet for weeks after that trip. These stones are so bad they stopped the pursuit that time."

"I often wondered how you two managed to get away. It was night when you reached here, wasn't it? I heard my brothers saying they lost you in the darkness, but they did not mention this."

"Doesn't look the same at night," Rhu grunted, wishing this part of the trip were over. Marda seemed to grow increasingly heavy and the task was more difficult than he had expected. Besides, his foot hurt cruelly where a jagged bit of obsidian had gashed it above the sandal.

Then he began to wonder about Hut and Haitee. Suppose he should drop her! Despite his anxiety to get across, he stopped and looked back. Hut was close behind. From their smiles, he guessed they were getting along famously, and he began to feel ashamed of his brusqueness with Marda.

"Hut has a lot of the prettiest pieces of this stuff," he volunteered. "We gathered them yesterday, and I know he meant them for you."

"How about you?" Marda asked, smiling to herself as she recognized his change of humor which she had mistakenly attributed to a touch of jealousy.

"Of course I have some for Haitee," he agreed. In telling about the many varieties they had found, Rhu forgot much of his pain and it was with about as much surprise as relief that he found they were leaving the place behind them.

"Better put me down now," Marda suggested thoughtfully.

"Not yet. There are still many pieces hidden in the grass. When we reach that white stone ahead of us, it will be safe." Then, after a brief silence, he asked the question which had been in his mind ever since they had started out with the girls.

"Don't you have any Elders among the Cari Yans?"

"Oh, I've heard inklings of such things, but never thought much about them. Sounded sort of foolish, what I heard, but if you and Hut have seen the Mu Yan ones, then I must change my way of thinking. Hut doesn't impress me as one who is easily fooled."

"Not that fox!" Rhu exclaimed. "Huh! He knows lots more than he lets on. Unlike me, he's always thinking ahead, while I'm usually too busy with today to fret much about tomorrow."

Marda giggled. "Oh yes? What about our coming along and your having already seen the Elders about us?"

"Huh! Even *I* get a bright idea once in a while! Well, here we are," he announced, squatting down so that she might stand upon her feet.

"Phew!" whistled Hut as he joined them and deposited Haitee upon the rock beside Marda. "I never before realized just how much Haitee there is under her deerskin!" He mopped the streaming sweat from his face, his fingers smearing the soot over it in amazingly terrifying designs.

"Gee, Rhu, but your face is a mess!" he exclaimed, his own smears making his smile so positively diabolical that the girls burst into gales of laughter.

"You're not exactly a thing of beauty yourself, Hut. Me, I'm going over to the spring and wash up," retorted Rhu, heading for the spot where he and Hut knew there was a good-sized spring.

A moment later, Hut's name rang sharply on the air. So urgent was the tone of Rhu's voice that Hut sped quickly to his side. There in the ooze was the mark of a great paw—a good foot across! The grass was just springing erect, and the lads knew it was but minutes old.

"A cave bear!" Hut cried excitedly.

"Yes, and a big one! It must have heard us coming. Hurry! Let's get back to the girls. It might attack them!" just as Marda screamed frantically.

Chapter Three

THE BATTLE WITH THE BEAR

VEN AS Rhu and Hut wheeled and both girls bounded to the top of the big stone, the shaggy head and shoulders of a mammoth, gray-coated bear came into view as it reared upon its hind feet, its roar almost deafening.

"You hold its attention," Rhu shouted to Hut as he crouched and slid off to the left through the brush.

That Hut complied without hesitation was certainly proof of his implicit confidence in Rhu, for even the most intrepid hunters avoided these monsters whenever possible. Most men of that time would have fled the scene. Of all beasts in that section, these were the most formidable, their very ferocity and utter savagery, even among themselves, fortunately keeping their numbers comparatively small.

Running past the big stone, Hut scooped up and hurled a rock, hitting the bear squarely upon the very tip of its sensitive nose, then daringly yelled to draw its further attention.

"Stay up there and keep still," he shouted to the girls as the great brute swung toward him. "Y-a-a-h!" he taunted, shaking his war club, a dare which the snarling monster was prompt to accept, roaring its defiance. If its intentions had been only a matter of curiosity before, the impact of that rock upon the end of its tender nose changed them to murderous intent, further intensified by the hairy man-thing prancing before it.

With deceptive deliberation, Hut moved ahead, supremely confident of his ability to keep just beyond the reach of those knifelike, lashing claws. "If only Rhu had his bow!" he mumbled as he led the bear away from the girls and began to wonder what plan his friend had, for he knew Rhu too well not to realize that he had some definite scheme in mind.

Only a few feet separating him from the bear, Hut essayed his first nimble dodge, forgetting that he still wore his sandals. And then, his usually agile feet with their prehensile toes shot from under him, and he fell flat . . . . just as the bear again reared up on its hind legs. Both horrified girls screamed.

As they did so, Rhu's body hurtled through the air in a prodigious leap, landing squarely upon the bear's wide back. Seizing one ear in his teeth, he clamped his legs about its massive body and with all his strength, drove his knife to its hilt in the creature's throat. *To his horror, the blade snapped at the hilt!*

With an agonized, gurgling bellow, the bear twisted to hurl this clinging thing from its back. So mighty was its effort that despite himself, Rhu was flung clear, but, carrying most of the ear in his clenched teeth, he lit upon his feet.

By now, Hut was up again, but intent upon Rhu, the bear apparently did not see him, launching itself upon its latest enemy, the blood pouring from mouth and throat. Seeing Hut upon his feet, Rhu fled before the berserk brute.

Hut sped after the bear, and switching his war club to his left hand, drew his knife. Rapidly, he gained upon the beast and when at its rump, slashed at the back of its leg in a desperate effort to hamstring it by cutting, or at least seriously injuring, the main tendon behind its heel. Sawing with all the strength he could muster while both were moving, he knew from its feel that the ragged, razor edge was cutting fast.

"Good!" Rhu yelled encouragingly, noting Hut's strategy from the tail of his eye and slowing his pace enough to hold the full attention of the raging brute from whose mouth great crimson gushers spewed at every coughing breath.

Hut redoubled his efforts, although it was impossible to keep cutting in the same spot due to their rapid movements. At last, with a lucky slash, he felt the tough tendon give place to softer flesh until his knife scraped the bone, and the leg began to drag. Immediately, he switched his attack to the other leg. Apparently, it was not until then that the bear realized it had a second adversary, and it wheeled so suddenly that Hut was knocked far to one side, at the same time affording Rhu a

Battle with the Bear

chance he was quick to grasp. With every ounce of his strength, he brought his stone-headed club down upon the creature's skull, feeling the roughly pointed stone sink in, and bringing the bear to its knees.

Grasping the club with both hands, Rhu swung again, and once more felt the skull crush beneath the impact. Hut, merely jarred and skinned by his fall, returned, and driving his knife to its hilt in the side nearest him, sawed away with both hands. He succeeded in cutting a gash over a foot long before the bear, with the tenacity of life for which that family is famous, staggered to its feet and turning, lashed out blindly.

Anticipating this, Hut was well away from it, however, and the effort, plus the nearly useless leg, caused the brute to fall again. Once more, it tried to get to its feet, but both Rhu and Hut realized the bear was done for and would soon be dead. Leaving it, they started back toward the girls who, as all women were trained to do, had obeyed and remained upon the rock.

"How did you happen to fall?" Rhu asked.

"These cursed things," Hut growled, and sitting down, immediately removed the sandals, started to fling them away, then reconsidered. "Guess I'd better keep them," he said lamely. "Gee! I thought I was a goner until I saw you light on its back!"

"So did I," Rhu said soberly and earnestly. "That's why I did it. I knew it was my only chance to save you. Phew!" and he spat disgustedly. "His ear surely needed washing! Wow! I can't get the taste out of my mouth!"

Hut's face was a study, his eyes very bright. "Rhu, I don't believe any other living man would have done that," he said softly.

"Well, I doubt whether I would have either if I'd known how it was going to taste." Rhu willfully distorted Hut's meaning.

Hut's eyes began to dance. He knew what he knew, and he was also aware that Rhu understood exactly what was in his heart, but the opportunity was too good to pass. "Why didn't you rub it with your taste rock first?" he asked, then dashed away as Rhu would have grabbed him. Boyhood was not so many years behind them although most of their kind had forgotten it by the time they were twenty-two.

"Come on down and help me stop this fellow!" Hut yelled as he dashed toward the girls.

Obediently, Marda slid down and rushed toward him, reaching for her flint knife, but Haitee took a flying leap and sped toward Rhu.

"Rhu!" she screamed. "Rhu! Don't you know me?" she cried tremulously.

But Rhu had dropped upon the ground and was rolling about, roaring with laughter. Staring in wild fright at this strangely bewildering behavior, Haitee faltered, then turned and fled toward Hut who was holding fast to Marda. However, the same queer and unseemly sounds were emanating from Hut, and Marda jerked free to stand staring at him for a moment, then threw her arms around Haitee, and both burst into tears.

Alas! Their mode of life thus far had developed in them little sense of humor. Small wonder they failed to understand these two fellows who risked a horrible death to save each other, then, after apparently starting to fight, suddenly began to laugh like those whose heads had been addled by the gods!

"We didn't know you were trying to save *us,*" Haitee explained seriously when, after a painful interlude, Rhu and Hut had finally convinced the girls that they were simply having a good time after saving them.

"D—do you mean," Marda stammered, "that Mu Yan men will fight to save their women?"

Hut sobered. "Don't the Cari Yans fight for theirs?" he demanded.

"Each other, yes," both girls chorused. "But women are plentiful, and these great bears are dangerous," Marda added.

"I'm afraid there are many Mu Yans who are no better," Rhu grumbled, "but Hut and I don't happen to be that sort. What is ours, we keep." As Hut glanced up quickly, he amended, "I refer to our women and families, of course."

It was very evident that while Rhu and Hut often puzzled the girls, they did realize and appreciate that these two were far superior to any men they had ever known. Even though they had many queer ideas, still, Marda and Haitee felt they had made a good bargain with which they were well content.

Together, the four went over to where the bear lay in a great pool of blood, to find it quite dead. Rhu hastened to dig out the blade of his precious knife, using Hut's for the purpose.

"It's going to be hard to handle," he said staring at it ruefully. "These edges are sharp!"

"Let's wrap it with a piece of skin," Hut suggested, and soon had a good handhold so that Rhu could use it once more.

Even with the willing help of the girls, it took them until almost dark to skin the bear. Then they had to hide the huge pelt where it would be safe until their return, first rubbing it thoroughly with some of the rock salt. All four were well smeared with blood before they were finished and though this seemed to bother none of them a whit, they did repair to the spring to wash off the stains.

"If we hurry," Rhu announced, squinting at the sun, "we can reach the Elders in time. The moon will be up soon, so let's eat."

"What shall we eat? That bear will be pretty tough, won't it?" Haitee asked dubiously. "It's only the very young ones that are tender enough to eat raw."

"Oh, this old fellow won't be so bad." Rhu's voice was serious, even as he winked at Hut. "We'll hunt for the tenderest parts."

"He smelled pretty strong to me," Marda remarked doubtfully. "I wouldn't mind that so much," she hastened to add lest Hut think her too particular, "it's just that it will be so tough and hard to chew."

"Rhu ought to know about that." Hut laughed. "He bit off its ear, and I think he ate it." Haitee's stare of disbelief caused him almost to choke with suppressed merriment.

"I spit it out," Rhu grunted, "but I was surely glad it was as tough as it was, or I could never have held on. Oh well, come on, Haitee. We'll cut off some of it while Hut and Marda gather some dry wood for a fire."

"Fire!" exclaimed both girls incredulously. "Why, at our home," Marda continued, "we have only one fire, and for nearly eight moons before the last Short Day, we had none as the rain put it out."

"Don't you keep it in a hut?" Rhu asked.

"I should say not!" and Marda's voice was quite emphatic. "One man tried it, and the fire god immediately burned down his hut!"

"Where did he place the fire in it?" Hut asked.

"By the wall, of course, where it would be out of the way, and my father's father, who was there, said they could hardly stay inside for the smoke. It was while they were all outside to get some air that the fire god slipped in and burned down the hut."

"So that's why the rains put out your fires, eh? The Mu Yan people keep their fires under thatched huts that have no sides so the smoke can blow out. When it rains, the women shield it with skins." There was just a touch of pride in Hut's voice.

"But that doesn't bring us any fire here," Haitee stated decisively, "so why argue about it? Come on, Rhu, let us get the meat."

Rhu and Hut grinned at each other as Rhu led the way to the bear, Haitee following demurely behind, as was right and proper in her eyes. Nor did she hesitate to help get out the tongue which Rhu said would be tender, while he opened up the carcass, removed the intestines, and crawling half inside, backed out with two long strips of meat which are known to us moderns as the tenderloins. Next, to Haitee's surprise, he dug out all the six to eight-inch claws and placed them in his bag. There were twenty of them, long, curved, and sharp as knives, although the outer ends were worn somewhat blunt from contact with the rocks. Rhu smiled at her but made no effort to satisfy her very apparent curiosity.

Returning to the spring to wash their hands, they found that Hut and Marda had a fire going. After placing the tongue in a bowl of hot water, they haggled off hunks of the tenderloin which, to the amazement of the girls, Rhu carefully rubbed with what they took to be a piece of rock. He then shoved long sharpened sticks through the hunks and handed one to each. Seating themselves beside the fire, they held them in the blaze, and soon the savory odor of broiling meat filled the air.

Handing each a piece of the rock, Rhu admonished them to follow his example. Presently, he withdrew his piece of sizzling meat from the fire, blew upon the most charred part, then biting off a chunk, rubbed the spot on the hunk with his stone, and began chewing away, while again shoving his spitted piece to the fire for further cooking, emulated by the others.

"Why!" cried Haitee, "I never tasted such good bear meat!" She hesitated a moment while she finished chewing her mouthful and swallowed it. "Does that magic stone make it taste so good?"

Rhu grinned. "Lick the stone once, and see for yourself."

Because of the confidence rapidly growing in her heart, Haitee did it. "H-m-m!" she said, "I can't say that I like it so much, but it's not bad, either. Try it, Marda," for Marda had hesitated.

"Um! *I* think it's good," she exclaimed.

"Be careful," Hut admonished her. "It will give you a great thirst, but that is what makes the meat so good," and as did the others, he gnawed off another chunk of the half raw and half scorched meat.

They made no move to leave the fire until the moon peeped over the mountains, although they could hear the growling and yapping of the wolves and jackals as they snarled at one another while they tore and slashed at the bear's carcass. Haitee crept closer to Rhu.

"Don't be scared," he said softly. "They're too busy and have too much to eat to be dangerous. Do you know, Hut, I'm going to get me a wolf whelp one of these days and try to tame it. I've an idea that one breed I know about can be tamed. I had one that would catch pieces of meat I'd toss him when he was only three or four steps away, and he was full grown. I believe that if I'd had time, I could have got him tame enough to touch him."

"Be careful," Hut commented. "They're treacherous, but I'd like to see one tamed. If he could be made to mind, a fellow could hunt easily."

"That's my idea," Rhu agreed. "Well, it's time we started. Do you want me to lead, Hut? I believe I can see better than you in this dim light."

"Like a hoogwar, you can see in the dark," Hut agreed as Rhu dropped the steaming tongue in their food skin for later use.

THE MOON was about half way to midheaven when Rhu paused at the base of a towering cliff, upon the very top of which a single pointed stone stood silhouetted against the sky. Reaching into his pouch, Rhu drew out a small stick—or so the interested Haitee thought it to be—and putting it to his lips, blew upon it softly, producing a thin, eerie sound, a plaintive whistle.

"Hut made this," he informed her confidentially. Presently, he repeated the whistling sound, followed by three short chirps. "Used to do it with my lips," he concluded, "but this can be heard farther and is easier."

As the sounds died away, what might have been an echo could be heard and Rhu gave one short note. Then he and Hut sat down, the girls doing likewise. Since neither of the men spoke, the girls also kept silent, each watching her man closely.

Beneath the Pinnacle

After what seemed an interminable time to the girls, Rhu and Hut got to their feet. As the girls arose, they discovered, standing a few feet distant, a tall, white-haired and bearded man, draped over whose shoulders and reaching almost to his feet was a garment of pure white fur such as they had never seen.

"Welcome, Rhu and Hut, and you, Haitee and Marda. We have been expecting you. You have all passed well your test upon the way, which makes you doubly welcome." The voice of this soft-spoken man was deep, rich, and vibrant, and his eyes, even in the dim moonlight, were as kindly as the gentle touch of his hands when they rested upon the heads of the girls who, intuitively and as one, knelt before him.

"May the Great N'Kul and those who serve Him ever bless and guide you. You are indeed all that Rhu has said and Hut believes you to be. Come, my children, to where peace and serenity ever dwell."

Turning, he walked toward the cliff, and Rhu, with Haitee's small hand upon his arm, and Hut, with Marda's hand clasped in his, followed. Turning to the right around a great boulder, they passed into a narrow cleft in the rock, and although there was neither torch nor fire, they found it sufficiently light to follow their guide easily. Some twenty steps they had taken along the sharply ascending path when there was a dull and heavy thud behind them.

"The stone door has closed," Rhu explained, and thus the girls passed on and into the beginning of a life of ever-increasing wonder.

FOR SEVERAL minutes, the little procession followed along the gradually ascending passage, the sides of which were smooth as glass and appeared to glow softly, and then up a flight of roughly hewn steps. Turning sharply to the right, they entered a great cave in which were burning several clear fires that gave off neither smoke nor heat as they passed close to them.

From the vaulted ceiling, great stalactites hung suspended, scintillating in the light of the fire which brought out and enhanced their colors of yellow, pink, green, and deep brownish red. Never having seen anything of this sort before, the girls peered about in silent awe. Their guide, however, continued on his way, leading them into another passage that had been cut through some white, chalky substance, eventually pausing before what appeared to be the end of the tunnel, not much higher than their heads.

Silently, and to the absolute amazement of Marda and Haitee, a massive section of the wall swung inward! Again resuming their journey, they could now hear soft and beautifully harmonious sounds . . . . the first music the girls had ever heard. The haunting chant of melodious voices steadily increased in volume as they advanced, and the sheer beauty of it all filled their beings with an indescribable sense of longing, strangely blended with the comfort and exhilaration of fulfillment. Though Hut and Rhu had heard it many times, tonight it seemed even more beautiful and reassuring than ever before.

Came a breath of fresh, cool air, laden with the scent of many flowers, and turning a corner in the passageway, they entered a vast open space. Above, the moon shone down serenely, so bright that the stars were dimmed, while all about them, carefully tended and blossoming plants were tastefully arranged.

But it was none of these which held the breathless interest of the awe-struck girls!

Seated in a circle were eleven men, so unlike the brutelike, uncouth creatures to which they were accustomed that they seemed actually beautiful to their unenlightened minds. Indeed, their noble bearing and serenity of countenance would, even today, arouse unusual interest. As Marda and Haitee stared, the one who had brought in the little party took the single vacant seat, thus completing the circle of twelve.

Yet, it was not these who caught and held their rapt attention!

It was the tall, golden-haired, blue-eyed man seated in the center of the circle, His raiment a violet-colored robe of rich, clinging texture bordered with what appeared to be golden fleece. Soft, wavy hair swept back from His high and noble brow, and His beard was as fine and soft as silken floss. All about Him was an aura of golden light.

As Rhu, Hut, Marda, and Haitee approached, He looked up at them, His eyes bespeaking gentle compassion and deep understanding. Then He smiled with such infinite tenderness, the four realized that here was not alone a friend and counselor, but One whose love was boundless. A great sense of peace, such as none of them had ever known, settled down upon them, enveloping them as gently as the down of swans, and creating a feeling of perfect ease. Beside Him, even the Elders looked almost as crude as did the four beside the gentle Elder who had been their guide.

Raising His slender, white hand, He silenced the chant. Then, in a voice as soft and mild as His appearance, He spoke. "My children, peace be unto you. Enter the circle of the Elders and be seated before me. I would commune with you."

Each taking one of the trembling girls by the hand, Hut and Rhu entered the circle reverently, seating themselves upon the soft skins spread before this Great One whom they had never seen before.

"It has been the custom of your people that by the mere taking of a single woman into your dwelling, you became man and wife. It is not fitting that this custom be permitted to continue indefinitely. My children, there is more to marriage than mere mating as the animals do, or that woman be no better than a mere necessary possession.

"Yet, even through many ages to come, will men and women so associate solely because of the urge of sex. But here and there among them will be those who will come to appreciate and understand the deeper significance of what should be a holy and sacred pact.

"You four have been chosen to inaugurate a new and better system because you have earned the right. In times past, about which you now have no knowledge, each of you has taken the same mate—by force, by cunning, and by mutual choice—but because you each were content with a single mate, you justly earned the karma which, in this life, even over mountain and through tribal differences, has drawn you together, as it will do through many ages to come.

"It is meet that you should part for a time, Haitee and Marda to remain here. As handmaidens to the Elders, they will learn

sufficient of the mysteries of life to equal the knowledge of Rhu
and Hut who have become as beloved sons of these noble men,
who through lives of self-denial and deep meditation, have
fitted themselves for the Great Work to which they have now
pledged themselves.

"You, Hut and Rhu, are to return to the outer world, there to
work out in your own way those matters which will afford you
the greatest possible opportunity for advancement and to fit
yourselves for your part in the Great Work of the Elders. You
may be secure in the knowledge that those you love are in safe
hands and that, when the proper time comes, you will be the
first to be wed through a holy ceremony that will find the utmost favor in the eyes of Melchizedek and God.

"You may now retire to the place where you will be shown
the home of Haitee and Marda during this period of separation. There you may bid them farewell, after which you will
rest, then be returned to the outer world.

"However, the decision as to whether you will do this rests
with each of you. There shall be no compulsion. Haitee, what
is your choice?"

Eyes brimming with unshed tears, Haitee looked up into the
kindly face, and in a voice trembling with emotion, replied, "I
shall do gladly as Rhu desires."

He smiled down at her with infinite understanding. "My
child, you have the right to make your own choice, yet do I admire you for your self effacement. And you, Marda?" He asked.
And because, through some occult power, neither she nor Hut
had been able to hear Haitee's decision, she, too, was left free
to decide for herself.

"I shall gladly do as you direct, still would I like that it
should be equally pleasing to Hut." Nor could either Haitee or
Rhu hear her reply.

With the same gentle smile, He looked down at Marda.
"Well said, my child, yet you must know that yours is the
privilege of free choice.

"Rhu, you have heard Haitee's reply. Fortunate the man who
has such a loyal companion, yet you must feel perfectly free to
choose."

"Your plan is best. Long since have I learned that a mere

suggestion from the Elders should be heeded implicitly, and though I fail many times, it is not by intention. If Haitee be willing to remain here, so be it. I believe our happiness will be the greater because of it. Still I would not like to go contrary to Hut's wishes."

Without comment, the Great One turned His eyes to Hut who had yet to learn Rhu's decision. "My son, have you made your choice? Speak freely for none may take from you your power of self-determination."

"May I ask a question?" Hut inquired.

"You may."

"Then, though I am perfectly willing and glad to have it as you suggest because I know it to be best, still would I like to conform with Rhu's desire. As you know, the tie between us is close, and I owe him much, even happiness, cost me what it may."

"Even so has Rhu expressed himself, and no greater test of friendship and brotherly love could be asked. So be it, then, and when the marriage ceremony comes to pass in due course, I, Hiroto, of the Venusians, shall perform the rites.

"Peace be upon the four of you. In the name of the Most High, do I bless you, and on the day of your marriage, I shall present you with that which shall be man's greatest blessing through the ages to come upon this plane." With His right hand, He made certain symbolic gestures which have come down through the ages, the full significance of which may not be revealed.

As the Elder who had brought them in led them away from the circle, the girls became aware for the first time that they were in a great valley walled in by towering cliffs of varying hues, and as they later were to learn, watered by many flowing springs. If there were any other entrance to it than the one through which they had come, none of the four ever learned of it.

"How could they possibly have heard your signal?" Marda asked Rhu. "No sound from the outer world can reach here."

With a smile, the Elder pointed to a long and slender pinnacle high above them, and which was clearly outlined in the dim moonlight. "That stone has a certain quality which causes it to magnify and intensify any sound made at the point where Rhu stood," he explained. "Even a whisper down there can be heard up here."

Along a path bordered with flowers, they were taken to a room which had been hewn in the chalky stratum of the cliff. Its only furnishing consisted of two low couches, or pallets, which were, in reality, piles of the same white fur as was worn by the Elders.   ·

"This, my children, will be your home while you are with us. Your duties will be simple. Each day you will be provided with a supply of food stuff with which you are to prepare a meal for us and for yourselves. Before this room stands a white rock around the flat top of which are stones of different colors. There is also a small thin triangular one which casts a shadow in the daytime. When the shadow touches the green stone, you will go to the place we shall show you with the coming of the next sun and there prepare the meal which you will bring to us in the adjoining room.

"You will always find a fire ready for the cooking of such things as are to be cooked, with vessels for that purpose, as well as those in which to serve them. You will be shown how to prepare the food and taught to recognize many herbs and plants that are good for that purpose, and most of which grow wild in the plains. Before that room also, is another white rock like that before this one, and when the shadow touches the red stone, we shall be assembled for the meal. Following that, you will be taught many things now known to Rhu and Hut.

"I shall leave you now that you may bid one another farewell. Rhu and Hut, I shall see you in the morning to conduct you through the passage. You will sleep where you always have. Peace be with you," and he moved silently away.

"DO YOU know, Rhu," Hut announced as they lay down and were drawing the warm furs over them, "I believe I can make one of those stone markers."

"Why don't you?" Rhu encouraged him. "What I am wondering is how they will work on cloudy or rainy days when the sun does not shine."

But Hut was already asleep. Rhu closed his eyes and all was silent, so quickly did complete relaxation come to them.

DAYLIGHT found Hut and Rhu already starting through the passage with the Elder, and they were soon on their way.

"Shall we see our fathers now?" Hut inquired.

"Not yet. I have a feeling that we shall never take the girls to our family huts. Otherwise, why should the Elders keep them and train them? While Lord Hiroto was speaking last night, I got a strange feeling that we shall not live with our people much longer, though why, I do not know."

"Odd, Rhu, but I felt the same way. What do you suppose it means? The Elders did not say a word although they looked queerly at us. At first, I thought it was because of the girls, but now, I am sure it was for some other reason."

"Let us get the bearskin and have it prepared. It is large enough to make a hut covering, and a warm one, too. It is the largest one I have ever seen. It must be a good five steps long and fully as wide. It will be fine for you and Marda."

"Why not for you and Haitee? By right of striking it the first blow, it is yours."

"You hit it first. Have you forgotten the stone you threw?" Rhu insisted.

"Let's wait until it's finished," Hut ended the matter, and soon, with the some two hundred pounds of bearskin slung on a pole between them, they headed for their homes, little suspecting what awaited them.

Chapter Four

FEATHERED ARROWS

BECAUSE OF the weight of the bearskin, Hut and Rhu found it necessary to stop and rest several times on their homeward journey, so that they were much slower than usual. It was mid-afternoon when they swung around the last clump of trees screening the Ku and Dan huts from them.

Hut, who was leading, stopped abruptly. "Rhu!" he exclaimed in a half choked voice.

As one, they dropped the skin, and Rhu sprang to his side. On the plain below them, they could see the struggle being waged. It was clearly evident that the Plains Dwellers were slowly but surely being forced back by the shaggy and much heavier Forest Dwellers who, while no greater in numbers, were giants as compared to the others.

Quick to grasp the situation, Rhu whispered, "If we slip around to the right, we should be able to get to my hut before they see us. Once there, we can get two of my bows and a big bunch of arrows. I believe you and I can outshoot those brutes and stop them before they can drive our folks back to the huts."

Hut nodded his understanding, and they sped into the brush, bending low as they raced for their objective. Accustomed to this sort of thing, they reached the hut and were inside without even their own people being aware of their coming.

"You swing to the right of our folks and I'll go to the left. When you get there and are ready to start shooting, I'll be watching for you. Take their leaders first, if you can, but shoot to kill," Rhu growled as they slung the quivers of arrows over their shoulders and picked up the bows.

Rhu Sol Ku

Disdaining cover, Hut left on the run while Rhu headed directly for the point he had in mind—a large boulder which would give him a clear view of the struggling men. So fleet of foot was Hut that as Rhu bounded to the top of the stone, he could see him already notching an arrow.

With seemingly calm deliberation, Rhu drew one of his own long arrows to his ear and launched it, having another notched by the time the first tore through the massive, hairy chest of the yelling savage who was battling Hut's father. As the stricken creature screamed in agony, Hut's arrow tore through the neck of the man nearest him, and a second later, Rhu's second arrow claimed a third victim. Then Hut's arrow ripped through the arm of a fourth, while Rhu's third arrow brought his third victim coughing to the earth with it through his throat.

So quickly had this come about that it was not until then that their people discovered the welcome allies, and with joyful cries of "Rhu!" and "Hut!" they took fresh heart. At almost the same moment, the attackers saw Rhu, and arrows started weaving toward him from their crude and heavy bows.

"Yah!" he yelled derisively, for the far-from-straight arrows flew wide of their mark. At the same time, the spiteful twangs of his long bow sent his own fairly straight ones speeding with such surprising accuracy that those of the enemy archers who were not struggling to drag his arrows from their bodies were quickly discouraged.

"E-E-yah!" Hut echoed Rhu's defiance as his scarcely less accurate archery accounted for two more.

By now, the heartened Plains Dwellers rallied, and the tide turned so swiftly that it was but a short time before the Forest Dwellers were in full flight. What might easily have proved to be a disaster was turned into a very real victory, though there was wailing in the family huts of both Kus and Dans that night, for there were eight dead among them, and all were wounded.

"GOOD!" grunted Rhu's father, as he sat beside the fire while Rhu's mother bound a strip of soft doeskin over a nasty, bleeding gash in his side where a stone knife had bared one of his ribs, binding it in place with a strip of soft leather.

"Good," he repeated, smiling at Rhu. "You shoot well, you and

Hut. Grut!" he snapped at the son who had disputed Rhu's right to the morsel at their last meal together. "The Ku man who dares reach before Rhu at my pot loses his right to eat from it."

Grut's grin looked positively wolfish. "But for Rhu's arrow today, I'd need no pot. He can have my share."

Rhu slapped him on his hairy shoulder, and eyes dancing, he growled, "There'd be no fun eating from the same pot without a contest. If I'm not fast enough to beat Grut, it's my fault, so don't blame him, Father."

"I have spoken," grunted the father sternly, but to their mother, he muttered softly, "Good boys."

Later, Rhu walked over to the Dan circle. Though nothing was said, there was no mistaking his welcome, Hut's mother even bringing him a bowl containing a stew of bear's tongue and greens.

"Hut has told me of the taste stone," she announced. "I would try it when you have some."

Rhu smiled up into her heavy featured but kindly and concerned face. It took courage of a rare sort for a woman to ask something of a man, let alone one from a different family. "Yes, Mother, and you are very welcome. Here is all I have with me, but Hut and I will get more tomorrow. Where is he?"

"He sits silently inside the hut," she said softly. "He did not eat."

"Neither did I," Rhu said stoutly. He did not add that his mother and sisters had been too busy to prepare the evening meal for, being first attacked, the Kus had suffered most at the initial onslaught. Not many minutes had elapsed, however, between the first Ku war cry and the arrival of every available Dan man.

"Well, Hut," Rhu announced as he entered the comparative darkness of the big abode and stood waiting for his eyes to accustom themselves to the gloom. "Didn't get hurt, did you?"

"No," Hut answered shortly. "But I feel a bit sick. I don't like fighting."

Rhu chuckled. "It didn't look as if you did. Huh! Your shooting improves! How'd you like that bow?"

Hut's face brightened and in his interest, he forgot himself. "It certainly pulls better than any I ever had in my hands. You surely know how to make them! Why, it didn't seem much harder to draw than a boy's, but how it drives those arrows! I was examining one after I'd cleaned it. You made the piercing end heavier than the notched one. Why?"

"Shoots straighter and doesn't come out so easily. Also, I always hold their points in the fire until they're almost ready to burn. It makes them much harder," Rhu explained. "That's the bow I've been making for you. Let me have it and then let's go outside. There's still a little finishing I want to do on it. By the time you're through eating, I'll have it ready for you to try."

Hut would have demurred, but feeling better somehow since Rhu had come, he followed. After one swift and understanding glance at the two, his mother brought him a big bowl of stew which, Rhu observed slyly, was mostly greens, although there was some bear's tongue in it.

"Bring Rhu some, Mother, with plenty of meat."

"Oh, I already had some," Rhu said, smiling at her, "but I could eat a little more. What's that green stuff in it, Hut?"

"Dandelion leaves, mostly, but I found a sort of green stuff growing at a spring, right in the water, and there's some of that in it. Bet you'll like it."

"It wasn't bad," Rhu agreed. "Do you mean that flat leafed stuff with straggly stems?"

"Yes," Hut agreed. "It's pretty good raw."

Rhu chuckled softly, but said nothing for a time as he began scraping on the bow which was already nearly perfect. "Better watch out," he cautioned finally, eyes twinkling. "Some day, one of those rams is going to mistake you for another one."

"That's what Yaug says," Hut agreed. "Got in bad with father for calling my stuff sheep food." Both laughed, as the brother he had mentioned came over and squatted beside them, grinning at Rhu.

"Good fight," he grunted. "Hut eat sheep feed, but fight like man," which was a rare compliment, coming from him.

Yaug, like most of them, had little humor, and that very crude, but, as Rhu well knew, he was a mighty good man to have at your back in time of trouble. His was the deadly, dangerous type, quick as lightning in temper and action, slow in thought and still slower of speech, but utterly fearless and loyal to his friends. In fact, these particular attributes were quite characteristic of the Plains Dwellers and set them well apart from the Forest Dwellers who were not only dangerous fighters, but were inclined to treachery and apt to think of themselves first and their friends afterwards.

Effortlessly drawing the string to his ear, Rhu now tried the bow several times, studying its curve and scraping one end lightly again and again while both Hut and Yaug looked on with avid interest. Finally, after snapping the string a few times, he heaved a sigh of satisfaction.

As though released from a spell, Hut sighed also. "It's certainly one fine bow," he breathed. "But why were you scraping it? It looks smooth to me."

"So each end will pull the same. Makes them shoot lots better. Here you are, Hut. If you'll scrub it with sand and water, it will get smoother, and if you rub it well with hot bear fat, it will work as well in wet as in dry weather, but the bowstring must be kept dry. I make mine by taking a strip of fresh hoogwar gut, twisting and rolling it under strain, then as it dries, working hot bear fat into it, in case you ever have to make one. There are always a few in my hut in that old quiver I had before you gave me my new one.

"Your bow and mine are exactly the same length, but mine is a bit heavier and stiffer. I still have to get perfect balance in its pull as I did yours. I have about two hundred good arrows that I'm soaking. If you'll help me, we'll try hanging a weight on them to make them perfectly straight."

"All right," Hut agreed readily enough, but his serious expression showed his thoughts were on another problem. "Say, Rhu," he broke out, "wouldn't a leather grip in the center of the bow help to strengthen it? Yours broke there."

"Pshaw! Why didn't *I* ever think of that?" Rhu demanded disgustedly, then smiled. "We seem destined to work together, don't we? I already have about fifty perfect arrows, so far as I can judge." As usual, his mind refused to be diverted from the original idea.

THE FOLLOWING morning found the two sitting upon the big boulder on which the hoogwar had been killed. From this vantage point, they overlooked much of the surrounding country. Eight miles away and far below them, the great Hatamukulian River which was a good two to four miles wide, appeared like a silver ribbon as it flowed through a vast green, rolling country that reached to the dim horizon . . . . and far beyond, as Rhu and Hut were destined to learn in time.

On its western side and merging with the blue-hazed mountains, lay the fertile Tama Valley, while to the east lay the seemingly limitless plains that reached to and beyond the Biblical Land of Nod. A few miles north of the Mu Valley, four great rivers, the Upata, the Mu, the Cari, and the Telha converged from the four main valleys and formed the source of the Hatamukulian River.

As far as Hut and Rhu knew, the magnificent country through which it flowed was unpopulated. The pass, once used by a few venturesome Mu Yans who sought to move there, had long since been closed when a great earthquake had caused the collapse of its towering walls, so that it was now almost impassable. Nor had the Tama Yans ever been able to devise any means for crossing the swift and mighty river.

"What a beautiful land! The grazing seems to be without limit." Hut sighed rapturously as he sat peering into its far reaches. "I've often wondered why we have never taken our herds out there. Here, we are confined to our valley and have to move them several times each Great Sun (year). We are never able to stay more than two or three moons in one place, and always lose some of the cattle each time we move. Out there, we could build substantial, permanent homes which would be more comfortable and where the old people could spend their remaining lives at ease. Every Great Sun, we also lose small children from exposure, and the old ones suffer much."

Rhu paused in the patient scraping of his new bow and smiled at Hut. "In the first place, we would no sooner get settled than tribes from the other valleys would swarm out and attack us, just as was done in ancient times. You know that is why it has never been populated. Of course," he added as Hut's face betrayed his disappointment, "we might be able to persuade a number of families to come with us, but the more there are, the greater the herds and the harder it would be to provide plenty of grazing without again having to move from place to place."

Hut grew thoughtful. He knew all that Rhu said was true, but there should be some way! Of that, he was convinced; yet if he could not persuade Rhu . . . ! Small wonder he could not hide his disappointment.

Laying aside his bow, and chin in hand, Rhu stared moodily into the distance, striving his best to help in the solution of the problems presented by Hut's idea. When it came to things he could do with his own hands, his thoughts flowed freely, but while his mental alertness was far above the average of his day, new departures from fixed habits and the usual routine of life called for slow and laborious thinking.

Only dimly at first, could he conceive such a radical move. Once the idea began to take root in his mind, however, the very tenacity which made those of that age so resistant to change, was an asset. The difference between the average folk of that day and these two lay in the fact that both Rhu and Hut were willing to consider new things. Thus, his thoughts once directed into the channel presented by this idea and the problems it involved, Rhu hung on to it with all the power of his determined nature.

"Hm-m-m!" he hummed half aloud. "Grazing for our flocks and those of others of the Plains Dwellers who might be persuaded to join us is a big problem, and we have to work it out before we think of anything else. I have noticed that if we do not let our herds, especially the sheep, graze too closely or too long in one place, the grass grows up again very soon. Also," as he warmed to the subject, "when we return to this locality each spring, in the places where our huts have stood and where the ground has been churned in the stock pens, the grass is always thickest and tallest. Maybe," he reflected aloud, "there is some way to make pastures last longer, or even to make them so much better that we wouldn't have to move our flocks at all."

Hut's eyes grew wide and bright as this new idea took hold. "You're right, Rhu. Now that you mention it, it always takes a long time for the stock to use up that longer and heavier growth. Perhaps," and the thought left him nearly breathless, "there may not only be some way to make grass grow better, but there may be different *kinds* of grass. Do you suppose we could get more of the better kind to grow?"

"I don't know," and Rhu shook his shaggy head dubiously, "but we could try, and I am sure the Elders can help. But if we succeed, then it won't be very long before the other tribes will try to take away our lands. On that great plain, there is no cover for fighting, and no barriers to slow down attacks. Of course, if we could persuade a large number of the Plains Dwellers to join with us, as the Ku and Dan families live, we might have a chance."

Rhu was now getting upon familiar ground, and his thoughts began to flow more rapidly. Suddenly, he almost shouted. "Hut! I have an idea! The Forest Dwellers are good fighters. They do not like to work and even hunt only from hunger, but *they love to fight.*

"Now just suppose we can bring along a goodly number of Plains Dwellers with their herds. With what we would save from not having to move them so often and because they will be so much easier to guard from losses to hoogwars and other animals, we could well afford to feed a big bunch of Forest Dwellers. In return for it, they would guard the pass and do most of our fighting for us. When those big, hairy fellows are armed with really good bows and arrows, other tribes would think twice before attacking us."

Hut frowned as he wrestled with another thought. "Yet, Rhu, if what the Elders say is right, might not our even preparing to resist *invite* attack? As you know, they teach that if we seek to live by fighting, we shall surely die by fighting."

It was Rhu's turn to frown. "But we are not seeking to live by fighting, Hut! We put roofs on our huts to keep us dry when it rains, but we do not all drown. We carry weapons to protect our herds, but the animals do not often attack us. It isn't as if we were preparing to *attack* anybody."

"There is a difference, I suppose," Hut agreed reluctantly.

"Of course there is. Did not Lord Lithargos say to choose the lesser of two ills. I certainly think that protecting ourselves and families and herds from attack is far better than sitting by and letting others kill them."

"Rhu, I wonder whether we could not build our homes so strong that we could hold them in case of attack?"

"Why not? If we can find how to build so that many families can live in one house in comfort, making one building large and strong enough to serve as a protection should not be so hard!"   .

For several minutes, the two sat motionless, each busy with his thoughts. Suddenly, Rhu began hurriedly stringing his bow with skilled fingers.

"Lie down, Hut, and don't move," he said, eying a low-lying hill beyond the deep canyon to their left. Then he notched an arrow. "Keep still," he cautioned further, just as a great eagle swept into view skimming the hill and watching intently for game. Steadily and swiftly it came across the Mu River and straight toward where the boys lay motionless on the stone. Rhu was now flat upon his back, his bow lying across his legs, arrow notched. In breathless silence, Hut, eyes fixed upon Rhu, observed that his right arm and shoulder hung over the edge of the rock so they could move freely.

When almost directly overhead, the eagle screamed, set its wide wings and started to swing almost straight upward as its keen, telescopic eyes detected the two man things. Like a flash, Rhu's bow arm described an arc, the arrow drawn to its head. Then the string twanged as the arrow sped on its way. Came another screech, a flurry of flying feathers, and the clawing, screaming bird, larger than our modern condor, plummeted to the earth, transfixed by the arrow. It was gasping its last when Hut and Rhu reached it, each with far different emotions. Hut was almost speechless at Rhu's uncanny skill and perfect markmanship, while Rhu was intent solely upon the plumage.

"It is the most powerful and agile of our birds of prey. Therefore, it should have the best feathers," he commented, waiting for the last clutching grip of those mammoth talons to relax and that razor-sharp, cruelly hooked bill to cease snapping. That these birds often carried off a full-grown sheep will afford some idea of their size and power.

"Grasp one wing, Hut, and be careful not to get close to either head or talon lest there be one final spark of life. Drop it quickly if it moves," he admonished, and it was thus that they carried it to the rock.

"It's by far the largest one I ever saw," Hut pronounced, "and certainly beautiful. I'll bet it's five steps from wing tip to wing tip, Rhu," missing it by only half a step for it was five and a half steps—some sixteen and one-half feet as we measure things.

Rhu then began examining the wings, plucking all the feathers of from four to six or seven inches in length, and straight. There was an imposing pile when he finally finished —probably over five hundred—for he had taken them from all parts of the body. Hut's eyes were wide with inquiry as he watched the silent Rhu's careful selection.

As he finished, Rhu caught the look and chuckled. "Wait and see," was all he said. "You might cut off his talons, though. They are certainly beauties. It's a shame to destroy the bird," he mused somewhat sadly, "but I believe it will be worth it." Then he picked up his bow, handling it almost caressingly. "It's a wonder," he breathed. "Its pull is perfect. Will you decorate it for me tonight, Hut? If you will, I think I'll have something real to show you tomorrow."

ALL that evening, and late into the night, Rhu labored patiently beside the fire which his mother tended as she watched with ill-concealed interest. He had several of his best arrows laid out before him. These, he grooved in line with their notch. Next, he carefully split each feather, fitting matching halves into each of the grooves, only to find that fastening them in place without making humps where they were bound presented a problem which he seemed unable to solve. Several of his precious feathers were already completely spoiled, and a less determined person would probably have given it up as a bad job.

"There must be some way," he muttered, frowning as he studied the problem before him.

Observing his mounting disappointment, Meta, his mother, got to her feet and, to his surprise, asked him to wait. Rhu's eyes followed her questioningly as she strode around behind the hut to the odoriferous pile of refuse consisting of sheep, beef, and deer hoofs, and gristly joints too tough for even their strong jaws. Returning with a quantity of these, she put them in a heavy earthen pot, added a little water, and placed the vessel over the fire. Presently, the smelly mess was bubbling frothily, and she skimmed off the scum from time to time until the hoofs and most of the gristle were either melted or very soft. Next, she brought out a large handful of dried strips of intestines which she had saved for sewing hides together as Rhu had taught her.

Taking one of the arrows from Rhu, she used a stick and liberally smeared the grooves with the thick mess in the pot. As carefully as Rhu, she inserted a split feather into each side, holding it taut for several minutes, until it remained in place when she released it. Next, she took a strip of gut and soaked it in some hot water until it was soft and pliable. This, she carefully wrapped, smoothly and tightly, at each end of the feather, biting it off so it lay almost perfectly flat about the shaft. With the stick, she smeared these with some of the glue from the pot, then set the arrow aside to dry.

For a long moment, Rhu sat staring. Then going to her side, he patted the wide, bare shoulder. "Mother, you're a wonder!" he said softly.

Her heavy-lidded, dark eyes brightened at this unexpected but very welcome praise. "Mahata has told me of that taste stone," she mumbled softly. "I—I would try it if I had some . . . . though I think she lied," she could not resist adding, glowering balefully.

Rhu chuckled and promptly went to his hut, returning with one of the pieces he and Hut had secured on their way home.

"Here, Mother," he said, handing it to her, "and you should know that Hut's mother told you the truth. Has not your stew been unusually good today?"

"It was fresh meat!" she growled, her eyes narrowing.

"Perhaps," Rhu said, edging away until just beyond her reach. "I put some of the rock in it this morning before I left!"

Like a flash, her heavy hand lashed out, the wind from its passing telling Rhu how sincerely earnest had been her attempt to slap him. As if badly scared, he darted frantically away, and her heavy features broke into a smile.

"It is not good to play pranks upon me," she growled, "but the stew was good."

"Use only about so much," Rhu explained, knowing she would die before asking, and likely spoil the next stew by tossing the whole lump into it.

"I know," she growled. "Mahata told me."

But Rhu observed that her sharp old eyes had watched closely. "Remember that I offered it first to you," he reminded her, for his people were proud and sensitive.

"Huh!" she snorted. "You and your silly notions. Do you expect that arrow to fly?" she demanded, at the same time reaching for another, and between the two of them, all fifty of his best arrows were feathered when another woman took his mother's place, and Rhu went to bed.

WHILE Rhu had been feathering arrows, Hut had labored patiently on Rhu's bow beside the fire his father had ordered kept fresh for as long as he desired to "play beside it," and it is doubtful whether any modern craftsman was ever more meticulously careful with his lines and striping. Each end of the bow was an exact duplicate of the other, line for line, and the geometrical designs were those of a master craftsman, while the grip was of plaited rawhide, applied wet and allowed to dry. The designs were carved into the hard wood with bits of the crystal fragments he had gathered, then carefully filled with coloring matter he had long since learned to prepare. These dyes never faded, and against the polished wood as he finished rubbing it smooth, were strikingly beautiful. This bow was ever after Rhu's chief delight.

When he took it and the feathered arrows out to try them the following morning, Hut was an admiring and interested observer. After dividing the arrows equally between them, Rhu invited Hut to try one first. "I don't know what will happen," he said, "but I think there will be no wobble in its flight. The feathers should make it fly straighter."

They were standing before a high, clay bank on which Rhu had made a small, rough circle. Stepping back some forty paces, Hut drew the feather to his ear, and the arrow's flight was a symphony of beauty as it sped unerringly toward its mark, landing about four inches above and to the left of the circle.

Next, Rhu stepped up and with a swift pull launched his arrow, apparently without aim, but it landed exactly in the center of the circle and stuck quivering in the clay. Without comment, he strode forward and retrieving the arrows, studied them intently.

"Hm-m-m!" he hummed through his nose. "I see. The feathers on your arrow, Hut, are not laid on perfectly straight. Had the arrow been turned over, it would have struck to the right. Try mine," and he handed his arrow to Hut, returning the defective one to his quiver upside down.

Hut's shot was well within the circle, which, considering it was not more than ten inches in diameter, was good shooting for anyone.

"Fine," Rhu praised as he himself launched a second arrow which landed in almost exactly the same spot as his first one, while Hut's next one struck close beside it. Fortunately, and due to Rhu's craftsmanship, they found but two defective arrows.

"Either of them is better than my best were before," Rhu announced. "With practice, we can do some real shooting. Let's go see how our others have come out. They should be dry and straight by now."

Already fairly straight, those they had hung out the night before were now practically perfect, so that after hanging out the other hundred, they spent the remainder of the day in feathering them.

"What in the world is this stuff?" Hut demanded as the pot of glue began to simmer and smell.

"The stuff Mother made to fasten on the feathers," Rhu explained, and they went to work.

Since the second batch of arrows was straight by mid-afternoon, they continued to labor, growing more and more adept with practice, ever mindful that the difference between perfection and carelessness might spell the difference between life and death. For the most part, they worked in silence. After an unusually long period, Hut voiced the thought which had been running through his mind.

"Rhu, you say that when the point is heavier than the main shaft, arrows are more accurate. Do you suppose the Cave Dwellers could make *stone* heads? That would not only make them more accurate, but sharper and more deadly."

Rhu stopped his work and lapsed into a deep study. "Maybe," he said at last. "But to fasten them on would be a very real problem. If one came loose, it would be spoiled, and we can take no chances."

Hut began tracing designs in the soft earth. Finally, his eyes brightened, and well they might inasmuch as he had drawn the arrowhead design that has come down through the ages.

"Cut a notch in the head of the shaft. Insert this," pointing to the concave neck of the arrowhead he had drawn. "Then bind it with this stuff," indicating the gut strips and the pot of glue, "and you would have one that would stay with you."

Rhu had been following him intently, and his response was enthusiastic. "You are right, Hut! They would be sharp of point and edge, and swelling in thickness so they'd make a clean hole for the shaft. What a weapon to train the Forest Dwellers to use in our defense!" he breathed. "None of the other tribes would dare molest us after they once got a . . . . taste . . . . of . . . ." His voice trailed off and he became lost in thought.

Accustomed to his friend's thoughtful moods and mindful of his own reveries, Hut remained silent, gazing off to the beautiful country before them.

Rhu's vibrant, "Hut! I have an idea!" broke the silence. "Why couldn't we make the *Cave Dwellers* a part of our plan and bring them on with the Plains Dwellers and the Forest Dwellers? They are so skilled in making knives and war ax heads that I know they can make these arrowheads. If they lived with us they could supply everything we need for defense, to say nothing of the knives necessary for skinning and cleaning our animals. What a blessing our mothers would consider it if they each might have a knife to make strips for lacings! And they have all sorts of things in their caves which they have devised from stone and which we could use. They could very easily earn their right to be with the rest of us . . . ." and he paused, going back into his own thoughts for a moment.

"Hut, do you know, I believe this is what the Lord Hiroto meant when He spoke of the Great Work we are to do. I feel He had in mind that we should gather the most intelligent of all the Mu Yans together so that each may supply the need of the other. I think He felt *we* could do it because our own families live together so harmoniously and that this is a condition He and the Elders would like to see spread further." Rhu's voice rang as he continued, "Yes! I believe this is it!"

Hut's being thrilled to the intensity of the thought, his blood seeming to surge with a great eagerness and a strange gladness. "Yes," he almost whispered, "I feel it too," and he heaved a tremulous sigh.

For some moments neither said a word, each engrossed with his own thoughts. Finally, Rhu spoke. "I'm willing to go among them and the Forest Dwellers to try to interest them. You could talk to the Plains Dwellers, Hut, and gather some of them together."

Hut demurred. "This is a really big undertaking, Rhu. Don't you think we should talk to the Elders about it?"

Rhu shook his head thoughtfully. "No, Hut. They know what it is we are to do, and they probably know how we feel about it. Let us at least make the attempt, then if we run into too much difficulty, we can go to them. If you will copy this arrowhead on a piece of bark so I can take it along, I think I shall approach the Cave Dwellers first and then go on to the Forest Dwellers." Getting his quiver, he dumped out the old inferior arrows, among them being the heavy stone he had found and forgotten.

"Huh!" he grunted. "Say, Hut, look at this stone. Did you ever see anything like it?"

As Hut took it, the unexpected weight caused it to drop from his hand so suddenly that it felt as if someone had actually jerked it away. He glanced at Rhu. "It felt as if you snatched it away! It must be magic!" he exclaimed.

"No, Hut, it's just heavy. Pick it up and you'll see."

Rather hesitantly, Hut reached for the stone, half expecting it to jump from his hand, but, of course, nothing of the sort happened.

"You should have seen the sparks fly when I struck it with my war club," Rhu commented. "Honestly, it almost blazed! Here," reaching for his club, "let's try it again." Taking the stone from Hut, Rhu struck it a glancing blow, the resulting sparks burning his bare leg so that he jumped.

Hut's eyes were wide. "It IS magic!" he asserted positively. "It is full of fire!"

"Fire?" grunted Rhu. "Say . . . . wait a moment!" Hurrying over to the pile of wood, he gathered some dry bark which was highly inflammable. Shredding some of this, he made a slight hollow in it. "That's to guide the sparks," he explained to Hut. Holding the stone above the hollow, he began striking it with the flint, and presently, to his delight, some of the sparks began to smoulder in the bark. Carefully blowing upon these, he coaxed them into a tiny blaze, as they often had to do when their coals were small.

For a long time the two sat silently looking at each other as though overcome by this great miracle.

"The fire god has been good to us," reverently murmured Rhu at last. "Let's break this stone so we may each have half."

This, however, was more easily said than done, and though they labored diligently, they had no success beyond myriads of sparks. Finally, Rhu laid it with its ends upon two hard rocks, struck it a heavy blow with his club, and it fell into four pieces. Carefully, they tried each of these and found them all equally good.

"You take one, Hut, and I'll keep one. The others I'm going to take with me to use with the Cave and Forest Dwellers. This might succeed should all else fail, for fire is precious."

"Let's fill a small skin with that dry bark," Hut suggested. "You might be unable to find any when you sorely need it. Besides, it will keep dry so you can always have a fire."

For a moment, he hesitated, then continued, "Rhu, I've been thinking about the Cave Dwellers. Do you suppose it might be possible that they could build *huts from stone?* They would last for all time to come and neither wind nor fire could harm them! Besides, they would be easier to defend. If such a thing were possible, our people would have homes forever and be reasonably safe from attack." His questioning eyes met the shining ones of Rhu.

"That certainly *would* be something, although the idea seems a little fantastic. No doubt, such a thing never occurred to the Cave Dwellers, Hut, but once they get the idea, they probably can do it. All this we shall know when we return from our journeys."

Chapter Five

THE CAVE DWELLERS

BY THE TIME Rhu reached the first of the towering lime-stone cliffs along the side of the Mu Valley and some hundred and fifty miles south of his starting point, he had grown quite adept at building fires with the use of his "fire stone." (Probably nickel-steel from some meteorite.) Thus, he had been enabled to make more rapid progress than hereto-fore when he carried coals as Hut had devised and had to stop from time to time to renew them. Even so, he had gone con-siderably out of his way in order to avoid contact with the Forest Dwellers—not that he feared them, but he knew that if he were to encounter them, it would result in delays. He had decided to contact the Cave Dwellers first, and once Rhu made up his mind, he clung tenaciously to an idea.

Many times, as he covered the miles to the cliffs, Hut's sug-gestion regarding the stone huts came to mind, and the oftener he thought of them, the greater and more important became the advantages they offered. Each resting spot found him gathering small stones and endeavoring to build tiny huts, but every attempt met with uniformly bad results. All the huts he had ever seen had rounded, dome-shaped roofs. Even the caves had them. Yet, each time he attempted to construct such a roof upon the carefully built sides of his little dwellings, the entire structure would collapse. But for the many advantages he saw in Hut's idea, he would have become utterly dis-couraged. As it was, however, the oftener he failed, the more adamant became his resolve to succeed.

Even now, during the last day of his journey, much of the

time he should have been devoting to sleep, he spent working
on a model building. Contriving a network of twigs to support
the stones as he placed them carefully over the top, he saw it
collapse before half completed. He tried stronger twigs, but
though he finally managed to get the roof covered after a
fashion, it fell to pieces when he tried to remove the first twig.
In disgust, he kicked and scattered the little mound of stones.

"Even if it did stand alone, it would not turn water unless it
was covered with skins or something," he growled. For a long
time he sat staring at the cliffs. "There must be some way," he
stated positively and half aloud, "and I'm going to find it!"

Well knowing the careful guard kept by the Cave Dwellers
to protect themselves from occasional marauding bands of Forest Dwellers, Rhu had long since decided that, despite the dan-
gers involved, he would time himself to arrive at night. He
wanted to contact Waugh, the most skilled of the stone
workers, before seeing any of the others. He had grown very
friendly with the old fellow on his previous trip, and while he
had never been invited into the deeper recesses of the cave,
Rhu had shown Waugh how to get fire into it.

All this day, Rhu had started no fire lest some keen-eyed
Cave Dweller see the smoke. Familiar landmarks were all
about him and with the approach of nightfall, he studied the
country ahead of him carefully. Of the several trails which
started up the cliffs, only one led anywhere, the others being
merely blinds to mislead those who did not belong among the
Cave Dwellers. There would be no moon. If the night remained as clear as it promised, the stars would afford him
ample light for, as Hut had remarked, his ability to see in the
gloom was almost catlike.

However, as often happened at this season, if it were to
cloud up suddenly, or a valley fog were to rise, he wanted to
be certain he knew exactly where he was. The path was narrow, tortuous, and none too safe to follow, even in a good light.
Besides, the Cave Dwellers were accustomed to placing devil-
ishly cunning traps along their main trails, and they were as
deadly as they were cleverly hidden. He had seen some of
them and what had happened to a great bear that had been
hurtled over a four-hundred-foot cliff by one.

As soon as he felt safe from observing eyes, Rhu started along the path he had located during the early morning. In addition to his bow and arrows, his war club, and his crudely repaired knife, he also carried a rude, stone-tipped spear. This was but a straight pole about seven feet long to which he had lashed one of the crude stone knives of his tribe.

"At least," he commented when finishing it just before leaving, "it is better than a mere club or staff such as I shall need for traveling in the dark."

As he moved silently upward, Rhu paused from time to time, ears alert for the slightest sound. Already, he had crept past two caves, apparently undetected since there had been no discernible movement or sound. Like a shadow he had also slipped past one sentry who was sound asleep.

To sleep while on guard was not as serious a neglect of duty as it sounds for, as was true of Rhu, most of those accustomed to depending upon their alertness for their very lives were almost as quick to detect a strange intruder by scent as by hearing. No matter how soundly they appeared to sleep, those highly developed senses could generally be depended upon. If not, their lives usually paid for their laxness. No more than a single person might hope to pass a sleeper undetected, and Rhu was indeed fortunate that scent or sound did not betray him.

During one of these pauses, Rhu's thought reverted to Lord Lithargos, and he started in surprise. He could have sworn he heard Him say, "I am with thee, my son. Thou hast done well, and I shall help thee in thy hour of need."

Strain his eyes as he might, however, there was not even the semblance of a shadowy form. The hair ridged along the nape of his neck, and his skin prickled, yet he felt encouraged. Almost, it was as if this Great One were by his side. With lighter heart, Rhu pressed forward, though he was not one whit less alert and careful. Later, he was to learn that he had actually passed through one deadly trap which, for some obscure reason, failed to function.

Then he approached the third cave, and his heart almost failed him when he saw one of the stooped but powerful men come to the entrance to stand sniffing the air and peering into the gloom. Breathlessly, Rhu pressed even closer to the rough wall, thankful that the deerskin garment he was wearing so nearly matched the stone as to make him seem a part of it. Carefully, he closed his eyes until they were mere slits. Eyes, as he had discovered, betrayed one very quickly since they reflected light as brilliantly as pools of clear water.

Evidently satisfied, the man disappeared into the cave, but Rhu was little better off than before. There was no way around the opening of that cave for the cliff overhung the narrow trail. Even though it did not, both above and below, the face of the cliff had been polished by countless driving storms until climbing or descending its face was a physical impossibility. To go back, even if he eluded detection, was to lose all he had gained, and morning was not far distant. In his extremity, he remembered the words of Lord Lithargos, and summoning all his courage, moved ahead, war club ready for any emergency.

At the very edge of the wide-mouthed cave, he paused and drew a long breath, then stooping, moved ahead with soft, pantherish silence, evenly and smoothly. Thus, either because he fooled the watcher into believing him to be one of the Cave Dwellers passing along the trail, or because, through some occult power, Lord Lithargos threw His mantle of protection about him, Rhu passed without either challenge or movement from within the cave.

Once safely beyond, he discovered that he was literally bathed in sweat, and the cool morning breeze chilled him so that, but for the danger of some untoward sound, he would have unrolled and wrapped about himself his sleeping skin. "Phew!" he whistled to himself. "That was close," and being what he was, thanked the Great One for what he firmly believed was His protection.

It was some five hundred yards and up a stiff incline, with hand-hewn steps in places, to Waugh's cave, and Rhu pressed forward. Waugh was old, and several years before had been so badly crippled in a fight with one of the big bears frequenting the region that he was no longer able to descend into the valley to hunt. Instead, he had developed such consummate skill in working the hard flint, obsidian, and other similar stones that his products were in great demand. As a consequence, he had been able to provide for himself many of the things he otherwise would have been denied, even by his beetle-browed sons, most of whose prowess it took to keep themselves supplied with food and skins.

Through Rhu's good offices on his previous visit, a contact had been made with some of the best Forest Dwellers septs who greatly prized Waugh's knives and cheerfully traded the spoils of many hunts for them. As a matter of fact, by the time Rhu left, Waugh had been lifted from actual want to a position of no inconsiderable power among his neighbors. He always had plenty of meat and skins with which to bargain for firewood—ever hard to procure in that barren section—as well as for supplies of flint and obsidian. He even traded for the inferior knives and ax heads of his neighbors which he greatly improved and then traded for something of more value. Since many of the Cave Dwellers were also skilled in making pottery cooking vessels, he could always enjoy the best, and being a shrewd bargainer, invariably profited from each transaction.

In other words, Waugh rapidly became wealthy and, even as is true today, the possession of wealth afforded him a standing which made his advice seem highly desirable. Therefore, his repeated assurances of Rhu's welcome at any time meant much.

"Now, if Waugh is still alive," Rhu growled, "the worst of this is over, but if not, I may find myself in a tight place." Boldly entering the cave, he squatted down in a niche inside the opening, draped his heavy sleeping skin over his shoulders and patiently waited for what the dawn might bring.

A sound like the faint or distant scraping of one stone against another roused him, and he shrugged the skin from his shoulders, gripped his war club, and prepared to leap into action if necessary. Presently, the labored, wheezy breathing and sound of a dragging foot at the end of a crooked leg brought a smile to Rhu's previously strained face.

"I am Rhu," he said softly. "How are you feeling, Waugh?"

The scraping noise in the deep gloom of the cave stopped abruptly.

"Rhu?" Waugh's rasping voice queried.

"Yes. Rhu of the Ku family of Plains Dwellers. Don't you

remember me? Phew!" under his breath. "Suppose, like some
of the old ones, he has lost his memory!"

"Stand before cave mouth," Waugh demanded.

Rhu complied, notwithstanding his full realization that in so
doing he made an excellent target against the now graying sky.

"Ugh!" grunted Waugh, and though Rhu could not see it, his
lined and bewhiskered old face broke into a broad smile that
disclosed age-yellowed and broken teeth. "Good! Rhu welcome. How Rhu reach cave alone safe? Waugh not understand. Lower Dwellers jealous Waugh rich. Rhu do. Hate Rhu.

"But Rhu here now." A sharp edge crept into his voice. "Let
others beware how treat Rhu, though Rhu need no help. Time
was Waugh fear no man, but few care for old who no longer
hunt. Waugh memory long. In Waugh cave, Rhu have only
friends. Even Dargh welcome Rhu, though an odd one. Still, of
all sons, Dargh alone have Waugh's skill in cutting stones.
Come." Waugh turned to lead the way. "Eat morning meal.
Fresh deer meat. Only week old. Scarcely smells."

Then Rhu saw what almost made his breath stop! Before
him, reaching from one side of the cave to the other, and from
floor to ceiling, was a wall of carefully matched stones, and in
its center an opening through which Waugh had passed!

Coming from the fresh outer air, the stench in the great cave
room was almost stifling, but Rhu was well accustomed to
smells, and it did not bother him. Furthermore, he was too full
of his recent discovery to be overly particular, for here seemed
to be the solution to his and Hut's perplexity. If only the problem of the roof could be solved as satisfactorily as Waugh had
provided for his family's protection with this thick stone wall,
they were well on their way to the accomplishment of their
ideal.

From the back of the room, other men began to emerge,
most of whom Rhu remembered well enough to call them by
name, receiving grunts in reply, for, like most of the folk of
their time, they spoke but little. Because their ideas were few
and seldom new, very few words were necessary, and these
mostly nouns and verbs. They were expressly people of action
rather than of words.

Over the family fire several pots of stew were steaming,

each being removed at this point by the women of the family to whom it belonged, the largest belonging to Waugh from whose pot all the unmarried men ate, an almost universal custom, even among the Forest Dwellers. This particular vessel, Rhu observed, was tended by three women, two of them young and comely, judged by Cave Dweller standards. Both men and women were stooped, carrying their heads well forward upon shorter necks than those of the folk who live in the open where headroom is not at a premium.

As Rhu had found on his previous trip, most of the caves had originally been animal dens, very few being high enough to enable one to stand erect. Thus, during the hundreds of years these people had lived in them, this posture had become peculiar to the Cave Dwellers as a whole. Theirs was a hard and rugged life, bare of the pleasures common to those accustomed to the open and the freedom of movement which that engenders, but they were, nevertheless, tremendously strong, and as brave as any of their tribe.

When he thought no one was looking, Rhu dropped some of the salt into his bowl and stirred it under the pretense of fishing for a choice morsel of meat. Without it, food no longer tasted as good, although he could and would eat it that way upon occasion, but not from choice. He was soon to learn, however, that his act had not passed entirely unnoticed.

The eyes of Dargh were ever alert, and of all the men in that room, with the possible exception of Waugh, he alone was not averse to trying new things. That he appeared to be sullen was not due to his disposition to be so, but rather to a burning desire for the open, frustrated by the fact that the necessities of life compelled him to stick close to the cave and the confining labor of making knives, axes, bone needles, and fishhooks.

Envy of Rhu's freedom to come and go as he pleased no doubt accounted for his seeming dislike of the Plains Dweller during the latter's previous visit. However, unlike so many with thwarted desires—perhaps because his ideas of freedom were dim—Dargh worked hard and diligently at what he had to do, taking pleasure in trying to improve upon the work of his now famous father, who had taught him all he learned of their craft.

After breakfast, Rhu showed Waugh and Dargh his knife, explaining how it had been broken, much to their delighted interest, for like most others of their time, they enjoyed stories of battle and struggle. Rhu, with his unusual command of language, went into such detail that when he had finished with the description of how Hut had hamstrung the bear and finally killed it by cutting the hole in its side, both were straining forward, sweat streaming down their faces, and their teeth bared in battle grins.

"Hu!" grunted Waugh, remembering *his* last fight. "Stab in throat kill bear. Bear dying all time. Bear die hard. Waugh know," he finished grimly.

Dargh appeared to be struggling with an idea. Grunting as though he had come to a decision, he got up and left to return a moment later with the most beautifully finished obsidian knife Rhu had ever seen. The chipping along its edges was so finely done that it was almost smooth, and its sharpness such that Rhu's incautious testing of it upon his calloused thumb resulted in a cut that bled profusely, but which went absolutely unnoticed in his great admiration for the knife.

"What do you want for it?" he asked eagerly. "I would surely like to own it, if I can trade something for it."

"Ugh!" grunted Dargh, shaking his shaggy head decisively. "No trade. Give," he finished.

"Give!" exclaimed Rhu, not believing his ears. "Do you mean you *give* it to me?"

"Yes," Dargh answered. Then unexpectedly, "What Rhu put in food?"

For a moment, Rhu stared at Dargh, puzzled, then remembered the taste stone. "Your eyes are sharp, Dargh," he praised. "It was some of this," opening his bag and taking out a sizable chunk. "I'll put some in your stew when we eat again and see if you like it. If you do, I'll give you some, and we will try to find some more around here before I leave. This knife, though. I do not like to take it without giving you something." Suddenly, his eyes brightened. "I'll make you a bow," he offered.

"Good!" Dargh agreed enthusiastically.

Rhu now drew out Hut's sketch of the arrowheads. "Dargh, do you suppose you could make some of these just this size?"

he asked. "They are to go on my arrows," he explained, getting one from his quiver and showing Dargh and Waugh how they should work, but their eyes were fixed upon the feathered shafts.

"Arrows fly?" demanded Dargh.

Rhu chuckled. "That's what my mother wanted to know. No, they don't fly, but they do shoot much straighter. Let us go outside, and if we can get a buzzard or eagle to fly close enough, I'll try one."

"Why waste good arrow?" Waugh demanded.

"I want feathers to use on Dargh's," Rhu explained.

"No man hit flying eagle," Waugh stated positively. "Never light close. Maybe *find* in valley."

Rhu simply grinned, well knowing that only seeing would convince Waugh, while Dargh's eyes bulged and his mouth hung open with wonder.

At first, Rhu was afraid they were to be disappointed for neither buzzard nor eagle flew near them. Observing the reason, Waugh sent Dargh to tell the women to bring out some of the bones accumulated in the back of the cave and which, as Rhu discovered when they passed him carrying them, were old and well rotted. These they hurled over the cliff. In a few minutes, the first of the buzzards appeared, swung high above them, then as others followed, started circling downward to the feast.

Stringing his bow, Rhu carefully selected an arrow, and picking out an exceptionally large bird, notched his shaft, drew the bow and shot. A flurry of feathers, and the croaking, screaming bird whirled head over end to its death below, the arrow having passed completely through it.

Turning to speak to Dargh, Rhu discovered him already flying down that crooked and narrow trail at such breakneck speed that, even knowing their goatlike ability, he more than half expected to see him go hurtling into the chasm.

Waugh, apparently, had no such worries for he simply said, "Hope Dargh reach first. Anybody touch bird, Dargh fight."

In a surprisingly short time, Dargh was back with the prize of Rhu's skill, and he also had the arrow. "Arrow hard find

among rocks," he growled. "Make take long get back," he apologized.

Waugh was studying the design for the arrowhead. "I make," he announced. "Flint stronger, but black rock sharper," he explained. "Dargh, start fire here. Dargh work flint. Waugh work black rock. Black rock kill big deer, hoogwar. Flint kill man, small game," and by his terseness, Rhu knew that his mind was busy with the problem of making these new devices. Shaking his tousled old head unbelievingly, Waugh continued to mumble. "No such shooting. Waugh not see, Waugh not believe."

Rhu smiled his pleasure for sincere praise was good to hear. "I'll show you a new way to start fires," he volunteered, opening his bag and getting out the fire stone and some of his bark.

Waugh eyed him and the stone in his hand. "Rhu brought fire Waugh's cave," he explained. "Only magic start fire without coals."

"You watch," Rhu suggested, grinning up at him, then proceeded to strike a shower of sparks with his flint-headed club. (It never occurred to Rhu that any other piece of flint might work equally as well.) By the time a spark had caught, and he was starting to blow on it to make it blaze, Dargh was an equally interested spectator.

"Magic," he breathed, eying Rhu dubiously. Things were coming almost too fast for his mind to grasp them, observing which, Rhu decided he would go no further until they had grown accustomed to this.

Old Waugh examined the fire stone. "Waugh never saw stone like this," he growled. "Where get?" Rhu explained. "Ax flint," Waugh continued. "Small piece do. Waugh try?"

Rhu agreed gladly, and to Waugh's infinite delight, he managed to start a fire of his own before reluctantly returning the stone to Rhu.

"You keep it," Rhu offered impulsively.

"No need. We keep fire. Waugh never leave cave."

"Then you keep it, Dargh, as part payment for the arrowheads, and later, we shall go look for a piece of good wood for your bow."

Dargh's face lit up with the first real enthusiasm Rhu had seen him display. "Dargh got wood like Rhu's, only dry," he volunteered. Again disappearing into the cave, he returned with two beautifully seasoned pieces, upon one of which Rhu promptly went to work with his new knife, and to his delight, made the most rapid progress he had ever experienced.

"This knife is a wonder, Dargh. I never saw anything like it! We'll have your bow well under way by night."

Dargh smiled all through the day as he chipped away. By the time they went in to eat, he had fashioned two practically perfect arrowheads. However, they did not seem to please Waugh who, for one reason or another, had discarded all he made though Rhu thought them perfect and later retrieved them while Waugh was resting.

Dargh gave his to Rhu without question. "Waugh cranky," he apologized.

At noon, the salted stew was such a great success and resulted in so much lip smacking and gurgling of the gravy that Rhu had to fix up the main pot with it. Their pleasure was so great that before leaving, he gave liberally of his supply, wisely deciding that this was perhaps the best means for gaining their interest in his and Hut's plan.

All that afternoon, it was a tossup which was the more interested in the work of the other, Rhu or Dargh. Three arrowheads so perfect that not even Waugh could find anything about them to criticize came from Dargh's labors. Waugh had four of his own, and Rhu had the bow almost shaped. It was a satisfied trio who went to sleep that night behind the closed stone door whose scraping as it swung upon its pivot had awakened Rhu that morning.

A WEEK passed and all of Rhu's arrows were tipped with either flint or obsidian heads, the flint predominating, for when Waugh had made fifty of the obsidian 'ones, he started with the flint. Even though he was old and crippled, his long years of working with stone told, and his production topped that of Dargh who strove his best to keep pace, much to Rhu's amusement.

As they finished making the second hundred arrowheads for Hut, Rhu decided it was time to broach the subject of the stone huts and the plan he and Hut had formed. Dargh's bow was completed and his supply of arrows ready for the new tips, much to his delight, while Rhu's prestige among the other Cave Dwellers had increased, due to the rock salt and his ability to use the fire stone. Everything pointed to this as being the right moment.

"Waugh," he began cautiously, "I have studied the stone wall you have in your cave. Do you suppose *huts* could be built of stone?"

"Why?" asked Waugh, and Dargh eyed Rhu speculatively.

Rhu drew a long breath. Many times before he had planned how he would begin, but now that he had started, he suddenly realized something of the proportions of the task before him. "Well . . . . my friend, Hut, and I have been thinking how fine it would be if all the three divisions of the Mu Yans could eventually live together on a great, open plain of which we know, but so organized that there would no longer be any strife between us."

"Dream!" snorted Waugh. "Nobody live near Forest Dwellers and not have fights."

"I'm not so sure about that," Rhu countered. "I have always managed to go among them and get along. The trouble is that each branch of the tribe wants everything its own way."

"Why not?" demanded Waugh. "Cave Dwellers live here safe many, many Great Suns."

"If you knew that you would always have plenty to eat, a

comfortable place in which to live, and that your safety was guaranteed so that you might go about as you pleased without fear of attack, would you not like that?"

"Phaugh!" scoffed Waugh. "Can't do. *Nobody* safe."

"Forest Dweller love fight," Dargh commented, but Rhu could see the gleam of interest in his eyes.

"Let's look at it from another angle," Rhu suggested. "You speak of your safety here, Waugh. Yet, I came up your trail in the dark and sat here in your cave a long time, and you had traps and sentries. So, you are not so safe, even here."

"No get past mouth of Waugh's cave!" Waugh denied. "Stone wall stop Rhu. Nobody pass through until Waugh open door from inside."

"Good!" Rhu agreed enthusiastically. "Would you not be just as safe if you were inside of *four* stone walls with a door fastened as securely as this one?"

Waugh simply snorted. While he was far from convinced, he seemed unable to think of a fitting answer.

"Of course you would." Rhu pursued his advantage. "And you must agree that it would be much pleasanter for you if you could have such a place out where the air is always fresh and among neighbors whom you could trust."

"Where find?" Waugh demanded. "Not *Forest Dwellers!* Even among Cave Dwellers always fight. Even Plains Dwellers fight and try steal from each other. Always plenty fresh air at mouth of Waugh's cave where Waugh see all want see."

"Yet, Waugh, *you* would not steal from your neighbors, nor would you pick quarrels with them, and there are many among the Plains Dwellers who are just as honest and hard working. Even among the Forest Dwellers there are those who are not cruel and treacherous."

"No Forest Dwellers! *All* bad!" Waugh was quite vehement in his statement.

"All right, Waugh, but suppose only those of the Cave Dwellers and the Plains Dwellers who are honest and peaceful are allowed to join us, and we would allow only a *few* of the Forest Dwellers to come in? You see, Waugh, Hut and I planned that this is exactly what we shall do. He is now going among the Plains Dwellers picking out those who really want to live in peace and security among others who also like peace and security and the happiness they bring. These will bring their flocks and herds with them.

"From the Cave Dwellers, we want to get people like you and Dargh who will eventually bring families. While you, who are skilled in working stone, carry on your work just as you do now, and build stone huts to shelter all of us, the Plains Dwellers will feed and clothe you, and in case of attack, fight for you, just as you would fight for us."

"What about Forest Dwellers?" Waugh's tone was belligerent.

"We plan to select a few who are good fighters and dependable, and who, because they do not like to work so very well, will be glad to have us support them. You will make their arrows and knives as well as ours, and they, in turn, are to do most of the fighting for all of us. There will be enough Plains and Cave Dwellers to hold these Forest Dwellers in line until they grow to be trusted."

"Then they turn on Rhu in night. Rob and kill Rhu," Waugh persisted, pessimistically.

"*I* like idea," Dargh put in unexpectedly. "I go, Rhu. Other Cave Dwellers go. I know."

For a moment, Rhu thought Waugh was going to strike Dargh. His face purpled with rage.

"Dargh go, Dargh never come back Waugh's cave!" he shouted. "And you," turning to Rhu, "you . . . . you . . . ."
His face suddenly distorted, Waugh's tongue appeared to choke him, and his face turning ashen, he fell over sideways.

"Water!" Rhu ordered Dargh, who fled to get it, but poor old Waugh was beyond all help.

Chapter Six

THE TAMING OF LEVI HAWK

UNLIKE RHU, Hut did not have far to go to contact the first of the Plains Dwellers, only about three hours' walk being necessary. Knowing that some of the younger men would be with the herds during the day, he did not start until after noon, spending the morning thinking over how he would approach them.

Hut well realized that there was none in the entire tribe who was anything like Rhu, who was closer to him than even his own brothers. Neither would many of them be likely to be much interested in something new like this, and there was no small amount of jealousy among them. He began to wish Rhu had not been quite so impulsive and had waited until they could talk to some of their own people before leaving on his arduous trip. Never before had he quite fully realized how much a part of each other they had become.

"If I could handle the bow and arrow like Rhu," he mused, "I could get them interested through my skill." Then it occurred to him to talk to his father, not that he hoped to win him over upon such short notice, but he could practice upon him. "He might have some suggestions," Hut thought hopefully as he went to see him.

"Father, have you ever wished that we did not have to move our herds in order to provide good grazing?" he began, shrewdly seeking the one point upon which he was sure they could agree from the start.

Old Mai eyed him closely. "Why wish what cannot be?" he countered suspiciously.

"Why can't it be?" Hut inquired with equal caution.

"Hut old enough to know," Mai growled. He did not like being questioned this way, a fact Hut was quick to sense.

"I know we always have done it because the herds exhaust all the grass. But suppose we could find a place where there would be so much of it and of such good quality that we did not have to move them?"

"Where?" demanded Mai with disconcerting bluntness.

To answer this question at this stage would, Hut knew, result only in a positive refusal to consider the idea at all. The interview was not progressing as he had hoped, so he decided to change his approach.

"Rhu has discovered such a place," he began, well knowing the high regard his father felt for Rhu, and justly so because Rhu had located many new meadows before.

"Why not take herds there?" Mai demanded.

"Then you would be willing to go to such a place? Provided, of course, that it was a safe one?" Hut added, anticipating his father's next question.

"Yes," Mai confirmed, "but place must be good and not too far away. Where this place?"

"I told Rhu I was sure you would agree," Hut again switched his line of attack. "It is not so very far, but there are problems to consider. Father, the Dan and Ku families have worked together harmoniously for many Great Suns (years), sharing good fortune and bad alike. Suppose we could get several other families to join with us. The Yaks, the Kuts, the Mauks, and the Tuks are all good people and friendly."

"Yes, but herds large. No land support all herded together. Combined *huts* cover almost as much ground as it takes to feed Dan and Ku herds," Mai demurred.

"But suppose we could devise a better kind of hut? If we had a grazing ground where all the herds could be fed without having to move them for many miles every two or three moons, we could have permanent homes."

"I thought there would be more to it," Mai growled into his beard.

Hut, however, was delighted that he did not veto the idea outright, and observed with satisfaction that the old man's eyes were alight with interest. "There *is* more to it," he said with surprising candor. "It would enable us to save many of the herds and would be much easier on the old people and the very small children."

"Huh?" Mai grunted interrogatively, jarred out of his usual composure by the very audacity of this unheard-of idea.

Hut hurried on before the inevitable negation would come. He well knew that as soon as his father became confused, he would lapse into sullen and adamant "No's" from which there was little likelihood of stirring him.

"Yes, Father, by having permanent homes, we could build them so that the old folk and the very small children would be better protected. Besides, they could be built so strong that it would be easy to defend them in case of attack by either man or beast. Only last year a hoogwar tore out the side of the Mauk hut and killed two of them before they could kill it. Bears, too, have broken into huts and stolen babies and even killed the old ones."

"What does Sol think about this?" Mai asked, referring to Rhu's father. "Mai do nothing without Sol."

"I have not spoken to him, Father. I thought you would do it for me while I go to the Yaks and see whether they will be interested. We are not yet ready, but we do want our families behind us when we are."

"The Dans and Kus always work together," Mai stated positively. "Sol do nothing unless Mai agree. Where Rhu?"

Here was a poser. If he explained what Rhu was doing, it might easily result in stubborn unreasoning opposition, for the Forest Dwellers were bitterly hated by all the Plains Dwellers. It would be difficult to convince Mai or Sol that there could ever be any cooperation between the Plains Dwellers and the Forest Dwellers. As for the Cave Dwellers, due to their inaccessibility and the fact that none of them ever ventured very far from their caves, they were but little known. Being little known meant they were to be distrusted.

"He has gone to the Cave Dwellers to see about getting stone tips for our arrows," Hut answered, disliking the subterfuge. Yet, he was too shrewd to risk losing the ground he had gained by explaining too much until both Mai and Sol had committed themselves as being in favor of all he had already suggested.

"Mai see Sol," agreed his father getting to his feet, and Hut heaved a great sigh of relief that his sketchy explanations had been accepted.

At the noonday meal, Mai announced that Sol was not averse to the idea, provided all things were as Hut had explained. "Good grazing come first," he stated, "then homes. But," and he eyed Hut grimly, "Sol and Mai see this wonderful place before move one hoof."

IT WAS with a lighter heart that Hut approached the camp of the Yaks. In his day, old Gar Yak had been an adventurous fellow and not unlike Rhu in his ability to get along with others. However, as the head of the Yak family, he had grown rather conservative in his later years. Hun Yak, about Hut's age, was quite friendly with both Hut and Rhu, and since he was much like his father had been in his youthful days, it was to him that Hut went first, sure that here he would find an ally. He found Hun seated beneath a tree watching a part of their flock, a heavy skin over his shoulders.

"Cool," he grunted as Hut neared him.

"Yes," Hut agreed, and began gathering up a few sticks. "Let's have a little fire."

"How?" grunted Hun. "None nearer than hut."

"Watch," Hut ordered, grinning into the other's puzzled face. Taking some of the bark from his pouch, he struck the fire stone with his flint ax head, and to the amazement—almost consternation—of Hun, soon had a blaze going.

"Magic!" grunted Hun, drawing away from the blaze.

"No," Hut reassured him. "It is a stone that Rhu found, and it is evidently blessed by the fire gods, for you saw how it works. Come on and sit down."

With a grunt, Hun complied, stretching out his hands to the welcome warmth, just as two of his brothers arrived on the run to see what had caused the smoke. Eventually, all had to try making the sparks fly. Their curiosity somewhat allayed, Hut decided he would see what their reactions to his proposal would be.

"How would you fellows like to live where you did not have to move your flocks every moon or two?" he asked.

"Where such place?" asked Kurg, Hun's oldest single brother.

"Rhu has found such a place," Hut explained, "and it is large enough for many herds. Do you suppose your father would be interested in moving his herds there and joining in with the Dans and Kus?"

Kurg's eyes grew round with wonder. "Meadow big enough so all herds stay one place?" he demanded.

"Yes," Hut assured him, "and even larger." For a moment he considered whether to continue, wisely deciding to wait until he could also talk to old Gar himself.

"Don't know where is," mumbled the puzzled Kurg, "but if have such place, Kurg say hurry before others grab."

"Let's talk to your father first," Hut suggested, and they all agreed that as soon as their relief watchers arrived, they would do so.

"YOU SAY Sol and Mai agree?" Gar questioned after Hut had explained what he had told the others.

"Yes, provided they are allowed to see it before anything definite is done."

"Sol and Mai want us come?" Gar asked.

"Yes, and others who are dependable. And not only that, Gar, but because the herds will not have to be moved as we now do, we can build permanent homes that will be more comfortable than our huts. Think of what that will mean to the old ones and the very small children."

"Who build? How?" Gar wanted to know.

Ever since he had talked with his father, Hut had been thinking how to meet this question. Did he dare advance his radical idea now? He decided against it. Instead, "Rhu and I plan to get a few of the unmarried men from each family we invite and take them to this place. Then we cannot only explore the great meadow fully, but can plan how to go about building. We will have places ready before anybody else moves."

Gar eyed his stalwart sons and Hut speculatively. "You three go with Hut and Rhu. If need more, send Hun back."

Hut's heart leaped. If this were all there was to it, his task would be easy. "All right," he agreed promptly. "I'm going to the Kuts next. When I come back with those whom I select, Hun and the others can join with us."

About four hours' walk south of the Yaks, the valley was divided by a ridge of stony ground that afforded no grazing. Since the present home of the Kuts lay about two hours' walk beyond that, Hut decided to leave the Yaks early the following morning, spending the remainder of the evening explaining why it was that his arrows were feathered and how Rhu had made his bow. Hun was especially interested from the first, but it was not until several of the others had tried out the bow and arrows that any desire to copy them was shown. Inasmuch as Hut was by no means a poor archer, by diverting their interest to this, he escaped the many inevitable questions he was not yet ready to answer.

THE HEAD of the Kut family was named Ku, a cousin of Sol, his mother having been the sister of Sol's father, a circumstance well known to Hut. Ku Kut was about the same age as Sol Ku, but the Kut family was one of the largest of the Mu Yan Plains Dwellers, and Hut expected no greater difficulty in getting recruits than he had with the Yaks.

As he crossed the Kut lands, he observed that the country was pastured almost bare, an unusual condition at this period. "Either their herds are unusually large or else the rains have been scant this spring," he mused.

The farther he went, however, the more evident it became that something very much out of the ordinary had occurred. It hardly seemed possible that there could have been a drought this close to his own home without their having had a like experience, but this had been a normal season for them thus far. In spite of himself, Hut began to have some misgivings which increased when he discovered that the Kuts were gone, their camp site indicating they had only recently departed.

It was nearing midafternoon before Hut found them, and the sight which confronted him caused him to hasten. Gathered about Ku were most of the younger Kut men. All were carrying war clubs and crude bows and arrows, and all listened in-

Hut Mai Dan

tently to Ku who appeared to be giving them orders. As he came nearer, Hut observed that many of them bore recent wounds.

Going directly to Ku, he demanded, "What's wrong?"

"The Hawks," Ku answered tersely. "Sneaked in. Grazed Kut lands."

"The Hawks!" Hut exclaimed. "Their lands lie far to the south. How did they get up here?"

"Sneaked," Ku repeated. "Caught two suns ago. Chased out," he finished.

"Why didn't you send word to the Yaks and to us?" Hut demanded. "We would have helped you."

"No time," grunted Ku.

"Where are they now?"

"Gone south," was the simple reply.

"How far?" Hut continued his questioning.

"Quarter sun," Ku answered. "Too close, but too many for chase."

"Were any of you killed?"

"No. Hawks run fast as herds travel. Kuts got some," and for the first time, Ku grinned.

"Men or cattle?" Hut persisted, wishing with all his heart that Ku would be more explicit.

"Killed four men. Got one herd cattle."

"Then they'll get Nurgs to join them and come back. Better send to the Yaks and have them bring some Kus and Dans. Killing them was bad enough, but taking their herds will bring them back. Your grazing is ruined, so how are you going to feed your stock?" Hut inquired, wondering whether this might not be a good time to begin expounding his idea.

"Nug already sent," mentioning the name of one of his sons. "May have to enter Mauk lands. Mauk herds small and land big," Ku answered.

"But that will bring about more fighting," Hut remonstrated.

"Have to feed cattle!" Ku's air of finality plainly indicated that his mind was definitely made up.

Hut thought rapidly. He could not afford a tribal war now, for once something of this sort started, the entire Mu Yan

Plains Dweller population would soon become involved. "Maybe you could trade some of the captured cattle to the Mauks for grazing until your own pasture is good again," he suggested.

"What Kuts take, Kuts keep," Ku asserted stubbornly.

"But the Mauks have never been anything but friendly to the Kuts," Hut reasoned. "The Elders say that what we take by force will be taken from us by force, and to attack friends this way is trying to take by force what is not rightfully your own, Ku. Neither Mai nor Sol will help you if you do that, and neither will the Yaks, for they will reason that if you would try to seize the Mauks' grazing lands, you might soon try to take theirs."

This was a bold stroke, and Hut was well aware that it might easily throw Ku into a dangerous rage. However, since the Kus and Dans were a most powerful combination, they were greatly respected by every Mu Yan family in the Valley, and he knew that even Ku would think twice before incurring their displeasure.

The older man glared at the lad before him. "You small boy threaten Ku," he snarled.

"I do not threaten," Hut answered quickly. "I am simply telling you what you already know, but may not have thought of. To fight the Hawks, who invaded your lands, is all right and proper, but for you to attack the Mauks, who are your friends, is wrong."

"Kuts not attack. Kuts just use Mauk land short time."

"Yet, that is exactly what you are fighting the Hawks for doing. They did not try to hold your land—only to use it for a time. Otherwise, they would have waylaid you and have tried to kill off enough of you so they could take your lands and keep them. Ku, you have always been a just man. I have heard my father often speak of your honorable dealings with all who know you. Do you think simply *taking* the grazing lands of the Mauks, even for a short time, without their permission, is either fair or just? How would *you* feel?" Hut demanded.

Ku hesitated. There was justice in what Hut said, and Ku was a just man when his passions were not too thoroughly aroused. Still, Hut should realize that it was not right that he part with any of the herd which were but a fair recompense for the spoiling of his own pastures!

"If your land had suffered a drought, Ku, and you needed grazing lands, you would not take them from your friends without first trying to make them some reasonable offer. You are justly angry now because of what has been done to you, and nobody can blame you for feeling so. But that does not make it right for you to try to take by force that which belongs to your friends and neighbors."

As if this last argument had convinced him, Ku drew a long breath, and Hut felt the cold sweat trickle down his back. "Right. Ku try what Hut say. But suppose Mauks won't?" he finished.

"I will ask them for you," Hut volunteered. "Dorg Mauk is a close friend of my father, and if I do not succeed, I will ask my father to try for you."

Ku's face brightened. "You never lie," he complimented Hut. "If Mai ask, Dorg not refuse. You Mai son. Ku give half new herd for two moons' grazing."

This was bargaining, as Hut well knew, and most Mu Yans were shrewd bargainers. "How many cattle will that be? And are they cows, bulls, rams, or ewes?"

Ku chuckled and his eyes snapped. "Hut got head," he praised. "Kuts took," counting with his hands by holding them with the fingers wide spread indicating ten, opening and closing them twenty times—two hundred. "They mostly cows, some with calves, not many. These Ku keep. Ku offer half, but pay twenty more if must, but Hut not tell!"

Hut's chuckle sounded a trifle hollow to his own ears, but the relief was enough to make anyone nervous. "My father has always said you would drive a hard bargain, but were just. You are. I think this is a fair offer, and if I know Dorg at all, he will agree, maybe for less, for he would not take advantage of a friend's misfortune."

Ku snorted, although his eyes twinkled. "Dorg take no advantage unless good chance!" But there was no venom in his words; rather, admiration for Dorg's astuteness.

"How long has Nug been gone?" Hut asked.

"Since noon," Ku answered. "Back tomorrow."

"I'll stay until he gets back with help," volunteered Hut, and seeing the smile on Ku's bewhiskered and grizzled face, felt his own grow hot. He knew he looked slight beside these big, hairy Kuts. "Who is your best archer?" he asked, unslinging his bow which Ku eyed with interest. As Hut drew out one of his feathered arrows, Ku's eyes widened while his lower jaw dropped in astonishment.

"Tun!" he ordered after a moment, and a tall, wide-shouldered fellow stepped forward. "Hut shoot with Tun. Choose target."

Tun looked at Hut somewhat disdainfully as he dragged out the great limb he used for a bow and selected the heaviest arrow from the bunch in his quiver. Beside this limb, Hut's bow looked almost strawlike. Striding to a nearby tree, Tun pinned a small piece of skin to it with a thorn. The leather was about ten inches across. Next, he counted twenty of his long strides, then smiled at Hut.

"You shoot first," Hut suggested.

With a wide grin, Tun drew his bow. The arrow struck the very edge of the hide, and Tun turned to Hut, grinning broadly. That they considered this good shooting was plainly evident from the pleased expressions of the Kuts now gathered around.

Stepping into Tun's tracks, Hut drew his arrow to his ear, and it struck exactly the center of the target.

Followed a moment of utter silence. Then Ku drew a long breath. "Do again, Hut, and Ku give what you ask."

"I do not want to spoil my other arrow," Hut bragged, very sure there was small danger of repeating as exactly as he had seen Rhu do, and this was a good excuse. Came the twang of his bowstring, and the second arrow landed about a finger breadth from his first!

This was shooting that not even Rhu would disdain, and the effect upon the Kuts was startling. As one, they gathered around Hut, examining his bow and arrows with eager eyes, while Tun strode to the tree, yanked his arrow free easily, then took hold of Hut's. He gave it an easy pull as he had done with his own, but the arrow remained fast in the tree. Nor was it until he pulled so hard that the great torso muscles writhed like serpents beneath his hairy skin that he tore it free, then its companion.

As tenderly as if they were something very precious, Tun regarded the slender arrows and their beautifully done job of feathering. Handing them to Hut, he asked, "See bow?" Several times he tried its pull, then extended it to Hut.

"Want to try it?" the latter asked.

"Yes," Tun answered briefly, and his smile was warm and friendly. With an ease that bespoke the strength of his mighty arms, he drew the arrow to its head, and struck almost where Hut's second arrow had pierced the skin. Again retrieving the arrow, he returned, handing it and the bow to Hut. "Good!" he grunted.

The gruff fellow had never been very friendly with Hut before, but from then on, he was always near him, ever eying that slender bow and arrows which seemed so frail beside the crude ones he had always made.

"Rhu made them," Hut explained. "Some day, maybe, I can get him to make you one. His is much heavier than mine, and you should see *him* shoot! I have seen him hit an eagle on the wing."

"Tun like see!" Tun exclaimed. "Rhu not shoot better than Hut."

"Yes, he can," Hut defended his friend stoutly. "Do you like adventure, to hunt and to travel in new places, Tun?"

"Yes. Why?"

"Tonight, I would like to talk to you and to Ku and any others who would like a better life than you now live, one where there will be no having to move every two or three moons."

"Tun be there," Tun agreed promptly. "Tun bring others."

SUPPER over, Tun squatted close beside Hut who sat facing Ku.

"Ku," Hut began, "how would you like to live where things such as have happened to you could not occur?"

"Where?" Ku asked.

"Rhu and I have located a place where many families can live with their herds without having to move from place to place every moon or two. The grass is always plentiful. In addition, because there will be no need to move, we can build permanent homes, easily defended. Just think what this will mean. First, there will be no losses of stock due to moving them from place to place, and by combining our interests, as the Ku and Dan families do, we can guard them from animals with less men than here. But best of all, think of what it is going to mean to the old ones and the very small children to be able to live in security and comfort all the time."

"Sound good. Where this place?"

"We are not ready to take it over yet. There must first be enough families who want to go."

"Who get best grounds?" Ku demanded. "Ku want know where so can get best for Kuts, next to Kus and Dans. Also, Ku want plenty land for big herds."

"All herds will be kept together, and all will share same grazing lands," Hut endeavored to explain.

"No good. Smart family soon have all and Kuts nothing."

This was a new angle, and for the moment, Hut was stumped. Then the usually slow Tun spoke.

"Kus and Dans do that, and nobody too smart. I like. If all cattle one, and all own alike, what smart man do?"

"Smart man steal eyes off Tun," grunted Ku, then grinned. "It might work if all put in same number."

"That's exactly it," Hut agreed immediately. "All cattle belong to whole group. All have same good homes where safe and comfortable." Hut smiled to himself. He was beginning to talk like the Kuts. "Things such as have just happened to you cannot occur, for who would dare attack such a big group?"

"Forest Dwellers might. Bad," growled Ku.

Hut frowned. Somehow, he had never quite reconciled himself to Rhu's idea of having the Forest Dwellers do the fighting. In fact, he was opposed to fighting when it could possibly be avoided, and already he could foresee that this might easily prove to be a bone of real contention and the stumbling block that would wreck the entire undertaking. He was almost sorry he had not opposed that part of the plan, but Rhu had a way that made his ideas seem very logical at the time. Suppose Rhu did succeed and bring some of the Forest Dwellers along, and

then those of the Plains Dwellers whom he, Hut, had influenced were to rebel? Could he conscientiously support Rhu?

Prey to these thoughts, Hut hesitated, mulling it over. Then,
almost as if someone had whispered into his ear, "Let Rhu
handle that," came to his mind, and his face brightened. So be
it. If Rhu could persuade any of those hardy devils to come
along, then he would also have the job of reconciling the dissatisfied ones.

"Perhaps you are right," Hut conceded, "but we have to admit that with all their shortcomings, the Forest Dwellers are
strong and hard fighters. Still, we will have such strong homes
that not even the Forest Dwellers can hurt us. Besides, Rhu
will show us how to make such superior weapons that we can
handle any who have the temerity to attack us. What would
you think of arrows with sharp, flint heads?"

"Can't do!" grunted Ku immediately.

"Cave Dwellers might make," grunted Tun, and Hut glanced
quickly at the big fellow.

"Cave Dwellers *wouldn't*," objected Ku, "even if they could
—not for Plains Dwellers."

"What do you think of this knife?" asked Hut, displaying the
one Rhu had given him.

With many grunts and much patent admiration, the men all
gathered around, passing the weapon from hand to hand.
Never before had they seen anything comparable to it.

"Where get?" Tun asked.

"Cave Dwellers gave it to Rhu who gave it to me," Hut explained. "He is with them now, or on his way to see them," he
amended. "It was his idea to try to persuade some of them to
come live with us and to make knives like these, arrowheads,
and other fighting tools for us."

"Not even Rhu get Cave Dwellers leave caves," Ku objected.

"Maybe not," Hut again conceded, "but he has been able to
visit among even the Forest Dwellers and come away without
a fight."

"Huh," grunted Ku, startled in spite of himself at this unheard-of feat. "Rhu lucky or mighty brave."

"Well, he did it," Hut asserted definitely and found it hard to
refrain from adding that Rhu was even considering enlisting

some of their best men, but his native caution warned him to be careful. "In fact, he even fixed it so that they now trade with the Cave Dwellers without fighting."

"Rhu good fighter," Tun chipped in. "Throw Tun once."

Ku stared at him in amazement for there was not one among the Kut family that Tun could not handle easily, and he was much larger than Rhu.

"Tun sick?" demanded Ku.

"No. Rhu fast. Rhu show new. . . ." Tun hesitated, groping for some word to describe what he had in mind, "hold!" he finished. Then wondering whether he had made it clear, he continued, "Rhu grab quick, twist hand, whirl body, Tun hit ground!" He grinned at the gaping crowd. "Rhu say do, Rhu do." There was no mistaking Tun's willingness to believe in Rhu.

Hut's heart warmed to the big fellow. It was good to hear Rhu praised by such men. Perhaps . . . . yes, there might well be others who would feel as did Tun, and Hut's heart was lighter than it had yet been.

"We would like to have four Kut men, single ones who will be able to stay and help, to come with me while I visit Mauks. Will you be able to spare them, Ku?" He put the question squarely.

"Tun come," that worthy asserted without waiting Ku's reply, and Ku almost glared at him, or so Hut thought. Sons seldom spoke before the head of the family had committed himself.

For a long moment, Ku hesitated, and all eyes were upon him. Only Tun seemed not to feel the tension in the air. However, Tun was a power all to himself and was regarded as second only to Ku in the management of their affairs.

"If we get rid of Hawks, they come," Ku broke the tension. "Tun pick men," he added. "Tun good man," he complimented, and Hut could hardly believe his own ears.

"I'll go see Levi Hawk tomorrow and try to straighten out this mess," Hut volunteered, rather startled at his own suggestion which seemed to have been entirely involuntary on his part.

"If Hut want, Tun go too," Tun volunteered.

"No," Hut answered, though he sorely wished he might accept the offer, for Tun's fame as a fighter was well known among all the Plains Dwellers. "It is best that I go alone. They have no quarrel with the Dans and Kus. I may be able to find out why they did as they did."

"No get back cattle!" stated Ku with finality.

"No," agreed Hut. "They have forfeited their right to them. I will leave at dawn so I can circle around and they will not know I have come from here until after I see how things are with them. When I come back to tell you, Tun and the others can join me."

HUT found the sixty-year-old Levi Hawk in a towering rage as he entered their temporary camp the following morning. Levi was the son of a Levi Yan mother whom his father had stolen from her tribe.

"Levi send Wug, twenty men north with six hundred cattle," he stormed at Hut when he asked what was wrong. "Being early, grass still short. No split herd . . . . scatter. No!" Levi's voice was sarcastic now. "Wug go *Kut* country. Graze close. Kuts find. Fight. Eight men die. Two hundred cattle gone," he wailed.

"Where were the rest of you?" Hut asked.

"Many sick. Stay behind with main herd. Get well. Come north. Wug not there. Leave women, children, and few men. Come on. Find yesterday two suns after fight. Hawks on Kut ground now. Bad."

As Hut followed Levi's raving, he could picture how, when the sick had recovered, Levi had brought them and the main herd to their northern grazing grounds only to find Wug and the cattle gone, and how Levi had trailed them into Kut territory, after leaving the women and children behind. No wonder Levi was incoherent, for he had lost both men and a third of the cattle Wug had brought. It did not escape Hut that Levi mentioned losing eight men instead of the four claimed by Ku Kut and he rightly guessed the additional four had probably died from wounds.

"What do you plan to do, Levi? You can't blame Kuts for fighting," Hut said. "Where is Wug?"

"Wug dead. Wrong use Kut land, but want cattle back."

"What about the Kuts? Their grazing is ruined for a long time. Where are the rest of your cattle?"

"Send back to Hawk land. Plenty grazing here for Kuts. Want cattle back," Levi insisted stubbornly.

Hut looked around, and there really was not much damage done to the grazing here, but the pasturage in sight, he estimated, would support the Kut herds only about a month, too little time for their northern pastures to recuperate. He also knew that the Hawk lands which stretched twenty miles to the south were narrow because of the constriction of the Valley at this point and afforded barely enough pasturage for their own flocks. Therefore, it would not be to the advantage of the Kuts to invade Hawk territory which they might otherwise have been tempted to do.

"Ku will never give them back," Hut announced bluntly. "You will be lucky if the Kuts do not come down into *your* lands and demand more cattle to repay them for their losses."

"Levi get Nurgs and fight. Want cattle back!" Levi spluttered in his rage over the loss.

"If you do, Ku will get Dans and Kus and Mauks. He has already sent to Sol and Mai for help, Levi."

"How you know?" demanded Levi.

"Nug came." Hut evaded a direct answer, allowing Levi to draw his own conclusion. "I came to find out why you invaded Kut lands."

Levi almost writhed in the throes of his dilemma. If the Kuts were to have such backing, he well knew that the days of the Hawks were numbered.

"Levi want cattle back!" he roared.

Now confident of his ground, Hut eyed the old man calmly. "You won't get one hoof of them back, Levi, and you know you are not entitled to get them. *You* would not return them under the same circumstances. Neither will Ku, and I see no reason why he should. You take the rest of your people and get off Kut land by tomorrow. When you have time to think straight, you send to Dan hut for me, and we will arrange so you may not have to give more cattle or lose some of your land."

"But we *need* cattle," Levi whined, abruptly changing his tactics, much to Hut's disgust.

"I thought you were Mu Yan," he almost sneered. "You talk like Levi Yan! Will you do as I say, or shall I return and report to my father that you intend to try to fight us?"

"We go," Levi capitulated.

"And don't come back," Hut snapped, and turning, strode out of the group of scowling men. When some forty paces distant, one of them started to fit an arrow to his bow, but Levi smashed his skull with his war club.

"Want all Hawks killed?" he stormed at the others.

Chapter Seven

ORD OF KURD

RHU LOOKED up at Dargh as he laid old Waugh's head back upon the floor of the cave. Mixed with his sorrow over the manner of the old man's passing was anxiety for its effect upon Dargh, for if Dargh turned against him, his mission among the Cave Dwellers was about as good as ruined.

Presently, Dargh looked into Rhu's eyes and smiled, then turned and entered the cave without a word, to return with the withered old crone who was Waugh's last remaining wife. She glared at Rhu, but Dargh laid a restraining hand upon her shoulder.

"Not Rhu's fault," he said simply, and his voice was both gentle and firm. "Rhu good man. Waugh old. Daugh now rule cave. Dargh find. Come," motioning to Rhu to follow him outside. "Daugh want rule long time. Waugh say Dargh rule. No want. Go with Rhu." As he talked, he led the way up to the next cave about two hundred yards away where the burly Daugh sat talking with a friend.

"Waugh dead," Dargh went directly to the point. "Daugh now rule cave. Dargh leave soon."

Without waiting to hear more, Daugh was already on his way to Waugh's cave. At nightfall, when Rhu and Dargh with four of Dargh's friends returned to the cave, Daugh met them at the entrance. "No come in," he snarled officiously.

With the speed of a striking rattler, Dargh grabbed Daugh, and before Rhu could remonstrate, even had he been so minded, hurled the shrieking man over the edge of the cliff, his echoing screeches suddenly stilled as the sound of a heavy impact drifted up from far below. Without a word, Dargh turned and strode inside, followed closely by the other four and Rhu.

"Daugh dead," he announced savagely. "Any more say Dargh can't enter family cave?" His great but skilled hands opened and closed convulsively.

Abysmal silence followed this definite challenge. As well as if they had witnessed what had happened, every occupant of the cave knew what had occurred outside. Few there were among the Cave Dwellers who would have dared emulate what Daugh had tried, let alone any among the members of this big family who knew something of the power in Dargh's great shoulders.

"Dargh and friends sleep in Waugh's room tonight. Tomorrow, Megh rule cave until Dargh come back. Megh, these my friends. Always welcome this cave while Dargh live. Make no mistake. Rule justly. If Dargh not come back, Megh rule always."

Megh got to his feet. "Megh hear," he grunted. "Do as Dargh says, always."

Eying the slender appearing young fellow, Rhu could not help wondering how long he would be able to maintain his position. His shifty eyes did not appeal to Rhu, but Dargh should know best.

Inside Waugh's old room, which was separated from the main cave by another stone wall, Dargh closed the heavy door. From a receptacle carved into the rock, he secured a number of bits of stone and odd-shaped articles for which Rhu could see no possible use. The other four interested onlookers evidently appreciated their worth, however, as their grunts and smiles plainly indicated. Placing these in skin bags, Dargh apportioned them among the four other Cave Dwellers.

"Waugh's tools," he explained to Rhu. "We," indicating his companions, "best stone workers this section." Then he grinned at Rhu. "Megh liar and cheat. Steal from Waugh. Try steal from me. Steal from all brothers, even try steal wife. Brothers no good. Soon all fight. Best man win. Now we leave." Here he smiled at the others. "You all get taste rock when we get where Rhu lead. Come."

Going to the back of Waugh's room, he fumbled along a

crevice in the wall and presently, a stone swung back. "Dargh help Waugh build," he explained. "Only Dargh and Waugh know secret," and even in the close cave room, Rhu could feel the incoming fresh air. Behind them, the door swung shut.

Taking Rhu's hand, Dargh lifted it to a nob high on the out- side of the wall above the stone door. He then pressed, and the door swung open, only to close a moment later when the pres- sure was released. Immediately, and without a word, he turned, heading along the narrow and steeply rising passage or natural tunnel leading through the mountains, its walls becom- ing smooth and damp until, at last, they were walking in run- ning water. Then they were in the open and beneath the stars. Just behind them rose a tall rounded rock.

"Remember rock," Dargh cautioned all of them. "Deep notch cut in it," and he led them into the night.

Accustomed to the stygian darkness they had just left, the night seemed less black. Rhu was able to discern that Dargh was leading them down a narrow but comparatively smooth trail. If the light had been better, he would have seen that, in places, it was cut into the cliff itself. In the gloom, he sensed the chasm yawning beside them, and while the Cave Dwellers strode along nonchalantly, he was careful to keep as close to the cliff as possible.

For perhaps half an hour, the little group had followed the winding trail when Dargh, who was immediately ahead of Rhu, reached back and taking him by the hand, turned ab- ruptly to the left for some twenty feet, then told him to lie down. "Path too rough to travel in dark. Rest here till dawn."

Emulating the others, Rhu unrolled his sleeping skin, then, remembering the savage cave bears and the hoogwars that in- fested the region, suggested that he would keep watch for a time, but Dargh assured him that it was unnecessary as they were in a spot safe enough for sleeping.

In the chill gray of coming dawn, Rhu awoke to find the others stirring. Glancing about him, he saw why Dargh had been so confident of their security the night before. They had been lying in a depression in the top of a high pinnacle of rock, joined to the towering cliff behind them by a strip of stone less

than *three feet wide!* Peering over the edge of the depression, Rhu caught his breath, for it was a sheer drop of perhaps two thousand feet to the bottom!

Following Dargh as he led them back across the narrow stone bridge, cold chills crept along Rhu's spine at the thought of how blithely he had walked along that narrow strip in the gloom of the night. To the Cave Dwellers, long accustomed to dizzy heights, this seemed to mean nothing at all, and Rhu would have died before letting them know how he felt.

Once across, Dargh led them down a narrow, winding trail in places scarcely a foot wide so that they had to walk sideways with their faces to the cliff in order to utilize it at all. Like goats, they scrambled down slopes that taxed all Rhu's strength and skill to keep on his feet and along with them. It was with a sigh of heartfelt relief that he reached the bottom. Glancing back along the tortuous path they had just descended, he could scarcely suppress a shudder. Seen from below, it seemed hardly possible that a human being could negotiate it!

Dargh grinned into Rhu's concerned face. "Took Waugh and Dargh five Great Suns make path so can use," he explained.

Knowing something of the fierce

fights the Cave Dwellers occasionally had among themselves, Rhu could understand that these two had performed this prodigious task in order that they might have a secret way of escape as well as a means enabling them to slip out of their cave to secure necessary food during those turbulent periods.

Demonstrating his complete confidence in Rhu and the Cave Dwellers accompanying them, Dargh led them to several cunningly contrived markers by which the beginning of the trail could be located from below, even at night. Without these guides, even though one knew of its existence and could see traces of it well up the beetling cliff, not even the sharp-eyed Rhu would have been able to locate its start without devoting much time to the task. Pursued by an enemy and with time at a premium, these shrewdly designed markers could easily spell the difference between life and death.

As they made their way along the scarcely discernible trails, Rhu pondered whether it would be best to go among the Forest Dwellers with his little band or have them go direct to the Ku and Dan huts while he pursued his dangerous mission alone. One of the Cave Dwellers, Pflugh by name, he had known before. The other three were strangers to him, but their friendliness and willingness soon made him feel as if they were old and tried friends. Besides, Dargh had vouched for them, having known them since they were toddlers, and the more Rhu saw of them, the better he liked them. He had hoped to gather at least ten Cave Dwellers, but Dargh had opposed trying to get more at this time.

"Dargh come back later," he commented. "Easier then. Cave Dwellers think slow. Want more taste stone soon," he finished, and Rhu realized that Dargh had a canny understanding of his own people.

Midafternoon found them at the edge of the great woods where the Forest Dwellers lived. "We'll stay here for tonight," Rhu decided. "The Forest Dwellers seldom come this way as there is but little game in this section, and we need rest."

As though he had been reading Rhu's thoughts earlier in the day, Dargh announced unexpectedly, "Dargh know Kurd. Make knife for Kurd. We go with you. Kurd big man. Plenty men. Rule this section," his sweeping arm embracing a large portion of the forest lying immediately before them.

"I want to get twenty of them," Rhu explained. "Too many for one family, so the work will be dangerous."

"We not afraid. Cave Dwellers good fighters. Forest Dwellers know."

As if this were all there was to it, each of the other four opened his sleeping skin and, for the first time, Rhu saw their beautifully made war axes, all with keen cutting edges and sharp-pointed backs—decidedly formidable weapons in their brawny hands. With a grin, Dargh opened his own bundle and handed Rhu one like them, but even more beautifully made and finished, the difference between a fine and a master craftsman's work.

"Yours," he grunted. "Mine," he added drawing out its duplicate. "Our arrows stop them. If any pass, axes finish," and the other four nodded their full agreement.

KURD was all that Dargh had said and instructed his oldest son, Ord, an exceptionally powerful, hairy giant who stood all of seven and a half feet tall, to select four others after several had volunteered.

While Ord's forehead was low and his brows beetling, his eyes were clear and set wide apart. His mouth was firm in contrast with the usual pendulous, drooling-lipped ones so common among the Forest Dwellers. In fact, all five were exceptionally intelligent men, and all nearly as big as Ord. Beside them, even the redoubtable Dargh looked almost small, but their respect for him was very evident, and they all eyed Rhu's and Dargh's bows. Theirs were but heavy limbs, roughly fashioned, though better than any Rhu had before seen among the Forest Dwellers.

The alert-eyed Dargh, observing this evident interest, looked at Rhu, then smiled. "Want see shoot?" he asked Ord.

"Ugh," the big fellow replied. "Look small," he remarked dubiously holding out his own great, club-like bow.

"How far Ord kill?" Dargh asked.

"Seventy-five steps," Ord responded proudly.

Dargh's grin widened. "See bird top tree?" pointing to a

crow so far away it looked no larger than a blackbird. The tree itself was a good hundred feet tall and probably a hundred yards away.

A chill ran up Rhu's back. Only sheer luck would enable anyone to hit that target! Again, however, he was underestimating the canny Dargh.

"If you come closer than Rhu, Dargh give you new knife," he dared Ord, who was quick to accept, although convinced that no human being could do much better than to shoot that far, let alone hit the bird.

"Ord scare, Ord get knife?" he demanded.

Dargh glanced at Rhu who nodded slightly. "Yes," he agreed.

Ord's heavy, crooked arrow flew so wide of its mark, however, that the bird paid not the slightest attention.

Carefully selecting his arrow, Rhu determined that he would at least make the bird move. Then his bow twanged, and the arrow described a beautiful arc, actually cutting some feathers from the bird. Too precious to lose, one of the Forest Dwellers fled toward the spot where the arrow should light.

Ord stared, seemingly unable to believe his own eyes. Never in his wildest dreams had he imagined such shooting. "Good!" he boomed from his great chest. "Good!" he repeated.

Kurd turned to Rhu. "Who make bow and arrows with feathers?" he asked.

"Rhu make bow and arrows. Dargh make stone tips," Dargh spoke up proudly.

"If make for Kurd family, will give ten men," Kurd volunteered.

"How many in family?" Rhu asked.

"Fifty men," Kurd answered, counting them off with his hands.

"If ten of your men go with me, I will make fifteen bows and ten arrows for each bow, but Dargh will have to say about stone points," bargained Rhu.

"Dargh make," Dargh agreed readily, "but not before our ten have good bows and arrows."

ANXIOUS to be on his way, Rhu with his fifteen men started due north through the very heart of the great forest. They had been lucky in locating Kurd so quickly, and by going through the center of the forest, he felt sure it would not be long until they would come across the trail of some of the other Forest Dwellers.

Elated at first by the ease with which he had secured the ten Kurd men, he began later to wonder why Kurd had been so willing to let a fifth of his men accompany him. At least one of them, he observed, was eying his bow and arrows. Instinctively, he gripped his keen-bladed ax more firmly. He realized that these big fellows were none too trustworthy and was determined to take no unnecessary chances. They were still close to Kurd, and before long it would be dark.

A moment later, Ord stepped to his side. "Open space ahead," he said softly. "Ord go get deer," and taking the very man who had caused Rhu's suspicion, disappeared silently into the brush.

Now Dargh took his place at Rhu's side. "Sud no good," he whispered. "Ord cure or come back alone. Ord good," he added, smiling into Rhu's face.

"How about the others?"

"Four good," Dargh grunted, studying the others who were plodding silently along ahead of them. "Ord pick."

FOR some time, the group traveled in silence until passing beneath an exceptionally large tree with wide spreading limbs, Rhu decided to camp.

"Shall we make fire?" asked Dargh.

Rhu nodded assent, smiling to himself as he surmised the canny Dargh's purpose. Squatting quietly, he made a tiny mound of dried bark, his every movement followed closely by the questioning, doubtful eyes of the Forest Dwellers, two of whom, rather surprisingly, although unenthusiastically, joined Dargh in gathering sticks. Reaching for his fire stone, Rhu looked up to see Ord and a somewhat disheveled and bloody-faced Sud, over whose shoulder was slung a deer.

Without further ado, Ord motioned for two of the other less prepossessing Forest Dwellers to join Sud in cleaning the deer, standing grimly over them as they went to work with more fear than desire to serve reflected in their heavy faces.

Dargh's grinning I-told-you-so expression passed unnoticed for so interested was Rhu in what was happening that he even forgot about starting the fire. Presently, he observed the two whispering to Sud as they worked, their backs toward Ord so that he could not see their faces. His keen ears, however, must have caught something they were saying for, as Rhu watched, Ord stepped up behind them. Grasping each one by the neck, he slammed their heads together so hard the thud was plainly audible to Rhu, a good thirty feet distant. With a grunt, he then swung them around to face him. Although neither had made any seeming effort to resist or dispute what he was do-ing, upon releasing their necks, his right and left hands smashed each so powerfully on the side of the head that they went sprawling.

With a yell of fury, one bounded to his feet, only to die in his tracks as Ord's heavy war club clove his skull. Sud and the other returned to their task with a speed that betrayed the deadly fear in their hearts for this giant brother of theirs.

Dargh grunted softly. "Ord good man," he repeated admir-ingly.

Rhu grinned back at Dargh, then began to strike his fire stone with the flint. At the second attempt, a spark caught. While the Forest Dwellers stood peering in awed amazement, he blew the smoldering spark into a tiny blaze, and a moment later, had a fire going.

"See?" Ord snapped to the two staring men who had now finished skinning the deer. "Magic! Just like shoot! Mind Rhu or die," he snarled, and turning his back on them, strode over to Rhu's side. Here he faced the remaining two men his father had selected. "Rhu chief. Ord Rhu's friend," and the vehe-mence with which they nodded their assent went far to calm Rhu's apprehensions.

Rhu now rubbed his piece of venison with the salt, and then that of the Cave Dwellers who presented theirs for the same treatment.

"What that?" Ord asked.

"Taste stone. Do you want to try it? It makes things taste much better."

"Ugh!" Ord grunted, smiling as he extended his big hunk of meat.

The four men whom he had selected presented theirs also, but the others seemed rather diffident.

"Come on, if you want to try it," Rhu invited them. "You'll like it."

As was usual when roasting meat, Rhu rubbed his after each bite, and now the others followed his example. There was such a smacking of lips, grunting, and mumbling as they wolfed down the meat that it was very evident the changed flavor appealed to them also.

Supper over, the fire was extinguished lest it betray them to some wandering band of hunters, although, as Rhu well knew, the Forest Dwellers seldom moved about much after dark.

Breakfast finished the deer meat. As they started ahead, Ord came to Rhu's side. "Try Gurd. Good men. Not many," he explained.

"Can you find him?" Rhu asked, and Ord nodded, leading them off in a northeasterly direction.

At about noon as Rhu, Dargh, and Ord were walking ahead of the others, Rhu's sharp eyes detected the fresh trail of some man's recent passing, probably within the hour, he guessed, and he turned to follow it. Ord looked at him in surprise, while Dargh tried his best to appear as if it were perfectly natural, but he, too, was as astonished as Ord at Rhu's trailing ability.

For perhaps a mile, they followed the trail, then Rhu held up his hand for silence, sniffing the air. "Smoke," he muttered. "Ord, do you suppose this is Gurd's place?"

Ord nodded. "I lead. Gurd know me," he explained striding ahead confidently. Presently, the big fellow was challenged sharply. "I am Ord of Kurd," he answered without slackening his stride or deviating from his path by so much as a hair, even though the guard stood squarely in his way. For a moment, it looked as if this sentry were going to dispute Ord's passage, but either he finally recognized the giant striding down upon him or decided that discretion was the better policy, for he stepped aside just beyond striking distance of Ord's heavy club.

"Ord's friends," Ord growled, nodding back toward the

others who were rapidly bearing down upon the two. As if this were all there was to it, he strode on into the opening where some twenty or twenty-five shaggy men sat around the usual bubbling pot, while their equally shaggy and unprepossessing women waited upon them.

One behemoth of a man, tall and mighty of frame, roared out in a stentorian voice, "Come eat, Ord. Who with Ord?"

"Friends," Ord boomed. "Hungry, Gurd. This Rhu Ku of Plains Dwellers."

"Ku?" bellowed Gurd who seemed unable to speak in ordinary tones. "Huh!" wiping off his greasy beard on his hairy fist. "Rhu whip Wud last moon. Rhu shoot good. Eat!" he invited, smiling his welcome.

THE MEAL over, Gurd stretched out his great, hairy legs and folded bristly hands over his stuffed paunch. After belching loudly, he dug a great chunk from between his tusklike teeth, spat, and grunted. "Wurt," he roared, "bring bow. Want see shoot with Rhu. Nobody yet beat Wurt," he boasted.

As the stalwart, youthful Wurt approached, Rhu was surprised to see that he had a real bow and that his arrows were unusually straight. He eyed the bow carefully, then walked over to Wurt.

"Where did you get that bow?" he asked.

"Wurt take from Wud's Kood who steal from Rhu," he explained.

Rhu grinned. "I thought I recognized it, Wurt. Those arrows look like mine, too."

"Wurt take all from Kood. Kood no good," Wurt replied, his attention on Rhu's beautifully decorated bow which was a great improvement over this old one he had made some years ago. Because the shape was different, it looked very slender by comparison. "Rhu's bow weak," he commented.

Rhu merely smiled. "What shall be our target?" he asked.

Wurt pointed to a deerskin which two Gurd men had stretched around a tree.

Rhu frowned. He did not want to spoil an arrow. "Why not place it against that clay bank?" he asked, pointing to the almost perpendicular bank of a stream fully eighty yards distant.

"Good," bellowed Gurd. "No break arrows and longer shot," smiling at Wurt, evidently figuring that the stronger bow would shoot farther.

Wurt probably felt the same way about it, for he grinned first at his father, then at Rhu.

At a signal from Rhu, Wurt shot first, striking near the circle drawn upon the skin with a charred stick. Rhu's arrow struck the center. Apparently, it was not till then that the Gurds observed the feathers and stone head, for one of them raced to the skin and secured the arrow which they passed from hand to hand.

"Shoot again!" Gurd shouted.

This time, Wurt's arrow struck almost exactly where Rhu's had been, and a great roar of approval went up from the Gurds. For the first time, Dargh and Ord seemed concerned. There could be no beating that shot. What would Rhu do?

With a smile, Rhu stepped up, shot, and to the utter amazement of everyone, his arrow split Wurt's from end to end as the flint head plowed straight through it.

Complete silence followed. Then Gurd got ponderously to his feet, and Rhu decided he had never seen such a monster of a man. Shaggy and unkempt, Gurd stood some eight and a half feet tall, the tremendous breadth of his shoulders in keeping with his height and bespeaking the might of the great brute he was. But his face was intelligent, though undeniably cruel.

"Accident!" he rumbled hoarsely, the sound resounding in his mighty chest. "Shoot again!" Striding over to Rhu, who seemed but a child beside him, he growled, "Rhu little, but Rhu shoot well. Rhu beat Wurt again, Rhu my friend. Wurt beat Rhu, Gurd crush Rhu . . . . so!" And he slowly closed his great fist that was larger than Rhu's head.

Ord promptly stepped up to him, and though there was no comparison between the two in size, there was no hesitation in Ord's manner. "Gurd touch Rhu, Ord kill before Gurd bat eye," he snarled. "No man yet ever beat Ord who killed Rood. Rood bigger than Gurd. Rood make Gurd run."

Gurd's eyes blazed, the great veins swelling in his low forehead until they looked like writhing snakes. The froth welled through his heavy lips as his fanglike teeth ground together in bestial rage. Quietly, Rhu notched an arrow, while his men each gripped his heavy ax and prepared for what they expected to follow.

"*Gurd!*" Rhu's voice cut like a whip, causing Gurd to look at him despite himself. "We came as friends. We hope to depart even better friends. I have no fear of you for all your size and strength. I have killed a bear with only a stone knife, and a flying eagle with an arrow. Sit down lest I forget our friendship and split your thick skull with this arrow. Your challenge is worthy of a boy, not of a man grown.

"Wurt, I will set you a mark. If my shot fails, we shall leave here quietly and we shall all forget what has passed. But if it succeeds and you cannot equal it, then," turning to the speechless Gurd, "you shall let Wurt and two other men of his choice come with us if he wants to after he hears what I shall have to say."

As he ceased speaking, the honk of flying geese winging their way northward could be heard. Rhu was sure they would soon be flying just above the tree tops, as was their usual custom. "Here come some geese, Wurt. I shall shoot one while you try to do the same."

Wurt notched an arrow but shook his head. "No man can do," he stated.

Waiting until they had actually passed over him and were heading away, Rhu picked one and shot, just a split second after Wurt's bowstring had twanged. Only Wurt shot straight up . . . . and missed, while Rhu's arrow struck, its sharp point tearing almost through the bird as they discovered when they picked it up.

"And now, Gurd, which shall it be? As I have said," notching another arrow, "or as you have said? Do you still want to crush my skull?"

The glint in Rhu's eyes told Gurd he meant exactly what he said, and the man who could do what Rhu had done was not one with whom to trifle. He shook his shaggy head and sat down heavily.

"You win," he growled hoarsely. Then, so unexpectedly that Rhu started and almost shot him, he burst into a great roar of laughter. "Bluffed by boy and scared by Ord!" he bellowed

The Taming of Gurd

between gales of mirth. "Gurd want scare Rhu so Rhu miss shot, but Ord make mad."

This was a very real apology, and everybody laughed, although Ord was the last to do so. Even when he sat down, Rhu could see the ridged hair along the nape of his neck and well down between his shoulders.

For most of the afternoon, Rhu and Ord worked, explaining repeatedly to Gurd and Wurt, as well as those who remained to listen, the reason for their visit. At first, it was hard for them to grasp the general idea, but once they did, Wurt was both willing and anxious to go. He became even more eager when he learned that he, too, would eventually have a bow and arrows like Rhu's—without the carving, to be sure, but that did not make much appeal to the practical minded Wurt. Neither did it to several of the others. Rhu, however, had asked for but three of Gurd's men, and Wurt promptly selected two from among his brothers and half brothers.

As they prepared to leave, Gurd turned to Rhu. "Rhu," he boomed, "when ready, send word to Gurd. Gurd pick men. Join Rhu. Rhu and Hut have good plan. Forest Dwellers fight too much among selves. Not good. Some day, work together like Kus and Dans. Rhu good boy."

"I now need eight more Forest Dwellers, Gurd. Have you any family in mind who would help us?"

"See Nod. Wurt know well."

WURT now led the way, no less amazed than his two brothers when, at dusk, Rhu started fires to cook the two deer they had killed but a short while before. By the time they had finished eating, almost all of Rhu's salt was gone, and having once tasted it, the salt starved Forest Dwellers were more than anxious to help him replenish his stock. Rhu knew then that he might expect plenty of speed on the balance of the trip after he had recruited his remaining men.

Nod was an old man, as Forest Dwellers go, being in his fifties and having many grandchildren who were fully grown, as well as a number of unmarried sons. As was true of the Mu Yans as a tribe, he had many wives, for the head of each family had as many as he could support provided he could take them, this latter being especially true of the Forest and Cave Dwellers. The Plains Dwellers usually were content with two or three whom they generally purchased from other families, whereas the Cave and Forest Dwellers took theirs by cunning and by main force. That the matter of love did not enter into this arrangement was largely responsible for the nature of the people, the women seemingly satisfied with their lot.

The Nod family was grouped under a grove of big trees whose bark was thick and red in color, averaging some two hundred feet in height, and beneath which was practically no brush or other growth. Of huts, the Forest Dwellers had none at all as they were almost continually on the move, following game and hunting women. Rhu estimated that there must be at least a hundred full grown men here and countless children. It was the largest family group he had ever encountered. When Nod died, as Rhu well knew, the family would probably divide into two or three groups, led by the strongest of the brothers remaining.

Nod himself was a big man, about the height of Ord, but wider of shoulder, and his hairy arms reached almost to his knees. Despite his age, he was alert and active, and the power of his rule was obvious. His welcome was neither effusive nor cold. In some respects, he reminded Rhu of his own father.

Most of the day and into the evening, he conversed with Rhu, unlike most of the forest folk, talking rather freely. It was just before supper when he told Rhu a surprising thing.

"Nod has brother living in secret place," he said. "Brother called Elder. Much older than Nod. Brother only Forest Dweller Elder. Three moons ago, brother came to Nod in night. Tell Nod Rhu come. Nod ask Rhu many questions. Rhu say same things as brother. Nod pick eight men for Rhu, but want men decide for themselves. They good men and single. Rhu depend on them. Now we eat."

Chapter Eight

OG YAK REBELS

BECAUSE HUT had been clever enough to foresee the difficulty of persuading the Plains Dwellers to accept Rhu's idea of enlisting the Forest Dwellers, he carefully avoided mention of it. Wisely, he decided to leave it to Rhu to harmonize the group. The fact of the matter was that he himself had succumbed to the feeling that the Forest Dweller idea was not so good. Hut did not like to fight and although he would do so upon occasion, it always seemed to him so futile, and to deliberately make this combative element of their tribe a part of the great undertaking seemed to him to be inviting trouble.

"Why can't people live together in peace?" he asked himself repeatedly as he mulled over the problem. "Surely, there must be some way to bring this about without the exercise of sheer brute force! It is too much like the animals—the strongest rules, and the weaklings are either killed or forced out of the herd."

Otherwise, however, his thoughts were on the success of his and Rhu's plan, doing much to clarify his ideas concerning it. The more he thought about the outcome of what they were setting out to do, the stronger grew the conviction that all those participating should eventually be governed by some simple set of rules that would insure justice without reverting to the use of force.

Leading an imposing cavalcade of Plains Dwellers, Hut approached the Dan and Ku huts about noon. At first, he had been puzzled by the fact that the larger the group he had with him, the easier it became to persuade others to join them. In the beginning he had been glad to get anybody who would come. Toward the last, he began to pick and choose, the result being that his recruits, as a whole, were getting steadily better in quality and understanding. By the time he had picked up Hun and the others first selected, he felt quite proud of the forty he had interested, and could not help speculating upon how long he would have to wait for Rhu.

He rather dreaded the wait. Even during the march homeward, some of his followers began asking awkward questions, showing signs of individual notions that required all his persuasive powers to keep from upsetting some of the others. If this amount of dissension was true among the Plains Dwellers, what *must* be the case with Rhu and those utterly savage and unbelievably truculent Forest Dwellers! And what about the Cave Dwellers? This would all be so entirely different from their ways, as he understood them from Rhu, that he began to fear for the safety of his closest friend.

Prey to these thoughts this last morning of his journey homeward, Hut's heart bounded when, as they came into view of the home huts, the first person he saw was Rhu. Surprisingly, he seemed to be on friendliest terms with two towering, shaggy Forest Dwellers and a shorter, powerful, short-necked and rather stooped man whom Hut immediately classed as a Cave Dweller. Gathered about a fire where they were preparing their noonday meal, he saw a group of mighty Forest Dwellers and four of the Cave Dwellers, all laughing and seemingly in excellent spirits. More remarkable still, among them, apparently the best of friends, were some of the Ku and Dan men.

A moment later, however, the scene changed as his followers also sighted the group about the fire, for they were ready to fight or to flee. As if sensing this, those great brutes of Forest Dwellers rose as one, each gripping his big war club, to stand glowering at Hut and his men, or at least, so it seemed to Hut.

"Hello there, Hut!" Rhu shouted, his face bright with the affection that welled up in his heart. "Boy! You surely have a fine looking bunch of fellows there!"

The tension among Hut's followers visibly relaxed.

"You didn't do so bad yourself," Hut shouted in return, the sting of tears in his eyes. Never before had Rhu looked so good to him, and he felt as if years had been lifted from his shoulders.

"Hut, I want you to meet Dargh," Rhu began as they drew close together. "What do you think of these?" he asked enthusiastically, showing Hut one of the flint-headed arrows. "Dargh has the ones for your arrows. He's the one who made most of them. And this is Ord of Kurd," reaching up and resting his hand familiarly upon the mighty, hairy shoulder of the taller of the two Forest Dwellers, "and this is Wurt of Gurd, a fine archer and my good friend."

Hut smiled up into the faces of each of the three as Rhu named them. Despite the utter savagery of their appearance, his heart warmed toward them. They must be good if Rhu called them friends. Still, Rhu looked very small beside them, especially Ord, by far the biggest man Hut had ever seen.

Ord's heavy face looked positively fiendish as he grinned down at Hut, then laid his great hairy hand on Rhu's shoulder. "Rhu Ord's best friend," he grunted simply, but the sincerity in his deep, growling voice expressed far more than the most flowery of speeches.

"Dargh's best friend, too," announced Dargh, at the same time handing Hut a heavy, leather bag. "For Hut," he added, smiling as the heavy bag he had handled with such consummate ease was almost whisked from Hut's hand by its unexpected weight.

Wurt said nothing, but there was no mistaking his rugged admiration as his black eyes peered down at Rhu from beneath beetling brows.

Turning to Hut's followers, Rhu said, "You fellows, just sit down with the rest of us and make yourselves comfortable. There is plenty for all to eat, and remember that you are among friends, so get acquainted while Hut and I go to see our folks."

For a moment, the two stood watching as the rather diffident Plains Dwellers joined the group. Contrary to what they evidently expected, the others proved to be as Rhu had said, friendly and entirely willing to share their food with the new arrivals, although, it must be said, they eyed one another speculatively. However, as Hut and Rhu knew, there is nothing equal to the sharing of food to make friends of strangers.

"I hear you tamed Levi Hawk," Rhu announced, hooking his arm through Hut's as they walked toward Mai's home. "You should have had Dargh, Ord, and Wurt with you," he said, launching into a brief outline of his experience at Gurd's. "Now, tell me all about your trip," he finished, belatedly realizing he had given Hut little opportunity to talk.

AT MAI DAN'S, the old man looked at Hut quizzically. "You got more than Mai expected," he praised. "Rhu arrive last night with his men. Never expected to sleep with Forest Dwellers close," he growled. Then grudgingly, "Seem all right. Big eaters," and he grinned at Rhu.

"Big hunters and big men, too," Rhu asserted a bit proudly, smiling at Hut's father.

"Bring in eight deer when come," Mai informed Hut.

"Look as if they could eat a deer apiece." Hut grinned at Rhu. "Your fighting force will take plenty of feeding, seems to me."

Mai looked sharply at Rhu. "You mean they will fight for us?" he asked incredulously.

"That's what I brought them to do, after we go to our new lands," Rhu declared.

"Gee!" cried Hut as, for the first time, he opened the bag of arrowheads and picked out an obsidian one. "I never saw such workmanship! Look, Father. Did you ever see anything like this?" handing the stone tip to Mai who promptly cut his finger trying its point and edge incautiously.

"Sharp!" he exclaimed.

"What do you think of this?" Rhu asked, extending his new knife to Hut. "Be careful. I cut myself with it the very first thing. It is so sharp it will cut hairs on your hand."

Hut immediately tried it, and to his infinite surprise, it actually shaved off some of the hair on the back of his hand.

"Dargh made it and gave it to me," Rhu explained. "Says it took him two moons to finish it."

"I don't wonder," Hut said softly. "Let me put a haft on it."

Rhu agreed only too gladly, commenting, "Dargh is a wonder, and the other four are nearly as good."

"Do you think they can build stone huts?" Hut asked his eternal question.

"Well, old Waugh, Dargh's father, and he built them a stone wall across their cave, closing it with a stone door almost as good as . . . . you know," Rhu ended lamely. "The wall was a good ten paces long and half as high. I haven't asked Dargh about building stone huts. In fact, I don't believe we can do it. I've tried almost every day to build one, but the roofs fall in every time. The wall would be easy for them, but I don't believe we can ever make stone roofs."

"I'll agree only after Dargh gives it up." Hut's positive tone rather surprised Rhu. "Anybody who can make knives and arrowheads like these," fondling those he had taken from the bag, "can make anything he starts out to do."

Rhu smiled widely. "Well, I almost agree with you, but have you ever tried to make one yourself?"

"No," Hut admitted reluctantly, wishing that it had occurred to him to try it. "Still, I'm sure it can be done. We'll see."

"How soon you want Dan men?" Mai broke in.

"Not until we send for them, Father," Hut answered. "First, we must see about getting out upon the Plains. We shall have to find an easier pass than we know about before we can possibly take any herds across. Besides, we should get the protecting buildings erected before we even think about the flocks. Let's get back to the men, Rhu," he suggested. "I want to be sure they get along all right."

"They will, if the Plains Dwellers don't start any arguments with them." Rhu's voice was warm and confident. "In any event, Ord will keep them in line. He is the one man those I brought all respect. So will the Plains Dwellers when they get to know him."

THE FOLLOWING morning, Rhu took the Forest and Cave Dwellers with him to a grove of what we now know as yew trees, for it was of this wood that he had made his and Hut's bows. Here, he showed them how to cut off suitable young trees by bending them over and cutting across the upper side with their stone knives. Because of their size and great strength, and need, therefore, for bigger and stronger bows, the Forest Dwellers selected taller and heavier trees than Rhu generally used.

As they were returning, Dargh remarked to Rhu that he believed he could fashion a blade which would work much better for shaping the bows, if he could get some obsidian or other similar stone that could be brought to a sharp edge. Immediately, Rhu thought of the place of shining stones.

"When we get back to our hut, I'll show you some pieces from a place where we can get an unlimited supply, though they are of many colors," he explained to Dargh, whose eyes lit up.

"Dargh like see. When go?"

Rhu glanced at the sun. "Too late today, but I'll take you there in the morning if you like. I have some pieces of the stuff at my hut and will show them to you when we get back."

By the time they reached the camp, it was noon, and though the rest immediately went to where the pots were already steaming, Dargh hesitated.

"Do you want to see the stones now?" Rhu asked.

Dargh nodded, and when Rhu brought out his supply, his enthusiasm knew no bounds.

"Fine stone!" he exclaimed, examining them almost lovingly. "Make fine knife, fine arrowhead, and pretty thing for . . . . for . . . . " rubbing his brow as he groped for some words to express the great idea that had come to him. Finally, his face brightened. "Make pretty . . . . pretty for around neck, like bear claw or hoogwar teeth," nodding his shaggy head enthusiastically.

Rhu's eyes widened. Why had *he* never before thought of such a thing? Still, how could they be fastened together? He had been going to make a necklace of the bear claws for Haitee, but these bright stones . . . . ! The thought left him breathless, and all the while, Dargh was turning over and over the stones he held.

"You keep them," Rhu offered promptly, and Dargh's smile was a veritable paean of thanks as he promptly stowed them carefully away in his leather bag.

Before daybreak, Rhu and Dargh left for the place of the shining stones, returning at dusk heavily laden. Tired though he unquestionably was, Dargh immediately began chipping away at a long, narrow bit of obsidian with Rhu, Hut, and the other Cave Dwellers deeply interested spectators.

SUNRISE of the next day found Rhu and Hut leading their entire force on the first journey of exploration. Arrived at the beginning of the trail the two had long since discovered, Dargh asked to take the other Cave Dwellers in search of a better passage. Rhu agreed readily because, having been raised in the mountains, they were as adept as wild goats in locating passes and paths through their jumbled masses.

The Plains Dwellers immediately began preparing a hut large enough for all of them, while Ord, with a group of the Forest Dwellers, went to get game for food. With the remainder of the Forest Dwellers, Rhu located some salt, returning at night to find the hut ready and the game for the evening meal dressed and ready for cooking. Within a short time, the Cave Dwellers returned to report they had found a pass that, by bridging a narrow canyon, should enable them to enter into the Great Plains in a body.

"It has been a good day," Rhu commented to Hut, who nodded his approval.

"We have a fine body of men for this job," he stated with no small degree of satisfaction. "I wonder what Dargh is making," for already Dargh was at his chipping.

Rhu explained. "It looks like a two-handled knife. That would be a great help in making bows."

THE FOLLOWING morning, the entire force followed Dargh and the other Cave Dwellers into the deep recesses of the mountains. Hut, unacquainted with the activities of the Cave Dwellers, was especially amazed at the ease with which they picked their way through the seeming maze of steep-walled canyons and along winding ledges. They finally stopped at the point where they were faced with the necessity for crossing the narrow but deep canyon formed by the confluence of the Telha and Cari Rivers as they roared through to join the Mu and Upata ones, and form the great Hatamukulian River.

"Rock here hard," Dargh explained laboriously. "Down," pointing below, "rock soft. River wear wide. Narrow here," motioning across to the other wall which was at about the same level and probably fifty feet distant.

Although the foaming waters were a good five or six hundred

feet below where they stood, Rhu and Hut could see that it was much wider down there than here at the top.

Hut's forehead furrowed in perplexity. "It *is* narrower here, but even so, how on earth are we to get across?" he demanded.

Ord turned to Rhu. "Get big tree," he boomed. "Make fall across," sweeping the span with his great, hairy arm.

"No trees here," Rhu objected, "and one large enough would weigh too much for us to carry."

Ord grinned widely, his black eyes twinkling. Pointing to the other grinning Forest Dwellers, he roared. "Big men, big tree. Get," holding up four fingers. "Bind together. Walk across. Drive sheep across. Forest Dwellers go get."

"Why not all of us go?" Rhu asked. "Then we might be able to carry two of them at one time."

"Forest Dwellers carry two. Plains Dwellers carry one. Cave Dwellers make place ready." Ord's big hand made a smoothing motion.

"You stay here with Dargh and the rest," Rhu advised Hut. "I'm going with them. I can't carry as much as Ord, but I'll bet I can show him an easy way to do it. We shall have to go almost back to our camp, so you fellows meet us there at supper. I surely wish there were some way to cut down live trees. They would be stronger and last longer."

"Dargh have idea," that worthy announced. "Here," opening the heavy bag he always carried and taking out two remarkably well-made flint ax heads. These were heavier and much sturdier than the obsidian war axes, having been designed for generally utilitarian purposes, such as chopping wood and breaking open large marrow bones. "Rhu make handles," Dargh continued. "Hack hole in side tree. Burn. Tree fall."

"And we thought *we* were smart," Rhu reproached himself.

"Water squirrels cut down fairly big trees, Rhu. Do you suppose we could do something like that?" Hut suggested.

"We can try," Rhu agreed enthusiastically. "It will take several days, but we'll get them. Dargh, you've saved the day."

BEFORE Rhu and Ord found the type of trees they wanted for their job, it was well into the afternoon. Rhu studied the towering yet comparatively slender redwoods, his fertile brain busy. To cut down four of these with their equipment would require days of hard labor. He had rather hoped they would find some that had been blown down during a recent storm, but although there were many such trees in the great forest, it was utterly out of the question to consider bringing them so far.

Studying some smaller trees, probably eight inches in diameter, an idea occurred to him, and promptly he set out to make it work. Cutting two comparatively heavy saplings with his knife, he laid them across two big stones and about eighteen inches apart. He then gathered a bunch of limbs which he proceeded to cut into two-foot lengths. Laying these across the two parallel limbs, he bound a few in place with some strips of bark from a willow, thus making a rough platform that soon began to shape up as a bridge.

Ord watched him closely, frowning and evidently deeply puzzled as to why Rhu should be playing this way. Suddenly, he broke out in a bellow of delight. "Ord see!" he roared so loudly that the others all came trooping over to stand staring at him. "Ord see!" he repeated. "Make wood trail with two logs! Ord see. Can do," and he nodded his head vehemently.

Rhu smiled up at him.

"Ugh!" Wurt grunted, nodding his head. "Wurt see too. Rhu put handle on axes?" he finished half questioningly. "Wurt get handles." The big fellow hurried away, returning shortly with two tough young saplings he had uprooted by pure brute strength.

As they walked back to their camp, it did Rhu's heart good to see how well the Forest and Plains Dwellers were beginning to fraternize, and it added to his zest as he worked on the springy handles for the axes. Although the Forest Dwellers were by far the most powerful of the men, he had an idea that the Plains Dwellers would do better with the axes, for he had long since learned that strength is not all there is to chopping. In fact, he assigned the cutting to two of his and two of Hut's brothers who were more accustomed to such work since they were experienced wood gatherers.

Nor was Rhu disappointed with the results for, by the following night, the Plains Dwellers had hacked a circle a good six

or eight inches deep around the two trees he and Ord had decided upon. They heaped earth and stones around both trees to the level of the encircling gashes and on top of these piles, they laid bands of fine, hot-burning sticks. Once the fires were burning well all around each tree, they kept them going through the night. The following morning, they discovered to their joy that the trees were burned in so far that it would take only a strong wind to make them fall. With renewed zest, they built fresh fires and toward morning of the next day, both trees crashed to the ground amid wild rejoicing.

Estimating the width of the canyon as some twenty paces, they cleared off the limbs for thirty paces, then built great fires toward the smaller end, first packing dirt around the trunk below where they

Felling the First Tree

wanted it to burn in two. The end of the fourth day found the two great trunks ready to be moved. Nearly three feet in diameter at their thicker ends, they tapered to about twenty inches at the top, not counting the thick bark which, at Rhu's suggestion, was removed with their knives and stone axes. Next, heavy poles about eight feet long were cut and inserted beneath the first log at about three-foot intervals. The Forest Dwellers voluntarily took the heavier end, and with a man on each end of these poles, twenty-eight of them actually lifted the great log and started marching away.

It was not until this monumental task was undertaken that Rhu fully realized something of the immense strength of the Cave Dwellers. At the end of the first half hour of staggering along with their heavy load, the Forest Dwellers paused to rest. With a grin, Dargh and Pflugh replaced Ord and Wurt at the butt of the tree where it was heaviest, while two others of the Cave Dwellers took the places of the two Forest Dwellers immediately ahead. Nor were the Cave Dwellers any more distressed by their gargantuan efforts than had been the Forest Dwellers when they paused for the next rest period.

By nightfall, Rhu and Hut estimated they were a good third of the way to their destination, and the following evening found them entering upon the last stage of their journey through the canyons. At one place, as they were going downgrade, they stopped to rest and to their amazement, the log started to travel ahead on the round poles by which they were carrying it. As one of these was left behind, an observing Forest Dweller picked it up and hurried forward to place it well ahead. Taking advantage of this and by pushing, they made quite rapid progress while actually resting from their tremendous task.

Then they reached the point where they had to skirt the canyon along the winding trail. Here, the path became so narrow as to afford room for only two men walking abreast. To carry the log along it was an utter impossibility! To make matters worse, a short curve lay between them and the place where they had planned to bridge the chasm! Consternation beset them. With less than a hundred paces farther to go, it looked as if they were faced with defeat. Had all their work been for naught?

Thoroughly disheartened, they dropped down beside the log to rest and consider the problem. Finally, Hut spoke.

"Rhu, do you suppose that if I were to go to the family huts and get thirty or forty more of our men to come up here to help, we could manage it?"

"I had thought of that, Hut, but not all of our men can work as it is."

Hut glanced up at the rocks above them. "Dargh, is that another path up there?"

"Yes," was the reply. "Goes up."

"If we could hold the log with heavy vines from up there, could we get it around this turn?"

"Man walk there," Dargh said, shaking his head, "but how carry log?"

Quick to see the possibility, Rhu sprang to his feet. "Take me up," he requested, and Dargh led him back up the trail to where they could climb to the upper one. This Rhu found to be rough and none too wide, but while it mounted steadily, he discovered that at no place near the turn was it more than twenty feet above the lower one.

"Ord," he shouted, "you and five or six men go get some heavy vines at least ten or twelve paces long and strong enough to hold the log. There are plenty in that ravine near our camp. As you suggested, Hut, we shall need at least twenty more men. How about sending someone back to get them? I think you have solved our problem."

THE NIGHT was a restless one for both Rhu and Hut. The more they thought of their problem, the worse it seemed. They had all worked until late getting the vines ready, and while they were strong, the lads realized something of the tremendous weight of that log. If one of the men were to get tangled in the vines and the log slipped, or some of the vines broke, tragedy could easily result, costing them not only the log, but life as well, or horrible injury.

Toward morning, Rhu spoke. "I've been thinking of Lord

Lithargos, Hut. If He were here I am sure He would know a way."

"Maybe He will come," Hut murmured.

"I surely hope so," Rhu sighed. But Hut had at last fallen asleep. With the thought of the Great Being, it was as if a heavy load had somehow been lifted from Rhu's shoulders. A deep conviction of success enwrapped him, and he, too, slept.

By noon all was ready for the attempt, and while Lord Lithargos did not appear, the sense of well-being remained with Hut and Rhu. With forty men above holding the log with the vines, two men to each vine, they lifted the log and began the difficult task of getting it around the curve. To the delight of all, this was accomplished without accident or slip, and soon, the log was at the point where they were to place it across the canyon.

The next step was to get it on end so that when lowered, the log would span the chasm. By main strength, some of the Forest Dwellers maneuvered it by means of the long vines fastened at its top until it was in the desired position while others of the Forest Dwellers, also holding vines to which it was attached, stood well ahead and far back up the trail so as to keep it from falling sideways. Then they started to lower it, and all watched anxiously the slow descent.

Halfway down, the vines proved to be too short!

Rhu drew a deep breath. Surely, Lord Lithargos knew their predicament, and by His great power would see the log safely placed.

"Drop it!" he shouted.

The log crashed into place, rebounded, twisted sideways, and plunged into the roaring river below!

Stunned, Hut and Rhu stood staring into the shadowy depths, almost unable to believe their own eyes. To have come this far only to fail at the very moment when success should have crowned their herculean efforts was a disheartening blow.

"And I thought Lord Lithargos was helping us!" Hut's voice was a trifle bitter.

"You sound too much like me, Hut. I thought the same thing while that log was turning over and over. Then I remembered the Elders telling us that we must not ask or expect help with those things we should be able to do ourselves. We did not ask Him to help us get the log across—only to get it around that bend. Besides, I should have had enough sense to know our vines would be too short. That was my fault. Next time, we won't make that mistake. Oh well! I suppose we might as well get back and start up with the other one. We can't accomplish much sitting here and wishing."

"Perhaps you are right, Rhu, but why take all the blame yourself? I should think of *some* things," Hut accused himself, just as Ord's snarl came to them from where he stood before the Forest Dwellers.

"Ord kill first Forest Dweller who say leave!" he roared.

As Hut and Rhu bounded to their feet and started toward them, Dargh and the four Cave Dwellers stepped to Ord's side, heavy war axes swinging easily in their powerful hands.

Came a deep-throated growl from the Forest Dwellers as Wurt stepped forward from their ranks. "No Forest Dweller mention leaving," he growled. "Wurt kill first man who do."

"Who said anything about leaving?" Rhu demanded as he neared Ord.

"Plains Dweller up there," pointing to the Plains Dwellers who were standing scowling down at them.

As Rhu glanced up, one of them hurled a rock, narrowly missing him. "Og said it," he snarled. "Too much work. Fool idea, anyhow."

To Rhu's amazement, several nodded their agreement and started edging toward the speaker, but Tun Kut stepped in front of them, balancing upon the balls of his feet, eyes alight and his heavy war club swinging freely in his hairy fist. He said no word, but the manner in which the advancing men stopped in their tracks told more plainly than words what they read in his eyes.

With a grunt of exertion, Hut would have bounded up the trail, but Rhu stopped him by holding out his hand.

"Og Yak," he said, "it is indeed a brave man who hurls rocks from where he thinks he is safe. Yet, with an arrow, I can kill you before you take two steps. But you are not worth risking such a good weapon upon. I have been watching you, and you feel very big and brave. I dare you to come down here and tell me face to face that you are a better man than a baby. You are a liar and a coward. You have not the courage of a jackal, and that has less than a rabbit. Otherwise, you would come down here and stop my talk.

"And as for the rest of you who have neither courage nor honor, join in with him and either leave now and for good, or else come down here and meet me as man to man."

With a roar, Og scrambled down, well knowing that to refuse would forever damn him among his people. With a wide grin, Rhu stood waiting until he could recover his feet and get ready. Ord frowned. Dargh eyed Rhu uneasily, then, noting the look in Rhu's eyes, grinned up at Ord who, in turn, relaxed and stood watching. In his eyes was that which boded no good for Og if he tried any trickery.

"Well, little boy, are you ready?" Rhu asked with heavy sarcasm, crouching slightly as the big Og dashed forward, his

The Taming of Og

hairy hands outstretched to grasp and crush the small man before him.

Like a flash, Rhu's hands shot out and grasped the thick wrist of Og. Exerting all his strength, Rhu whirled, swinging the heavy, bellowing man over his head, and then let him crash to the stony trail with a thud. Reaching down, he snatched away Og's heavy stone knife and tossed it aside.

"Little boys shouldn't carry such things," he stated, and there was a well-defined snicker from Plains and Forest Dwellers alike, while Dargh and his companions chuckled aloud.

Og got to his feet, but with every ounce of his strength, Rhu drove his iron hard fist into Og's face, knocking him flat. Groggily, Og tried to rise, and Rhu helped him up, then stepped lightly aside just beyond reach as the bleary-eyed man struck out ineffectually. Stepping close to him, Rhu swung once more, again knocking him down. Then he dragged the big fellow to a trickling stream beside the trail and washed his bloody face.

"Now get back with the others, Og, unless you want some more. And if you want to go back to be laughed out of camp, go ahead. Otherwise, eat your supper, then come to see me. And as for you others who would have joined Og, come with him. I want to talk to you. Hut and I want no man to stay unwillingly, nor do we want any more stuff like this. The next time it happens, I shall let Ord, who is at the head of the Forest Dwellers, take whatever action he thinks best. I can't be bothered." Turning away, he took Hut by the arm and started back to their camp.

As they made the last turn in the trail, Hut glanced back, then chuckled. "Ord, Wurt, and Dargh are the last of the column, Rhu, and those Plains Dwellers look like sheep. I'll bet we have no more trouble like that."

"I wish I could say the same, Hut. I truly do, but not everyone can take disappointments, you know. I have my doubts."

Chapter Nine

THE BRIDGE

SUPPER OVER, Og and some ten of the Plains Dwellers, closely followed by Ord and Dargh, approached Rhu and Hut who sat beside their fire.

"Well, Og," Hut began when they stopped before Rhu and him, "I must admit that right now, I feel very much ashamed of my selection. I am sure Gar will be equally so. However, Rhu has asked me to give you a chance to defend yourself and to say what you have to say before we decide upon what we shall do about it."

Og's face darkened under its whiskers, his mouth still puffed from Rhu's fist. "Think idea foolish. Og come because Gar say come. When bridge made, no cattle cross. Where new pastures?"

"Where only those who are willing to work with us may go," Rhu said shortly. "Og, you told Hut that no Forest Dweller could be trusted, yet these have not only done more work than you, but not one of them has complained. Every Cave Dweller has done his part gladly. Only you and these ten have objected, and you are the ones who have done the least. You say this whole idea is foolish, yet Sol and Mai think it is a fine one. Gar thought to send his best men. Are only the Plains Dwellers undependable?"

Og began to sweat. "Foolish idea," he persisted stubbornly.

"Why?" Rhu demanded bluntly, and as Og seemed unable to answer, "Just what *is* our idea?"

Og's utterly blank stare showed how little of it he really

knew. "No good," he snarled, his great fists bunching, and Ord stepped to his side, glowering down at him.

"What no good?" Ord demanded. "*Og* no good. Idea good." It was clearly evident that the towering giant was hoping only that Og deny his assertion.

"No, Ord, Og is all right," Rhu startled everybody by defending the uneasy fellow. "He just doesn't understand what it's all about, and because he doesn't, he feels it is no good.

"Og," turning to the staring Plains Dweller, "how would you like to live where you did not have to move your flocks, never had to go out into the storms to look for lost cattle and sheep, could always sleep where it is dry and warm, and knew that neither man nor beast could reach you to attack you during the night?"

"Safe. . . . Warm. . . . Dry. . . . " Og's slow working mind strove to comprehend all Rhu had just said.

"Yes, and no stray cattle. No moving of herds," Rhu repeated.

"Og like safe, warm, dry. Cattle stray. Must eat." Thus Og voiced his real objection, while the ten others with him all nodded their shaggy heads in agreement.

"Good." Again Rhu surprised them by agreeing. "Sit down, all of you. Dargh, bring everybody here."

With the entire group, including those who had come up from the Dan and Ku families to help with the log, all seated around him, Rhu began at the start, carefully and thoroughly explaining his and Hut's big plan, using the simplest terms and repeating many times the most salient of the points until by their many nods of comprehension, he was sure that all of them fully understood the prospective program. He even explained why none of the Plains Dwellers from the Mu Yan or other valleys had ever before utilized the Great Plains which he promised to show them the following morning. Then, he told them about the proposed stone huts.

"And now, Og, that you understand the plan, do you still think it is a foolish one?" Rhu concluded.

"*Good* plan. Og work hard now." For a long moment, the big fellow seemed to struggle with himself. Then, "Og sorry throw rock. Og sorry," he repeated, looking anxiously into Rhu's face.

Rhu chuckled, and there was a visible relaxing of the tension among the entire force. "We had a good fight, anyhow, didn't we, Og?"

Og's heavy face lit up and he smiled at Rhu. "You good fighter. Og whipped. Now Og fight for Rhu." Turning to the ten who had followed his lead, he growled, "You work?" There was a distinct menace in his tone.

"No, Og," Rhu admonished. "Let them make their own decision. How about it?" he asked of them.

"We stay. We work hard." There was every evidence of their sincerity, and for the first time, Hut smiled. Rhu certainly was making very real headway with these men.

"What is it, Dargh?" Rhu asked as he saw the big Cave Dweller struggling to say something.

"Dargh think can build stone hut, but have flat roof," he announced, and his four companions nodded their shaggy heads in agreement.

"*Flat* roof!" Hut exclaimed.

"Why not?" Rhu asked, inwardly as surprised as Hut and wondering why such a solution had never occurred to him. "If Dargh says he can build one, then it will be built," he concluded.

THE NEXT DAY after Rhu and Hut had led them to their stone so that they might see the Great Plains, the second log was moved as far as the bend. In the meantime, a small group of Plains Dwellers were felling another tree by the same method they had previously used under the direction of Og, who seemed to be unable to do enough to show his enthusiasm.

"Og have tree ready tonight," he assured Rhu the following morning before the remainder of the force went to carry the log past the bend and place it across the canyon.

This time they succeeded, and as if it were a mere walk along a smooth trail, Dargh strode easily across the great log, followed by the other Cave Dwellers to whom such dizzy heights were as nothing. Breathlessly, Hut and Rhu watched them until they reached the other side. Then, on hands and knees, clinging desperately to the log, they inched themselves along, while even the most intrepid of the Forest Dwellers followed their example. On the other side, by dint of might, they finally got the log in place and properly braced with heavy stones so that it could neither shift nor roll in the heavy winds which sometimes roared through these deep canyons.

Two days later, the log Og and his men had felled was in place, and the entire force went to secure seven to eight-foot logs for the floor of the bridge Rhu had devised. Og insisted that it be made wider than originally planned because he was sure that otherwise, they would be unable to get the cattle to cross it. To get these logs ready and lashed in place with strips of rawhide cut from the skins taken from their game was quite an undertaking and took more than a week. This done, they covered the entire structure with gravel and dirt, which was carried in skin bags, and then proceeded to make the approach easy of access by building a runway to it.

It was also Og who suggested that a crude railing be lashed in place along both sides of the bridge. Rhu then conceived the idea of building railings on each side of the runways leading to it, so that once the herds were driven into it, their only outlet lay across to the other side. Later, this idea led to fenc-

Moving the Log

ing in the herds at night, and still later, to dividing the land into great pastures.

Beyond the bridge—and before the Great Plains could be reached—lay a deep gorge, or canyon, some five to six miles in length and varying from two miles to fifty feet in width. At the time of the great earthquake, countless tons of great boulders had split loose from the face of the cliffs and crashed into it, forming veritable mountains of stone replete with blind passes and narrow slits barely large enough for a man to wriggle through. To find a safe and easy passage in this vast labyrinth through which to drive their herds and bring their families and few household possessions, presented still another problem.

Like mountain goats, Dargh and the Cave Dwellers, accompanied by the more cautious Rhu, scrambled over obstacles that fairly took the latter's breath, undertaking to find such a pass. From these dizzy heights, they were able to locate routes otherwise almost impossible to find, although it was only after two full days of climbing and traveling five miles along the Hatamukulian River that they finally discovered a passage suitable to their needs.

DARGH spent his evenings working upon his knife for the making of the bows, grinding it with sandstone and a mixture of obsidian chips and a hard sandlike substance until its edge was almost as smooth and keen as that on Rhu's knife. Every night after its completion found Rhu working upon the bows, the first being for Ord—a great seven-foot affair whose pull must have been a good hundred and twenty pounds or more, and for which four-foot arrows were required. To the delight of both Rhu and Dargh, the new knife proved to be a big success and so facilitated the work that Rhu was able to finish Ord's bow in three evenings. In the meantime, Dargh and the other Cave Dwellers were chipping some larger heads for the longer arrows.

Rhu was preparing to string the bow when Ord came in with some dry, fine, straight-grained wood he had found for his arrows, and under Rhu's guidance began splitting it into strips of suitable length for the purpose. When he had finished, he had well over two hundred pieces that were beautifully straight, so much so that Rhu decided they would do without straightening them further.

Dargh, who had been an interested spectator, produced a small obsidian knife which proved ideal for shaping the slender shafts, and with practice, Ord became quite expert at the task. Dargh further surprised them all by bringing out a piece of very light, fine-grained stone (pumice) in which he had made a groove. Taking the arrows, he began rubbing them through this hard abrasive, and the resulting polished smoothness caused even Hut to comment upon them. Two of the Plains Dwellers proved to be quite adept at this and even with the feathering, once Rhu had taught them how to do it, so that before very long, Ord had not only his bow, but a dozen fine arrows.

With Ord thus equipped, and after much careful planning and overhauling of their other weapons, the first trip out upon the Great Plains was made. Their first glimpse as they emerged from the gloomy pass was of grassy meadows as far as eye could reach, broken here and there by groves of stately trees.

As they wandered on to the Plains, they found the grass steadily improving in quality and luxuriance. In many of the groves were fine, clear springs, the streams from which later formed many small lakes. Along the banks of the streams and lakes, the grass was rather coarse and of a bluish tinge, so that in speaking of it they called it blue grass. Digging into its luxuriant stand with a stone-tipped spear, they found it grew from massed roots, forming the first real sod they had ever seen.

"This grass cannot be pulled up by its roots," Rhu announced after trying to do that very thing. "That means it will not be so quickly destroyed by the grazing herds. It is so thick that by spreading them over a bit wider range, I doubt whether they can graze it down."

"And it appears to be almost limitless," Hut observed with delight. "It is no wonder that there used to be such fierce battles for its possession."

"I wonder what these little things are that we see on the tips of so much of it," and Rhu stripped off some of the seed. Putting it into his mouth, he tried to chew it. "It seems to be rather hard," he commented. "Doesn't have much taste, either," spitting forcibly as he strove to rid his mouth of the fine seed. "I wonder what it can be. Must have *some* good purpose."

"Let's take some to the Elders and see whether they know," Hut suggested.

At this moment, Ord's new bowstring twanged loudly, followed by his bellow of delight.

"Look!" he shouted, for he had transfixed a deer with his first shot from the weapon which was now his chief treasure. With effortless ease, he picked up the deer and pointed to the arrow, the head of which protruded a good foot. "Through!" he roared as if afraid no one could hear him, and grasping the head, pulled the arrow on through. Anxiously, he examined the feathered end and to his huge satisfaction, found it unscathed, though bloody. Tenderly, he wiped it off upon his hairy leg. "Never such bow! Never such arrow!" he boasted, and the fact that no one a mile away heard him was only because there was none there to hear.

Nightfall found them camped at the outlet of the canyon where two of the Forest Dwellers kept watch. There was no telling whether enemy eyes had spied upon them, and it was no part of Hut or Rhu's intention that they be caught by surprise.

All the following day was spent tramping along the base of the towering cliffs in which the mountains to the east of the entrance to the valley terminated.

"We must be sure that tradition is right and that some of these other valley dwellers cannot slip in this way to attack us," Rhu remarked to Hut. "As far as I could see, there seems to be no break in these bluffs, but that means little. I'm not so much afraid of the Tama Yans. They are pretty decent people, those of them I have seen, and besides, they would have plenty of trouble getting across the great river. But the Xion Yans and the Cari Yans are all fighters, and the Hata Yans, who live just beyond these mountains, are the worst of all, as I understand it."

"You're probably right, Rhu, and I, too, think we should be careful. Yet, I don't believe in expecting trouble. The Elders say that we always find that which we sincerely seek, and that could also mean that if we are always *expecting* something to happen, it will happen. We started out expecting to find a better way to live, and I believe we are finding it."

"That may well be true, Hut, and I surely do not question the wisdom of the Elders, but I sometimes wonder whether we don't go too far with our own ideas of what They really mean. Do you think that it is only because we carry weapons that a hoogwar will attack us? We know from bitter experience that they attack the unarmed as readily as they do those who are prepared to defend themselves. It is their nature. We know this is so and we prepare for it. It isn't that we *expect* to be attacked, but isn't it only common sense to be prepared for being attacked because we know from the experience of others that everybody who has tried to live on the Great Plains has been attacked?"

Hut frowned. "You always think of such odd ways to make your points, Rhu. It seems to me that this is different, but maybe you are right. At least, only a fool would make his camp where he knows freshets and floods occur every time there is a hard rain in the hills. Yet," and he hesitated doubtfully, "the Elders say that to *fear* anything is to make it possible for it to happen."

"Who's *afraid* of being attacked?" Rhu demanded with a trace of heat. "I just don't believe in taking unnecessary chances. I'd rather be prepared for trouble and never have it happen than be caught without being prepared. But that does not mean one *expects* trouble. Only a fool would tickle a sleeping hoogwar, Hut, and our moving into this place amounts to the same thing if we are so foolish as to be unprepared for what has always happened."

"You are probably right," Hut agreed although he continued to frown thoughtfully. "But I'm going to ask the Elders, just the same."

AFTER three days of searching, they returned to the entrance of the canyon, having found nothing in the way of a pass into the mountains.

"If we had a high stone wall across this place," Hut commented, "nobody could pass through to the Great Plains unless we let them."

"Not unless they found some way to climb over it," Rhu answered. "Dargh and the Cave Dwellers would get over. They cut notches in poles which they use to climb up to their caves in some places. After they are all inside, they pull up the pole. Of course, we could build it so high this could not be done, but it would take a long, long time to do it. Dargh suggests that we make a high wall wide enough so fighters can stand on it and beat back any who try climbing over."

"Maybe we could make it a big *hut* with that flat roof Dargh was talking about," Hut proposed. "Then the wall would serve a double purpose."

"A good idea!" exclaimed Rhu. "Let's talk to Dargh about it."

"Can do," Dargh agreed readily when Hut's idea had been explained to him. "Build wall first. Quicker. Make stone door. We start wall now." He frowned and became lost in thought.

Since these were the usual signs preceding his broaching a new idea, Rhu asked softly, "What is it, Dargh?"

"River run down," Dargh began heavily, at the same time scratching a sloping, wavy line on the smooth earth where they sat. "Cliff where build hut here," and he scratched another sloping line almost parallel to the first but several inches above it. "Cave Dwellers cut . . . ." He hesitated, cupping his hairy hand and groping for the proper word.

"Groove?" Rhu suggested. "Groove as in your arrow polisher?"

Dargh's face brightened. "Yes," he agreed. "Groove run along cliff, so . . . ." drawing a straight line midway between the two previous ones.

Rhu and Hut could see that it started at the surface of the river, running along the face of the cliff upon which the building was to be placed until it reached the surface of the plain.

"End in big hole," Dargh continued, scooping out a small one at this point. "Water come down for drink," he finished, looking anxiously at Rhu to see whether he understood.

The eyes of Rhu and Hut were round with wonder.

"You mean that the water from the river up there," pointing

up the canyon where the roaring river came rushing downward from high above them, "will run down your groove to
empty into a big basin or hole here so that we shall have
plenty of drinking water?"

"Yes! Water for drink! For cook!"

But Rhu and Hut were puzzled. The river ran far below the
cliff. How was Dargh to get down there to dig his canal?

"That canyon is deep and smooth. How can you possibly get
down there to do it?" Hut demanded.

Dargh chuckled as he did often lately, something Rhu had
rarely seen Cave Dwellers do in their homes. Dargh was changing in many surprising ways.

"Dargh not go down," he explained. "Begin where empty
into pool. Dig into cliff wall till reach water. Most rock soft.
Cut easy."

Although the river itself ran far below where the pool was
to be located, it came roaring down such a steep incline that
at the point where it would connect with the channel, below
the site of the proposed building, it was actually higher than
the pool would be.

Rhu was not a little chagrined because it had not occurred
to him that by starting at the pool, it was possible for Dargh
and the other Cave Dwellers to gouge out the channel in the
cliff as they went, until the channel met the river. How practical Dargh was and how well he worked out his ideas before
presenting them! Some of the river water would run naturally
into the man-made runway, and what a help and comfort it
would be for those who would locate on this portion of the
Plains to have water so readily available!

Realizing the need for more men to carry out these two
great projects, Hut announced, "I will send Dargh to the Cave
Dwellers, Ord to the Forest Dwellers, and Hun to the Plains
Dwellers."

Rhu glanced at him in surprise. It was not like Hut thus to
take the full initiative without first saying something to him.

"It seems to me that it might be better to have Ord stay
here," he said thoughtfully. "But let him select the proper man
to send. It is Ord whom they really obey, Hut, and I do not
believe in doing anything to interfere with his standing. The

same thing applies to the Cave Dwellers, and Dargh knows best which one to send. As for the Plains Dwellers, it makes no particular difference, but Og has been so faithful and now seems to understand so thoroughly that I believe he would welcome this chance to serve."

"Rhu right," Dargh agreed so promptly that both Hut and Rhu were somewhat startled. "Dargh send Pflugh. Pflugh know many. Cave Dwellers like Pflugh."

"Never thought of that," Hut agreed readily, "and I think you are right about Ord, Rhu. Shall we ask him whom to send?"

"Surely," Rhu smiled.

"Hey, Ord," Hut called to the big man who came to them with a wide grin. "Ord, we are going to need more Forest Dwellers. Whom do you think we should send?"

"Wurt," Ord answered promptly. "Wurt good man."

"He's the one I would have selected," Rhu said addressing Hut. "It is going to take a man who really knows the Forest Dwellers to select them, and Wurt's reputation is good and widespread. As to Hun or Og, you use your own judgment."

"Since you mention it, Rhu, I believe Og would be the best one to send," Hut decided. "Hun is a good man, but he is a dreamer—much more so than Og who has the courage of his convictions, at least."

The following morning, Og and Pflugh left on their missions, Wurt remaining until the next day while he and Ord discussed whom he should go to see. Rhu had reworked Wurt's bow, and he now had a dozen stone-tipped and feathered arrows. Next to Rhu, he was probably the best archer in the entire group.

Chapter Ten

HUT AND RHU VISIT THE ELDERS

AFTER WURT left for the homeland of the Forest Dwellers, Rhu and Hut departed for a visit they had long discussed, but which their work had prevented.

"It's almost four moons since we visited the Elders," Hut remarked sincerely.

The astute Rhu, undeceived by the very apparent excuse, and heartily in accord with what he felt lay back of it, agreed at once. "Yes, I think we should see them before we go much further with our plans. We are going to need their advice, for I am rapidly becoming convinced that nothing we have planned is more than a beginning. The more I think about this, Hut, the more certain I become that we are starting something that is going to change the entire lives, not alone of the Mu Yans, but eventually of all tribes. If we can bring harmonious understanding among the three divisions of our own tribe, why can't it be expanded to cover all people?"

"That's a big idea, Rhu, a big idea," Hut mused. "However, we still have far to go before this part of any such program is completed. We have only a few single men now, but when it comes to moving in whole families and getting them all to live peaceably together, we are going to face some real problems."

Rhu made no reply as he tried to picture what such a wonderful program as he had in mind would be like. "What do you mean?" he asked after a bit.

"Well, Rhu, there are many Plains Dweller families who will come, and each will have its own herd. Each family will want to keep its herd. We know, too, that there are among them those who do not hesitate to steal from the herds of others when they get the chance, and some plan must be devised to take care of that. The really serious thing, however, is that neither the Cave nor the Forest Dwellers have herds of any sort, and I doubt whether they will want any, at least not for a long time. To support all the Forest Dwellers, even a few of them, is going to make heavy demands upon us.

"Since they will be unable to hunt here as they were accustomed to doing in their forests, what, besides serving as guards, can they offer in exchange for the cattle they eat? Except when we are attacked, they will be idle most of the time and won't be compensating in any way. Yes, Rhu, I foresee many complexities," and Hut shook his head.

This problem had also presented itself to Rhu, but had been resolutely thrust into the background while he concentrated upon the more immediate ones confronting them. Instinctively, he reverted to this same line of reasoning now.

"First, we have still to get enough of the Mu Yans together to get a real start," he objected. "Then we can take care of these things as they come up."

It was Rhu's custom to work out each situation as it arose. The truth of the matter was that neither was accustomed to thinking very far in advance, and this venture was assuming undreamed-of proportions. Heretofore, the very nature of their manner of living necessitated a constant alertness and resourcefulness that precluded too much planning for the future, and now, having taken this monumental step ahead, they were already beginning to wonder just where it was leading them.

Being what they were, the very stubbornness which made them a pair to be reckoned with at any time held them to their endeavor, and it can be said to their credit that the thought of dropping it never so much as occurred to either of them. In fact, the entire thing appealed to their inherent spirit of adventure. Had they given any thought at all to going back to the old life, they would soon have come to realize that something far greater than themselves was steadily and surely holding them to the path. They were yet to learn that once started upon the work of the Great Ones, there can be no turning back.

UPON reaching the place where they were accustomed to signal for admittance to the retreat of the Elders, they found their usual guide awaiting them.

"Welcome, my sons," he announced, smiling at them. "Lord Hiroto told us you would arrive at this time, and He awaits your coming that He may discuss with you the further problems of organizing your work." His kindly eyes began to twinkle, and his smile became very gentle as he answered the unspoken question uppermost in the minds of each. "The girls are well and anxiously await you. Come." And he led them to the already open doorway.

Entering the great cave, they could see that many important changes had been made in it during their absence, but these things were all forgotten when, from behind a great stalagmite where they had been hiding, Haitee and Marda emerged. To the entranced Hut and Rhu, they had never seemed lovelier. Instead of deerskins, they were wearing the most beautiful garments Hut and Rhu had ever seen. Flowing robes of a beautiful shade of green, so pale that it appeared to be almost colorless, and of a texture so fine and soft as to be comparable only to a spider's web, partly concealed and greatly enhanced the physical perfection of both girls.

Yet, great an improvement as this was, a subtle change in the girls themselves held the two ardent admirers almost breathless, hesitating even to touch them although their understanding guide had left them alone for this meeting. And be it said, the changes were not confined to the girls alone. The responsibilities and work Rhu and Hut had assumed had given them a certain sureness of bearing, a restrained virility and composure such as comes only to those who, through sheer ability, have become leaders of men.

Thus it was that for a moment, the four stood breathlessly striving to say something, yet strangely restrained from their old free camaraderie. Haitee was first to break the silence. Impulsive and high-strung, she suddenly held out her arms and fluttered into those of the delighted Rhu.

"You—you are beautiful!" he breathed, burying his flushed face in the luxuriant hair which, instead of being worn loosely as was the usual custom, was now knotted on the top of

Haitee's head, framing her fresh young face with its silken softness.

"It—it's good to see you!" Hut said rather stiffly. The spell broken, Marda was in his arms and for the moment, all else was forgotten. "What beautiful stuff," he remarked after an interval, fingering the cloth of her robe with one hand while holding her close with the other.

"The Lord Hiroto promised that we shall be taught to make it," Marda answered. "At least," she amended, "something very like it, for the material from which this is made cannot be found near here."

"How long has He been here?" asked Hut. Without waiting for a reply, he whispered, "You are even more beautiful than ever." From the corner of his eye, he glanced at Rhu, but he need not have been concerned for Rhu was too busy whispering into the blushing Haitee's very pink little ear to notice anything else.

"We—we must not keep the Lord Hiroto waiting too long," Haitee said softly, rather practically calling Rhu's attention to the importance of deferring their ardent greeting until a more propitious occasion.

"I do not believe He would begrudge us these few moments together." Rhu's reluctance was ill-concealed. "But then, I guess you are right," he conceded. "Come on, Hut. We'd better be on our way." His arm about Haitee, he moved toward the other side of the cave.

"Rhu, do you notice anything different in here?" Hut asked as he and Marda followed.

"Yes. It looks as if it were being used as a meeting place—or about to be used as one," observing that several stone chairs were still unfinished.

"They are making this into what Lord Hiroto calls a temple," Marda explained, "whatever that can be."

"It is to be a place for teaching a very select few many of the things the Elders have already taught you two," Haitee amplified Marda's statement. "I think it is to be also a sort of place for worship. The Lord Hiroto says that we are to be the first vestals to serve in here because we have earned that right through our service to the Elders."

"Who are to be these 'selected few'?" Rhu asked.

"I believe they will be certain ones whom you and Hut select," Haitee explained. "Do you know anyone named Darkh?" she inquired.

"Dargh?" Rhu asked.

"Yes, that is the name. The Elders say that he will probably be among the first. What an odd name! Who is he?"

"A Mu Yan Cave Dweller, Haitee, and one of our most trusted men," Rhu answered promptly. "Did they ever mention Ord or Og?"

"Yes, now that I come to think about it, but Dargh seemed to be the most important. At least, it seemed that way to me," Haitee explained.

Hut's face was alight with an idea. "I believe this will be the ultimate solution of everything, Rhu. If we could possibly get together a group of leaders of the three groups of Mu Yans and have them trained by the Elders, there is almost no limit to what we could do!"

Then, because the girls seemed so much a part of themselves, Rhu and Hut did something unheard of in those days. They explained to them as much of their great idea as was possible as they proceeded along the tunnel to the great valley of the Elders.

"Welcome, my children," Lord Hiroto's deep and gentle voice greeted them as they emerged from the passage. "You have done well and justly merit the confidence Lord Lithargos reposes in you. He will join us presently. Marda and Haitee, take them with you and see they have something to eat, after which the four of you will meet us at the place of assembly."

While they were eating, Rhu took from his pouch two crystal pieces of a beautiful green shade. "Dargh shaped this stone, then broke it in half. See," placing them together, "they fit perfectly. I am to keep one, and you, Haitee, the other. If ever you need me, or if ever I need you to come, we are to send our half with the messenger. Unless the stone exactly fits, we may thus know that the message is false."

"How beautiful it is!" Haitee exclaimed, examining her half with delight. The crystal seemed to be almost fluid as the light radiated from its depths. "Rhu," she said musingly, "these stones represent you and me. We are two matching parts of a single whole."

Rhu's eyes widened at her philosophical suggestion.

"The Elders have been telling us how a man and wife should make a perfect unit . . . . or be as one, each supplying certain things the other needs," Haitee continued.

Rhu's heart almost skipped a beat. This was a new and startling idea. Besides, Haitee's pleasure in the stone caused him to recall what Dargh had said about suspending smaller stones upon a thong to wear about the neck. Rhu could well imagine her reaction to a necklace of the most beautiful of the many colored crystals.

While this was taking place, Marda glanced at Hut who grinned back at her, at the same time reaching into his own skin pouch from which he brought forth a similar, but dark blue stone, also broken as had been Rhu's. This he handed to Marda without comment, and her delight was no less than that of Haitee.

Lunch over, the four repaired to the council place where the Elders and the Lords Hiroto and Lithargos were seated. It was the first time the girls had seen Lord Lithargos, and Haitee thought He seemed rather austere, but when He smiled at her, she decided that in some vague way, He reminded her of Rhu. In just what way, she was unable to decide, but she did know He created the feeling of being absolutely just and ever understanding.

Then she decided that He reminded her of Hut, and that Lord Hiroto was more like Rhu, only to come to the final decision that regardless of all else, she would gladly follow the advice of either of the Great Ones without question, knowing They would never err. Glancing at Marda, she smiled to herself, for it was clearly evident that much the same thoughts were passing through her mind.

"Draw near, my children, and be seated," Lord Hiroto invited the four. "At this time, it is well that all of you should hear what is to be told, for while Marda and Haitee shall remain here for some time, yet it is best that they understand from the beginning something of the Great Work in which Hut and Rhu are now engaged.

"Rhu, those bits you removed from the grass are the seeds from which more of its kind will grow. In due course, you will be taught how to gather and to plant them so that you may not only have plentiful pasturage, but may improve its quality so that all you have visualized may come to pass. I shall further instruct you in the matter of raising for food certain things which are now unknown to you, as well as how to improve the quality of the soil so that your crops will ever increase in abundance and quality. As Lord Lithargos will tell you, this work will eventually be the backbone of the support of the government which He will teach you to inaugurate and maintain.

"For a time, however, the matter of proper organization must supersede all others, but once well established, stock raising and agriculture will form the basis for the continual maintenance of your society."

Lord Lithargos nodded His head in full agreement. "Yes, my children, no government or society can continue to exist unless it is properly organized. It must be made self-sufficient—that is, able to support itself without outside help. It can *grow* or expand only as it produces more than it consumes. Such is the first law for proper organization."

"The basis for the permanent success and growth of your community is excess service, both as it relates to that which each individual member or citizen renders to the organization as a whole, and as it relates to the service the organization as a whole renders the individual member or citizen thereof.

"Since no form of government can long endure or prosper except as each individual member thereof prospers, so, too, may no individual citizen thereof prosper unless the government as a whole prospers. For either the government or the individual citizen thereof to seek to prosper at the expense of the other, or of another, spells ultimate failure and disintegration. This is the second point of the law.

"Thus we come to the basic law of all laws, the law which embraces all others including that of which I have just spoken. *For whatsoever ye do to or for another, so shall it be done to or for you.* Stated otherwise, action and reaction are always equal in force but opposite in direction.

"For example, the force required to draw your arrow to its head is the exact force that is used to drive it from the bow. . . . The drawing, we call action, and the shot is the reaction, or resulting action. . . . Observe that as you draw your shaft for shooting, you pull it in exactly the opposite direction from that in which the shaft takes its flight. Accordingly, as one serves, so shall he in turn be served; in direct proportion as he gives, so shall he receive. Take a thing by force and sooner or later, it will be taken from you by force.

"These essentials you must learn as you know the palm of your hand. This is the fundamental rule of all proper government, and you, my sons, are now embarking upon the building of the first government upon this earth planet. Lord Hiroto and I are but two of Those to come for the express purpose of helping in its establishment.

"There are many things that you would like to know, but to try to instruct you now would serve only to confuse you when you need most a clear understanding. Only this morning were you both discussing a fair distribution among your forming citizenry. Because we must, according to the Great Law, get as we give, it follows that those who contribute most shall receive the most, be that what it may—good or bad.

"Since much of this compensation will lie within your powers, you must learn to weigh values. To the thirsting man, a drink of cool water is of greater value than all the land in the Great Plains you seek for your government, yet it is of little value to the one who has plenty. It may even be a curse in the time of flood, so far as the individual is concerned. Its fair value lies in the measure of its ability to serve. Thus is the value of all things measured.

"One thing more: Everything in moderation. Be ever alert to observe the reactions of that which is too much and that which is too little. In moderation lies balance, and neither the balanced individual or group of individuals, such as will be your government, can greatly err.

"The more you think upon these matters, my sons, the more they will mean to you.

"Let this be your lesson for today." So saying, Lord Lithargos sat back and closed his eyes.

Presently, Lord Hiroto took up the discourse. "You will think of many questions with the passing days, my sons. Talk them over together, and on your next visit, we shall be glad to discuss your decisions with you.

"And now we come to your immediate problems. First, the objective set forth by Rhu as you came here this morning is the ultimate end for which you are to work. First things must come first, however, and your initial step is the completion of the first stone building, or house, as your homes shall be called when buildings are used for that purpose.

"Dargh and his men will construct these with the help which you must provide them. Ord and his men will assume, as their prime duty, the protection of the workers. With their superior strength, they will also help to bear the heavier burdens, of which there will be many. Og and his men will bring in a small herd for food when there is not time for the hunt, and otherwise will help with the building and in such other ways as you may direct.

"For a time, you, Rhu, will direct, for your understanding of the handling of men will be needed. Your conversion of Og from a potential trouble maker to an enthusiastic helper proved this to our satisfaction. But, all ideas you have which will contribute to the efficiency and well-being of the group should be entered into with Rhu and later with those most concerned in carrying them out. In connection with this, you will also give much thought to the matter of making the homes of the members of your society so attractive and comfortable as to make your people quite happy.

"There shall be no taking of women by force in the new order. This must be approached by education, for willing wives become willing helpers and bear strong and obedient children. Peace can come only when all things are accomplished by peaceful means.

"Let no man take from another without giving an equal return.

"Deny no man the opportunity to serve to the best of his ability, but put no man to a task beyond his ability to perform. Thus will come only satisfaction and real accomplishment. There will ever be the drawers of water and the gatherers of wood, but this is just as worthy and honorable a service as that of the man who may become the highest official in the government. The man who honestly gives the best he has to give is as worthy as the one who is able to give more, for none can do better than his best.

"Stint not in commendation for those who serve faithfully, no matter how humble the service, and forget not those who have rendered such service, though their hands may later falter.

"Ever seek to lead rather than to drive. When the time comes to drive, then will you both be given new instructions.

"Be ever just, but measure justice with kindliness and compassion. Judge no man by appearances. Remember Og.

"With those who will come back with your present messengers, you will have sufficient force to bring about the first step in your program."

Lord Hiroto paused. As one, the Elders and Lord Lithargos rose, Hut, Rhu, and the girls doing likewise, then stood with bowed heads and closed eyes.

"Almighty Creator, in Thy tender and understanding hands do we place these two young men. Guard, guide, and aid them in all ways essential to Thy desires that they may never falter in their Great Work and that their path may be made easy. And so it is."

When Rhu and Hut opened their eyes, neither of the Great Ones was to be seen, but the Elders gathered around them, the warmth of their smiles and words of kindly praise being most welcome to Hut and Rhu.

"And now, my children, since the remainder of the day is short, let the four of you go about our valley, seeing what you will and we hope, profiting therefrom. The girls will be able to tell you much, for they have been apt students and willing learners. You, Marda and Haitee, accompany them and give no thought this night to your usual tasks for you, too, have well merited these few hours of happiness with those whom you love. Peace be with you." Quietly, the Elders withdrew to be about their several duties.

Walking through the fields, Rhu and Hut were amazed at what they saw. On every side, or so it seemed to them, were fields which they called meadows until the girls told them they were raising many things to eat. Some of these, they called herbs, while a broad-bladed growth, they called maize. The Elders had told them this produced a seed which was ground into meal and used in cooking. Haitee promised to use some of it later so that Hut and Rhu could taste it. There was also a sort of reedlike growth which the girls explained were onions, a root that was very tasty either raw or cooked. Marda pulled some, and upon munching it, both Hut and Rhu pronounced it far tastier than the reed roots which had been their nearest approach to such a food.

As they walked arm in arm, the four also discussed the many things each had done during the period while they were separated, as well as such other matters as are of interest to those in love. In this respect, Hut and Rhu showed, more than in any other, the effects of their association with the Elders, for it was rare for women to be shown much consideration, and love, as we understand it today, was unusual. Marda and Haitee were vaguely beginning to realize that characteristics they had sometimes regarded as weaknesses on the part of Hut and Rhu were really consideration for them and represented a sort of strength that was as new to them as it was pleasantly surprising.

It was nearing mealtime when the girls suggested they return to the living quarters.

"We feel it our duty to prepare the meal," Haitee explained. "The Elders have been so good and kind to us that we find serving them one of our greatest pleasures. Every time we serve them they always thank us and commend us upon our cleanliness and care, although," she added with a giggle in which Marda joined, "some of our first efforts at cooking as they would have it done must have been pretty awful."

Having been there many times before, much of the food served that evening was not new to Rhu and Hut, but this was the first time either had known what it was they ate. The tasty little cakes made from the maize meal disappeared at an alarming rate, much to the evident amusement of the Elders. Besides being a food for humans, one of them remarked that, according to Lord Hiroto, the entire stalks when cut and dried would make wonderful feed for cattle.

After supper, Lord Lithargos joined the circle, which was much more informal than either Hut or Rhu ever remembered their usual meetings with the Elders to be. Summoning up his courage, Rhu asked Him why it was that they had had no help from either Him or Lord Hiroto while they were building the bridge. "I had asked your help," he added, "and felt that you were with us until the first log was lost."

"My son," Lord Lithargos answered, "when you were nearing the cave of Dargh, you did all that lay in your power in the way of caution, skill, and daring courage, so I helped you to pass the cave where the watcher was alert. With the log, you both were fully capable of accomplishing your task, and for me to have helped you would have detracted from the value of your accomplishment so far as your own advancement is concerned.

"Never ask or expect help with those things which you are capable of accomplishing unaided. It is thus that you acquire knowledge. No matter what you may be told nor how thorough your understanding and belief in its truth, it is only information—*something told you*. When you have *acted* upon such information and proved it to be right by your own experience, then it becomes knowledge, and not before. Knowledge comes to each one only through personal experience.

"In the case of the log, a little more intensive thought would have told you that your guiding lines were too short before you raised the log into position for lowering it across the chasm. Your dearly bought experience taught you the wisdom of using foresight, which is but another name for reason based upon known facts. Had either Lord Hiroto or I helped you, then would you have failed to learn this most valuable lesson. Instead of really helping you in the development of your powers to lead, we would have but weakened you."

"Does that mean we should not help others when they are in trouble?" Hut asked, eyes wide.

"Much, my son, depends upon what you mean by that. If a man struggles to overcome an attacking bear, you would be a poor person indeed not to go to his aid, just as Rhu was helped in his hour of peril when visiting the Cave Dwellers. Also, if a man falter through lack of knowledge in performing his task, there is no harm in showing him a better way. But ever remember that to give advice to other than one with whom you are working at a common task, *unless you are asked for it,* is apt to prove to be a thankless undertaking. Like what Rhu and you call your taste stone, and which in reality is salt, a little adds savor, but too much spoils it. Advice unasked for is much like salt. A little of it goes a long way. Be sparing with it.

"Tomorrow, you will return to your labors, my sons. You are quite right in building the first stone house where it will close the entrance to the Great Plains which shall henceforth be known as the Rhu Hut Plains. Peace go with you and may N'Kul bless your great undertaking."

Chapter Eleven

PLANNING WORLD'S FIRST BUILDING

RHU, JUST what do you make of what Lord Lithargos said about knowledge and information?" Hut asked the next morning as he and Rhu were on their way back to the Rhu Hut Plains. "To me, they have always seemed to mean the same thing."

Rhu scratched his head as he strove to frame some suitable answer. That the same question had been troubling him ever since the talk, he had been reluctant to admit, thinking that Hut probably understood. It was quite a relief to have him broach the subject.

"Well," he began hestitatingly, "I never thought much about it. I have always been too busy trying to *do* things to think much about something like that. Still, He must have had some good reason for saying it. At least, we both know now that we'd better be sure we have done all we can before we ask for help."

"Y-e-e-s," drawled Hut, frowning in his effort to comprehend. "Of course, when *you* tell me anything, I accept it as a fact because I know you have tried it or have seen it done before you say it is so. Usually you say you have seen it in such cases. Pshaw! I should have asked Him what about seeing things done! Well, anyhow, it seems that unless we actually do something ourselves, we don't actually KNOW it can be done.

"Do you know, Rhu, there is more to this than at first seems to be true. When we have done anything ourselves, we not only know it can be done, but HOW to go about doing it. There were the trees we cut down by using fire. None of us had ever seen that done. But we did it."

"Yes, but all of us had seen trees burned down during forest fires and that gave Dargh the idea. I confess I had serious doubts about that ring of fire working. That's knowledge, Hut, according to Lord Lithargos, just as knowing how to get a tree across a chasm is knowledge. But if we try to tell somebody about it, he gets only information. The same would be true if we told him about burning down the tree. He'd probably not believe, anyhow, and not try it.

"Say, Hut, maybe that is the difference! When we are told something, we can believe it or not, or somebody may shake our faith, but when we have actually done it, then there is no room left for doubt. We KNOW it can be done that way no matter what *anybody* may say. This would mean that the only way to *know* a thing is to do it. Until then, it is nothing more than an idea which we can believe or not, depending upon the amount of confidence we have in the one who told us about it."

Hut's brow was still furrowed in thought. Rhu always made things *sound* logical and he, Hut, wanted to KNOW. Suddenly, he had a fresh idea. "That's right! You can always convince me, even though you may not be right, but when I have tried it and made it work, then I KNOW. The KNOWING of something is knowledge. The BELIEVING of it is something else . . . . but I think we should always listen, anyhow."

"Salt," Rhu grunted. "Lord Lithargos said a little of it goes a long way, but just what has salt to do with what He said?"

Hut chuckled softly. "He said that to give advice when nobody has asked for it is like salt, and since we use but little of it at a time, so should we give only a little advice. That really doesn't sound right to me. Seems sort of selfish."

"Oh, I don't know!" Rhu disagreed. "How would you like for me to advise you as to how to decorate a bow or a bowl? It wouldn't take much of that to get you ready to fight. But, if you had asked my advice, then you could not very well object to my passing it out to you.

"If I've tried once to tell Grut how and why he should make his bows like mine, I have done it a dozen times, but do you think he would listen? No, sir! He'd just get mad and refuse to talk or else say I thought I was smarter than he was. But after the fight with the Forest Dwellers, he surprised me by asking how to do it, and now he is working at it. I think it is only when people *ask* for help that they really listen or are anywhere near willing to try your ideas."

This philosophizing was growing a bit deep for Rhu's direct mind, and he broke off, grumbling, "Oh, well, I'm more interested in this thing of planting that maize stuff. I can see some sense to that."

At this abrupt change in Rhu's line of thought, Hut frowned in earnest. "Does it ever occur to you, Rhu, that things like this matter of knowledge and information may explain much and be of vast help later?" he asked reprovingly. "You always seem to be interested in the more material things—those which you call practical, things to do rather than those about which to think."

"Why not?" Rhu demanded with a bit of heat. "All this vague talk doesn't do a fellow much good when he's hungry. I'm betting we get more real good from learning how to plant and raise all those plants like the onions, maize, and herbs than we shall ever get from worrying about whether what we learn is information or knowledge!"

Hut eyed Rhu speculatively, uncertain whether he was in real earnest or just trying to start an argument. Then his eyes twinkled. He would fool Rhu by keeping silent! He had long since discovered that this was the surest way to draw out his friend. Besides, who can argue with one who neither fights back nor pays any attention to attempts to promote a controversy?

Thus it was that for a good mile, they walked in silence. Finally, Rhu glanced at Hut and chuckled.

"Is your discretion based upon information or knowledge?" he asked, rather startling Hut whose mind was still occupied with the subject. "Silence in the face of a good subject for argument must indicate one or the other unless, of course, a fellow can't think up a good retort or if he's trying to make the other fellow talk. Which is it?"

Hut opened his mouth to reply, but closed it quickly, for from around a bend in the trail, running swiftly, came Dargh, his anxious face lighting up as he saw them.

"Hurry!" he shouted, stopping and waiting for the two to reach him, and they lost no time. "Fight with Cari Yans," he explained briefly, and before either could question him, he turned to race back along the trail, Hut and Rhu following closely on his heels.

Nearing the end of the trail where it entered upon the Rhu Hut Plains, Dargh slowed down, at the same time signaling them for silence. Cautiously, he moved forward. Hut and Rhu strung their bows and notched their arrows. Then Dargh stopped, and Rhu slipped silently to his side while Hut came close enough to peer over his shoulder. Less than a hundred feet from where they stood, the battling Cari Yans were locked in a struggle with the Forest Dwellers, whose hoarse war cries the three had been hearing during most of their run. Although greatly outnumbered, the latter seemed undaunted and their great war axes were taking a terrible toll.

Suddenly, Ord was attacked by five shaggy Cari Yan Forest Dwellers, and Rhu shot, his stone-tipped arrow transfixing one through the chest. A second later, Hut's arrow claimed another, while, with a wild cry, Ord slew two of the remaining three. The remaining one turned to flee just as Rhu shot again. Even as the stricken warrior fell with Rhu's arrow embedded in his brain, Hut's bowstring twanged and the great shaggy man who was evidently the Cari Yan leader, sprang into the air, clawing at the arrow driven through his throat.

Evidently having had enough, the Cari Yans turned to flee the scene, Dargh, Rhu, and Hut slipping behind the surrounding boulders to let them pass. But for Ord, the Mu Yans would unquestionably have pursued the escaping foe.

"Ord know better," he later explained to Rhu. "Cari Yans hide. Let Mu Yans pass. Hit in back."

"Do you think they will return?" asked Hut.

"Not soon. This hunters. Later, more come." Here Ord grinned savagely. "Wurt back soon. Plenty Mu Yan fighters."

Rhu was already among the men, greatly relieved to find none had been killed, and giving simple aid to those who were wounded. In the early evening as he sat musing beside his fire, Ord approached.

"Ord start many bows," he announced, proudly showing Rhu

the several which he had begun shaping with the special knife Dargh had fashioned.

"You are doing fine," Rhu complimented him. "Later, I'll finish them so they will be best suited for each man. Let one of the least hurt men begin making bowstrings from the deer gut we have saved. You know how I do it."

ALTHOUGH Hut and Rhu had been gone only two days, Dargh, with the aid of all the others in their camp, had moved a goodly number of stones to the site where the wall was to be erected. Under Dargh's personal supervision, these were being placed so as to close the entrance. But for an eight-foot gap, the wall was already some three feet high completely across the opening into the valley. Even at this height, the wall had served as a protection in the fight with the Cari Yans. Ord had forbidden all but the Forest Dwellers to emerge from behind it, thus accounting for the fact that so few suffered severe injuries.

Two days after Hut and Rhu returned, Dargh struck his first real trouble. Since he had constructed only straight stone walls previously, he failed to take corners into consideration. It was only when the wall had been built to almost five feet in height that he realized walls of a building must be tied together. It was not until then that either Rhu or Hut fully appreciated Dargh's handicraft, for it became necessary to tear out the end of the construction which had been laid stone by stone, each one so bracing the next that it was impossible to shift any once they were in place. So cunningly were they placed that later it was found that the wall afforded no hand or foothold for an attacker to use in its scaling. It also proved to be completely watertight.

To tear out the end of the wall was quite an undertaking, but after several days of careful labor, Dargh finally had the first corner turned to his satisfaction. He then assigned to his fellow Cave Dwellers the task of supervising the Plains Dwellers in laying the side wall and in the selection of the stones to be used.

"You are true Mu sons," Rhu complimented the Cave Dwellers the evening after the corner had been completed.

"Mu sons?" Dargh repeated, questioningly.

Hut's face brightened. "Dargh," he said, "to say Cave Dwellers every time we want to refer to you and your men is laborious. From this day forward, if you like, we shall call you 'Musons'."

With the passing of time, this has been changed to "masons" for artificers in stone, just as the word Mu Yans has become Mayans (pronounced Mä yän).

"Dargh like!"

The smiles of his companions reflected his pleasure, and the term "Cave Dweller" gradually dropped from use among the Rhu Hut Plains people, the founders of civilization.

SEATED beside the fire the evening following the battle with the Cari Yans, Rhu's eyes twinkled as he spoke to Hut. "For a fellow who was so concerned about this matter of killing when we talked to Lord Lithargos the first time, you are doing very well, it seems to me."

Hut eyed him levelly. "Still, I don't like it, Rhu. It does seem to me there should be some other way. But as Lord Lithargos said, a fellow can't stand by and allow his friends to be killed without trying to do something to prevent it, and I don't know what else I could have done."

Rhu sobered. "Hut, I don't like killing a bit better than you do. I never get into a fight that I don't wish there were some other way out, but since we have to protect ourselves against those who fight us, there seems to be nothing left to do except out-fight them."

"The Elders say two wrongs do not make a right," Hut asserted rather stiffly. "If killing is wrong in one instance, it must be so in another. I confess that I just don't see how it is or what one should do. However, I *will not* attack."

"No?" Rhu commented rather skeptically. "Hut, I've learned one thing from the Elders and that is never to say what I won't do. Every time I make such a statement, I have to do it or back down. I don't mean promises, for promises are made to be kept. I mean positive statements of personal intentions or opinions, and especially, of threats."

Hut's mood changed, and he laughed freely. "What about

you and Gurd? Seems to me there were some threats made then."

"Maybe so," Rhu admitted grudgingly, "but that was in the course of a heated argument. Huh! What about you and Levi?"

"Well," Hut hedged, "neither of us had to make good."

Rhu grinned. "I hope you weren't as scared as I was," and both broke into hearty laughs.

The following day brought the first ten new Plains Dwellers, all from the Ku and Dan families, and from that time forward, almost every day found more and more of them arriving as the result of Og's work among them. All were immediately put to work under Dargh's supervision.

Since the distance between the edge of the canyon of the Hatamukulian River and the towering cliff which was to form one wall was some fifty odd feet, it was finally agreed that the building itself should be that long. After much argument and conversation, it had been decided to make it thirty feet wide. With the passing of time, these became the accepted proportions for later Mukulian structures, including their pyramids.

When the wall was about ten feet high, Dargh led up to the great idea he had in mind. "Wall must be high to stop attacks," he began.

Rhu and Hut nodded as Dargh waited, apparently for their confirmation.

Then he made a startling suggestion. "If first house high for Ord, second high for Hut, and third high for Musons, Dargh like." Naively, he added, "Musons like live high up!"

Hut and Rhu stared at him greatly puzzled. "What do you mean, Dargh?" asked Rhu. "We are building only one hut here, and we will all live in it together for the time being."

Dargh grinned. "Have new idea. Build huts top each other. Make three in one," he explained, illustrating his meaning by a rough sketch in the dirt before the wall. "Forest Dwellers big men. Need plenty room. Make first room so," drawing a rectangular shape to represent the ground floor of the proposed building. "Next room on top first. Smaller for Plains Dwellers." He drew a line cutting the rectangle into a space a little more than three-quarters the width of the lower floor. This in turn, he divided by another line to represent the third floor which would be a little more than half the width of the ground floor.

(As a matter of fact, since the ground floor of the completed building was about thirty by fifty feet, the second floor was about twenty-four by fifty, and the third about eighteen by fifty.)

"Looks fine to me," said Hut enthusiastically, his mind looking ahead to other imposing structures.

However, Rhu, who had been intently studying the sketch, now shook his head. "I can see all the advantages of what you suggest, Dargh, but let us build the hut as originally planned," he said. "It has no roof on it yet, and I do not see how even that is to be done. If we had the entire Mu tribe here, we could not lift and carry a stone big enough to cover this hut. When I see the stone roof on this, I'll be ready to talk about more huts above it. We can make the wall next to the pass higher so that we can shoot over it, but by the time we get the hut finished, I think we are going to find out a lot of things, just as you did with the corner."

Dargh listened attentively to all that Rhu said, then erased his drawing with his foot and hastily sketched a crude likeness of the following diagram. We have inserted figures on the

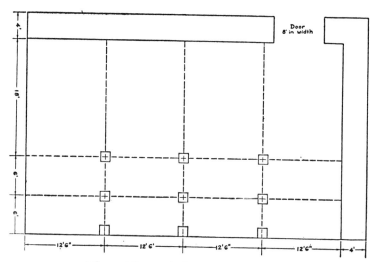

Floor Plan of the First Building

drawing for greater clarity. Of course, such markings were beyond the capacity of folk of that period. Also, the measurements indicated are only approximate as they used "hands," or "spans," and "steps," or "paces" to designate their measurements.

At about six foot intervals from front to back and about twelve feet from center to center from end to end of the building, Dargh had scratched three rows of small squares. He now drew light lines which crossed each other at right angles in the center of each of the small squares.

"Build stone piles from floor to roof," he explained, pointing to the small squares. "Hold flat rocks for roof. Dargh know where flat rock. Musons cut same size," running the stick he used for sketching around the rectangular spaces made by the fine lines. "Small so can carry. Men carry flat rock to roof and rest on stone piles. Cut *some* edges so." He sketched a flat rock, making a step or notch half the stone's thickness and of equal length, probably six inches as we measure. ⌐ "Other edges we cut so," and he made another step on the under side ⌐ so that when two such stones were fitted together, they would form what we call a "lap joint." "Make clay mud and lay in notch before put on second rock. Make tight. All stone on, got roof. Flat. No leak. Build second hut on first."

Rhu and Hut hung upon Dargh's every word while the other Musons nodded enthusiastically as the plan unfolded.

"See, Rhu! Look how easy it will be!" Hut enthused.

Rhu's eyes were very bright, yet he shook his head stubbornly. "I still don't believe the other huts will work."

"But, Rhu!" exclaimed Hut somewhat impatiently, a bit nettled at his friend's apparent obstinacy in refusing to see the advantages of Dargh's plan. "Surely you can see that it is nothing more than simply making another building on top of the first one, can't you?"

"Yes, I can see that, Hut, but these walls are heavy. One of them would crush any stone we could carry. I stepped upon a piece of those great flat stones Dargh mentions, and though it was a good two fingers thick, it broke under me and I almost fell into the river below. One strong enough to hold these walls would have to be at least three *hands* thick, and who can carry one up here, let alone place it? Dargh, how thick do you plan these roof stones to be?" Rhu asked.

While Rhu had been speaking, Dargh was frowning deeply, his eyes never leaving those of his friend.

"Two hands," he answered, and without waiting for any comment, "Rhu right. Dargh forget. Stone never carry such load. Dargh sorry. Two hands not safe. We build one roof with wall breast high behind, but make room much higher than Dargh said."

"I'm sorry, Hut and Dargh. I don't want to be obstinate, but if this should cave in, it would kill everybody in it, and they are our best friends. Dargh, do you suppose there is any way to carry the roof stones if they were three hands thick?"

Dargh got to his feet and went to the pile of stones brought in that afternoon. With a grunt, he lifted a slab about ten inches thick and a good two feet square, bringing it over to Hut and Rhu. "Dargh carry back today. Thirty men with poles carry big one. If three hands, take forty men," indicating his numbers with his hands.

"Twenty Forest Dwellers carry," grunted Ord, who had been a deeply interested listener. He may not have understood it all, but he had grasped enough to get this much clear in his mind.

The problem thus solved, Rhu's inquiring mind was already on something else. "Why not have the rooms all the same size?" he asked. "Then we would need only two rows of stone piles, one for the front and one in the center."

Dargh grinned widely and made another sketch. "First roof come here," he said, indicating the front of the building. "Second roof come only here," indicating the second row of squares. "Third roof come here," indicating the third row. "Always have open space before caves. Have open space here." He eyed Rhu intently to be sure he understood.

Rhu's face brightened as he grasped Dargh's idea, whereupon Dargh nodded vigorously.

And though they could not then know it, it was in this manner that porches, now evolving into patios, originated.

Chapter Twelve

SHADOWS OF
FORTHCOMING EVENTS

A YEAR HAD PASSED. The three-story building was complete, and no modern skyscraper was ever viewed by its builders with any greater degree of pride than that expressed by Hut and Rhu. True, the side toward the valley was open, but that was no disadvantage in the eyes of the builders, for did it not enable them to see across their beautiful Plains as well as provide an excellent view of all that took place among those gathered there?

No engineering feat was ever regarded with greater satisfaction than the great eight-foot stone door which was the only entrance to the Plains from the pass. It was a good eighteen inches thick, nine feet high, and, as was to be expected, its weight was tremendous. Rhu and Hut never ceased to marvel at Dargh's ingenuity as they watched it swing upon its central stone pivot, affording a double entrance. It required two Forest Dwellers to swing it open from the inside, and once closed and secured by a simple mechanism of Dargh's contrivance, nothing known to man in that age might open it from the outside.

Placed near the end of the building that nestled on the very edge of the yawning abyss through which the mighty Hatamukulian River roared some two hundred feet below, to approach it, one was compelled to come along the thirty-four foot high wall. Thus, any who were intent upon attack were directly exposed to the ever-present guard on the roof above. The parapet was four feet high on the inside and tapered outward so that archers might shoot down upon any enemy with the minimum of exposure to themselves. In addition, there were piles of jagged stones which the watchful Forest Dwellers could hurl down upon their attackers. These were no mean weapons in their powerful hands and later experience proved this method of defense far more efficacious than even Dargh had dared hope. Those they did not crush, suffered terrible gashes when struck.

Hut shook his tousled head. "I dread to think of using those against human beings," he mourned.

"Then they should not try to take from us by force that which we have created!" Rhu asserted stoutly. "When it comes to protecting our own people against such marauders, we cannot be too particular. Do you think they would hesitate to do the same?" he demanded.

Before Hut could reply, the bellowing of an approaching herd interrupted him. "There they come!" he shouted.

There was a concerted rush to the parapet by all who heard, their shouts bringing the now more than two hundred workers below to witness the arrival of the first of the Ku and Dan herds.

"I'll bet they will be astonished when they see this building!" Hut shouted to Rhu.

With a wide grin, Rhu joined him in his hurried flight down to greet their families. This, they felt, was a day long to be remembered by all.

The leaders of the approaching herd started to mill around when they reached the stone wall of the building. By this time, however, a number of Plains Dwellers, anticipating this, had hidden hurriedly among the rocks, and these now prodded the leaders through the open door. Yet, despite their efforts, before some semblance of order was gained, several were crowded over the unguarded cliff and into the river far below.

Well knowing how highly their people regarded their cattle, Rhu and Hut realized this was a bad start. It was not until later that they learned this was not the first tragedy of this epochal hegira, and so were none too well prepared for what followed when their fathers arrived with the women and children.

With scarcely more than a glance at the structure which Hut and Rhu so pridefully considered as most imposing, the Ku

and Dan families streamed through and into the open beyond
where their cattle already were beginning to feast upon the
rich grasses of the valley.

"Where huts?" demanded Sol Ku of Rhu. "Hut promised to
have ready!"

"What about cattle lost?" stormed Mai. "Two best bulls and
several cattle break through line of poles crossing chasm!"

Hut and Rhu were destined to learn that things lost are always the most valuable in the eyes of their losers.

"Not best," growled Grut, unexpectedly coming to Rhu's aid.
"Young," he added, stepping to his brother's side.

"*What?*" demanded Mai, eyes blazing. "Grut say Mai lie?"

"Bulls young," Grut insisted stubbornly. "Besides, belong Ku
herd."

Sol moved toward Grut, his great, gnarled fist doubled up.

"I own eight good bulls," Rhu said mildly. "Take four of
them. As to a place in which to live, we can erect regular huts
until your buildings are ready."

"You promise stone huts," Sol stated stubbornly, at the same
time coming nearer to Grut. He was not one to allow his sons
to question his or Mai's word.

Once more Rhu intervened. Quietly, he stepped between
them, and something in his level eyes made even Sol hesitate.
The past year had brought about many changes in Rhu, not the
least of which was confidence in himself and a courage of his
convictions that neither Mai nor Sol could crush.

"Father, Grut spoke as he believed to be right. It may as well
be understood now that here all men have a right to express
their honest opinions. It is not good that my father and Hut's
should be the first to break this rule. We promised you stone
huts, yes, but just how long do you think it takes to make such
a one as you just passed through?"

Rhu took a deep breath, then without waiting for a reply,
continued, "Has this great opportunity to select the first and
best lands for the Ku and Dan families made you two less fair
than you have always been? I have offered liberal payment for
the two bulls you complain about losing. I admire Grut's desire
for the justice I have always respected and come to consider
part of our fathers' standard. If," and his voice took on a keen

edge, "your coming to this wonderful land means that you two intend to become as Levi Hawk about whom Hut has told me, then it would be best that you take your herds and return to your own lands. There was no disrespect in Grut's words. He is my brother, and I shall stand by him."

There was no mistaking Rhu's meaning, even without the presence of the slowly gathering Forest and Cave Dwellers who were ready to obey him implicitly. For a long moment, both Sol and Mai stood, mouths agape. This was something so new in their experience as to give them pause.

Mai turned to Hut. "D-do you . . . . is this your idea of respect for your father?" he stammered.

Beads of cold sweat stood upon Hut's brow. Twice he swallowed before he could speak. Never before in the history of their families had a son as young as he or Rhu dared speak to his father as Rhu had done. Hut's ears roared, and his father's grim face told him he was faced with the necessity for making a monumental decision from which there could be no retreat.

Were their own families going to defeat the work which had grown to be so much a part of his and Rhu's very existence?

"Father, I owe more than my life to Rhu. As with you and Sol, whatever decision Rhu makes is as my own. This is more than a mere family affair. This is the start of the greatest thing ever to come to our tribe. Are you willing to be the ones to start tearing it down?"

Sol stepped to Mai's side, his rugged and bewhiskered old face a mixture of emotions. "For eight hundred Great Suns, the Kus and Dans have stood shoulder to shoulder, and I will not be the first to change it. Mai, you and I are old men. Times are changing. It is hard for us to change. What you decide, that will I do.

"Today, we have seen something no man has done in all Mu Yan history. It is not Hut, but Rhu who has defied us. Yes, even Grut has stood by Rhu, and now, Hut is on Rhu's side. Can it be possible that we are wrong, that we are growing old and childishly stubborn? Or are these merely defiant boys to be cast out from our clan?"

"Humph!" snorted Mai. "Are they or *we* to be cast out? I always thought this foolish idea, but when I see Forest Dwellers ready to fight for Plains Dweller, nothing more can ever surprise me. Let us forget bulls. Rhu, I admire bravery. I admire loyalty, and you have often proved both. Sol, let us erect our huts and give boys a chance. Besides, Mai never saw such grazing lands before."

Rhu drew a great breath of relief. Hut mopped his brow with his hairy forearm. The hulking Forest Dwellers grinned at Rhu with ill-concealed admiration. Only Dargh seemed unaffected.

"Let us eat," he grunted. "Foolish talk for women," he added succinctly and turned to where ten deer were being roasted over great beds of coals. Picking up a bowl from the stack close at hand and stepping to the nearest deer, he hacked off a big hunk, pouring over it some of the liquid from one of the large, steaming, earthen cooking vessels. Then, as Sol and Mai watched, he reached for a hunk of something entirely new to either of them—bread made of maize meal from their first crop —*the first harvest from any cultivation except that of the Elders ever to be had upon this earth plane.*

"Father, you and Mai are next," Rhu invited.

The two old men took prompt advantage of the opportunity, although both eyed quizzically the still hot "corn bread" even as they helped themselves as they had seen Dargh do.

"What this stuff?" Mai growled.

"The Elders call it maize bread," Hut explained. "They taught us how to raise the maize and to make this bread from the seed. You will like it."

"Yes," Rhu added. "The crop also makes fine stock feed even after the seeds are removed. The Elders say that its use will make our cattle grow into better and larger stock, but it is hard to raise," and he frowned. "We have to dig up the ground with sticks before it can be planted, but Dargh is working upon a stone tool that should make it easier. It took ten men a moon to prepare the ground for this crop. Dargh thinks that with his new tool, we can more than double the next crop with no more effort or time."

"Maize . . . ? Crop . . . ? Seed . . . ?" Sol demanded,

tasting the bread. "H-m-m-m. Good!" smacking his lips over
the delicacy so new to him.

"We shall show you and Mai after we eat," Rhu offered.
"Also, we shall explain how it is raised. Try dipping the bread
in the stew," he suggested to Mai whose loud lip-smacking as
he complied and tasted it proclaimed more than words his full
agreement, closely seconded by Sol.

"Humph!" snorted Rhu's mother half an hour later when
Rhu offered her the first taste of the hot bread just taken from
their crude oven. "More of your foolish ideas," she complained,
although it was noticeable that she immediately reached for a
much larger hunk. "At least, it is filling," she admitted grudgingly. "Makes stew too thick," she grumbled as the crumbling
bread mixed with the gravy.

Rhu and Hut smiled at one another as she gave her entire
attention to the food, carefully scooping out the last remains
from her bowl and making sure that not a single drop escaped
her probing fingers which she licked clean.

"How make?" Hut's mother asked Rhu, too proud to ask Hut.

"Mix meal with water, then bake," Rhu explained to her.

"Taste stone make better," she suggested.

"Elders add bird eggs," said Rhu, "but we cannot find
enough."

Hut's mother said nothing, but a few minutes later was seen
talking busily with Rhu's mother whose violent negative head
shakes gradually turned to nods of approval as the full significance of Mahata's breath-taking idea began to dawn in her
slow-working mind. Soon, the two of them had gathered about
them all the mature women of each family. Presently, all the
children old enough for their purpose were called, and the
following morning, these children scattered about the Plain in
every direction.

Hut and Rhu were too busy with other matters to notice.
Neither did they observe that while most of the women were
busy erecting frames for the family huts, Mahata, Rhu's
mother, and three of the older women were busily working
upon an entirely new type of structure. They were building a
long, low pen of rather closely woven branches. It was not high
enough for a dwelling, yet covered an area comparable to a

family hut. Nightfall found a portion of it divided into a few small rooms, or cages, with thatched roofs, the larger portion, however, having only the outer walls.

The following morning, the children again departed. This time, each carried a net of woven rushes from a neighboring bit of marshland and upon which their mothers had labored well into the night beside the family fires. Mahata and the same women returned to their previous day's work, and by evening, the entire structure was covered. When the children returned, each carrying a bag containing birds very much like our modern pheasants and grouse, there was a great squawking and fluttering of wings as the older women released them inside the completed pen. The children spent the next day gathering from plants and grasses the seeds they had seen the birds eating. These were spread liberally about in piles convenient to shallow vessels of water the women had placed inside the structure.

It was soon found that some of the species of birds would not breed in captivity and that others could not stand the restricted life. It took time to discover and provide proper foods for them, and the mortality was high. Many survived and even throve in their new environment, however, and the children were kept busy trapping more of this sort. With the passing of

A Family Hut

time they grew quite tame, and their eggs became an important food item. Nor was anything wasted, for those fowl which died were added to the food supply.

Thus, from the simple desire to provide eggs for the maize bread, the development of domesticated fowl was begun. It proved to be a long and laborious task, but with the help of the Elders, the flocks evolved into the forerunners of our modern chickens, and subsequently, became the means of livelihood for many people.

It was in this way that each new development of the forming race began, starting for some similarly simple end only to grow eventually into industries of vast importance to the entire people.

FOR A TIME, all went well, and the group gradually became accustomed to the new order of things. The Yaks, the Kuts, and the Mauks soon joined them, and then came the problem Rhu and Hut had foreseen—the division of the herds. Not all had the same number of cattle. Some had more sheep than cattle, and none of their herds equalled a half of those of the combined Ku and Dan families. It also soon became evident that it was next to impossible to keep the herds from mixing unless they spread too far apart to make the main plan feasible, and as old Ku Kut had prophesied, dissension arose.

The grumbling and dissatisfaction grew, and Rhu and Hut became desperate in their efforts to restore the original harmony. Hut would have called upon the Elders, but Rhu clung persistently to the idea that they should be able to solve this by themselves. They did call their fathers into conference, however, and for the better part of three days, the four argued and schemed.

Finally, Sol offered a solution. "Count all cattle and divide into five equal parts. Then all have equal share and equal interest," he said.

To this, Mai immediately disagreed, taking the stand that it was not fair to themselves to give away the several hundred head of cattle necessary to make this division.

Emphatically, Sol shook his grizzled head. When Mai had finished, he spoke, and Rhu and Hut were astonished to see how much of their philosophy he had grasped. Nor was his increasing ability to make his thoughts clear much less astonishing.

"No, Mai," he said, "unless each family thrives, group as whole cannot succeed. Even with dividing herds, Dans and Kus better off than ever before. All start equal. Each new family come in on equal basis. If have less cattle, must supply so many cattle's worth of labor or extra help to earn enough to make equal."

Mai frowned heavily. It was a foregone conclusion that he would not refuse to do as Sol said. It was thus that their families had prospered, always sharing their prosperity and losses equally. He could see the justice of Sol's contention, still he did not like the idea of giving away any of their own stock. However: "If Sol say, Mai do," he agreed grudgingly, "but will Yaks, Kuts, and Mauks agree?"

Here, Rhu took part in the discussion. "They have all worked hard with us and often done more than their share to help," he said. "Besides, Hut told Ku Kut we would all share equally. Of the three, his herds most nearly equal ours. Let's call him in and see what he says. Since he, too, will have to make some sacrifice, he should have his say."

"Good," agreed Sol and Mai as one. "Ku shrewd."

To the surprise of all, Ku agreed to Sol's suggestion without argument. "Kuts too happy here to argue over small matter. Herds soon big enough for all. Hut's idea right when he talk to Ku."

"I want this matter settled, so I will call in Gar Yak and Dorg Mauk," Hut announced. "I have always thought all should share equally, and I shall establish the rule now," he added.

Rhu glanced at him in surprise, for it was not like Hut to assume so much. Mai also eyed his son sharply, but said nothing.

"I have brought you all together to discuss a very important matter which affects us all," Hut stated when he returned with Gar and Dorg. Having explained the situation, he continued, "Sol, father, and Ku have agreed and since they have the largest herds, I think this is a fair solution. Therefore, let us begin the count tonight when the herds are bedded down."

"Don't you think that Gar and Dorg should be given a chance to express their ideas?" asked Rhu.

"I have already given them the main idea," Hut replied. "But of course, if they have anything to say, now is the time. How about it?"

Gar Yak eyed Hut shrewdly. "All in Yak and Mauk's favor," he said slowly, "so should not object. But before Gar agree, Gar like Rhu's opinion. Rhu find this place, Hut say. Rhu always fair. Gar ask no favors. Some complain because Gar's herd smallest. Not good," he finished.

"You have some fine bulls," Rhu answered, "and the Elders say they are important. Besides, you have always been ready to help in every way, so I think the idea is fair, especially since Sol suggested it."

"What Sol say, Gar do," Gar stated simply.

"Fine," Rhu commended, and Gar smiled at him warmly. "That is the spirit which will carry us far. Mai and Sol have long experience in working together. What do you think about it, Dorg?"

Dorg's shrewd old eyes bored directly into Rhu's. "Rhu, you good boy," he said. "What you say, Dorg do. Dorg ask no unfair advantage. Dorg have three tame cows. Use milk for motherless baby. Dorg tame more so all have milk."

"What!" Rhu demanded, his exclamation echoed by the others, including Hut whose eyes were shining. "Do you mean you can take milk from cows?"

This was certainly a new and startling idea with many possibilities.

"Yes," Dorg confirmed. "Milk fine drink. Dorg keep secret. Cows hard to tame," he finished.

Rhu chuckled, well knowing that in the old days, it would have been hard to keep such cows once other families heard of this. That Dorg felt free to tell of it now spoke volumes for his high regard for their forming group. Every year, motherless babies died in some of the families where there were no other mothers to nurse them.

"If you can tame more, you can render a service worth many hundred head of cattle," Rhu said.

"Dorg can do," and as all listened breathlessly, "Dorg will."

TO THE surprise of Rhu and Hut, the herds were counted and distributed with little or none of the customary bickering and argument, a fact that was also quickly recognized by those participating. They were discovering that when a thing is commonly agreed upon, all can go about it intelligently and without the uncertainty which so often follows when only one directs.

A few mornings later, as Rhu and Hut prepared to go about their daily activities, the former gave expression to the thought which had been forming in his mind.

"Hut," he said, "I believe it would be a good thing always to have a meeting of the patriarchs when we have a problem involving any or all the people on the Plains. We had fine results talking over the division of the cattle. However, I do think Dargh and Ord should be included. We certainly never could have accomplished what we have without them, and besides, it seems to me that all three divisions of our tribe should always be represented."

"W-e-l-l," drawled Hut, frowning as he concentrated upon the suggestion, "I think the idea is good as far as it goes, and I'm in favor of it. However, Rhu, you and I are the real leaders, and I think we should be very careful not to do anything that could possibly weaken our position. I hadn't thought about Ord and Dargh, but I agree with you. I'll call them in and tell them about it."

On the verge of agreeing, a fresh idea occurred to Rhu, "Don't you think we should speak to our fathers and the other patriarchs about it first?"

Again Hut frowned. "I'm not so sure, Rhu," he hedged. "As I said, you and I are the leaders, and if we say a thing is to be done, they will have to agree."

Rhu shook his shaggy head. "I suppose we could do it that way, but we have made a good beginning, and I wouldn't want to do anything to upset what we have gained. I'm sure they will agree, and if they have a voice in it, they'll like it better. If we simply call in Ord and Dargh the next time without saying anything to them, they might resent the idea, Ku Kut especially. He might not *say* anything, but he's sensitive about being ordered to do things. If he feels that he has been consulted first, I'll bet he'll be a lot more enthusiastic."

It was Hut's turn to shake his head. "If he and the others get the idea that they have to be consulted all the time about everything we want to do, won't it weaken us in their eyes?" he protested. "After all, Rhu, *we* are the leaders," he repeated, holding stubbornly to his idea.

Knowing his people, Rhu well realized the need for strong direction, at the same time sensing that leadership was significant of something deeper than the exercise of arbitrary authority, or of mere personality. Also, he felt vaguely that if the people were to work together harmoniously, they should have a voice in matters affecting the common welfare.

"If we are the leaders, Hut," he said thoughtfully, "it seems to me that our leadership will be even more effective with their backing. If they all agree to having Ord and Dargh, and I'm sure they will, then our leadership will be even more secure. Don't you think so?"

"Well, Ord and Dargh will always be sure to do as we want, and I am sure father and Sol will, so we can count upon six out of the nine. Since it was agreed to do as the majority want, it should work out all right. It isn't that I am not in favor of having them in the group, Rhu. It is just that I do not like the idea of subjecting *ourselves* to the wishes of the group. But you may be right, and with the backing of father and Sol, we are sure to be able to have our own way. So let's get them together and bring up the idea."

As they went to find the five patriarchs, Rhu's mind continued to turn over the matter. Vaguely, he felt it was right to have their unanimous approval although, in an emergency, he would not hesitate to assert his and Hut's authority. Still, his mind held tenaciously to the idea that only in absolute unanimity lay the possibility of real and lasting success.

Observing his silence, Hut seized the opportunity to present another idea he had been thoughtfully considering for some time. "I've been thinking of a set of rules based upon what Lord Hiroto said on one of our visits," he said.

"Good idea," Rhu agreed. "But, somehow, Hut, I feel this is not a good time to propose them. We are just getting our people to work as a unit, and I think they will do better if we let *them* make some suggestions first. As Lord Lithargos said, 'Make no rules that govern yourself less than others.' I like that. Rules are so easy to break and once broken, lead to dissension and misunderstandings that are hard to overcome." Almost, it was as if the words had sprung from some separate source, and Rhu was as surprised at them as Hut.

"I dislike unnecessary rules," Rhu continued. "Never have I been forbidden to do a thing than I wanted to do it more than anything else."

"Like the time when we were all forbidden to go near the great forests," Hut chuckled. "It was only three days later that you told me of your visit with the Forest Dweller family when you came so nearly getting killed. But for your shooting into the hornet's nest behind you and starting them on the warpath, those savages would have caught you." Hut laughed aloud at the memory of Rhu's description of what followed as the mighty Forest Dwellers fled ignominiously with the angry hornets in hot pursuit.

"Well, Rhu, you are probably right, as usual, so let's forget it until we can formulate the plans together. Still, I do think there should be some sort of rules for the group meetings. Don't you?"

"Maybe," Rhu agreed half-heartedly. "Let's see what happens first," he hedged.

And so it was agreed.

Chapter Thirteen

THE STORM

ALTHOUGH THE adage, "Uneasy lies the head that wears a crown," lay many millennia ahead of them, Rhu and Hut were beginning to realize that being leaders of men carries with it many problems and complexities that even the sleep of perfect health cannot banish. At this particular time arose a situation entirely new to their experience, the settlement of which sorely perplexed them.

One of the big Forest Dwellers, Nord by name, had become enamored of Nana, a daughter of Ku Kut. As was customary among his folk, without so much as intimating his intention to her or anyone else, Nord had quietly entered Ku's hut at night and taken her away with him. Pursued by her brothers, and still carrying his fair burden, Nord fled to the stone house where Rhu intercepted him and to the amazement and dissatisfaction of Nord and his friends, bade him release her.

"We shall settle this matter tomorrow," he assured the growling Nord. "Tonight, she shall stay here with her brothers who have followed you and who will remain."

Far into the night, Rhu and Hut discussed the matter. Had it been other than a Forest Dweller, it is open to question whether old Ku would have objected seriously. For one of his family to become the mate of a Forest Dweller, however, was, to him at least, utterly unthinkable. Nor was he at all reluctant to say as much. For the first time during their association, even Ord seemed disturbed by this situation, but being what he was, backed up Rhu's order.

It was the spring of the year, and for the past two days the oppressive heat and heaviness of air which presages a storm had been increasing steadily. Rhu and Hut had not yet fallen asleep when it broke in all its pent up fury. Despite the heavy skin curtain lashed in place before the space where the two maintained their sleeping quarters, the blinding lightning flashes kept the shadowy room light as day, while the reverberations of the mighty thunder claps shook even the sturdy building. The violence of the wind was such as neither of them had ever experienced.

Through the downpour and gale, one of the Kut men burst in to tell them that the Kut hut had been blown to bits.

"Go bring them up here!" Rhu shouted.

He and Hut hastened to have those Plains Dwellers who still slept on that floor lash skins across the front, then to find refuge with the Musons and Forest Dwellers on the other two floors, while Nana and her brothers hastily prepared for the rest of their family. Through the storm, they soon came staggering in, drenched and miserable, the wails of the children adding a dismal note to the general hubbub.

It was only because the storm had broken from the south and roared down through the Hatamukulian River gorge that the stout hides now laced across the front of the building had been able to withstand it. Still, they snapped wildly, threatening momentarily to tear loose. Even after the confusion following the arrival of the Kuts had subsided, such was the violence of the raging elements that Rhu and Hut's sleep was broken and uneasy, and morning found their problem still unsolved.

Shouting to make himself heard above the uproar, Hut aroused Rhu as the leaden dawn began to make objects distinguishable. "I wonder how *our* family huts are standing this?" he cried.

With a grunt, Rhu sat up, rubbing his heavy eyes. "Our mothers are good builders, Hut, but I'll bet they wish they were all up here. Aside from where the wind eddies in at the front, this place is dry and comfortable." He chuckled. "Now Mai and father will give us no peace until their stone houses are finished. There also will be more enthusiasm among the Plains Dwellers about carrying in stones for their own homes, I'm sure. Dargh was right when he insisted that their houses be enclosed with four walls, and now there will be less objection to the extra work entailed. If that wind were from the north, we would be good and wet!"

Getting to his feet, Hut walked to the front of the big room, closely followed by Rhu. "I'm glad this place is large enough to hold the Kuts," he remarked, then frowned as the thought of the impending problem was thus suggested.

"It ought to teach them to respect the Musons, anyhow," Rhu grunted. "I wish Nord had been a bit more circumspect," he growled. "Even Ord seems to think what he did was right."

"This is why I wanted to establish some rules last moon," Hut declared. "Had all been made to understand that there was to be no more taking women by force and without their consent, this would not have happened."

For a moment, Rhu eyed Hut quizzically. "You were much interested in that matter about experience bringing knowledge," he said grinning broadly. "Well, it looks to me as if we are all going to gain some knowledge this day. It may make us more trouble, Hut, but I still feel that more good will come out of this than if we had set up a rule regarding it. I'm betting Nord would have ignored such a rule, anyway, and then we would have had a *real* problem. Now, nobody can be blamed, and old Ku is just the one who would have insisted upon direct and drastic punishment. Good will come of this or I miss my guess."

"Hadn't thought of it in that light," Hut growled, only half convinced. Although he was forced to admit that there was more than a little truth in what Rhu said, his mind held stubbornly to the idea of the rules he had formulated. "If there just wasn't such an ingrained prejudice against the Forest Dwellers!" he lamented. "Nord is not a bad fellow at heart."

"He's Ord's brother from the same mother," Rhu stated simply. "I like him. Say! I have an idea."

Without giving Hut a chance to satisfy his curiosity, he hastened back to where the girl of Nord's choice was sitting beside the fire just kindled for the preparing of the Kut breakfast. "Nana," he said, smiling down into her questioning face, "I wish you would come over here for a moment. I want to have a little talk with you."

Silently and obediently, she got to her feet, and for the first time, Rhu took note of her exceptionally prepossessing looks. Well formed, tall, willowy, strong, and despite her youthfulness—she was only some sixteen years old—she was well developed, and he rather wondered that she had not already been claimed by some Plains Dweller. Also, there was about her an air of confidence and sturdy independence that was quite unlike that of most women of his acquaintance.

In some respects, she reminded Rhu of her father, and his eyes brightened. She had not been struggling very hard when Nord had arrived with her, and it was quite obvious that had she been serious in her desire to escape him, even the big Forest Dweller would have found her far from easy to manage. Nor did Rhu recall any scratches or other marks of violence upon Nord's face or body, now that he came to think of it.

It was this inherent ability to observe and catalogue everything that happened while it was occurring that made Rhu a factor with which to reckon at all times. Therefore, it was not surprising that he should have observed all this, even though the incident had been so unexpected.

"Nana," he began, again smiling at her as they neared his and Hut's section of the big room, "I think Nord has good taste."

Nana's eyes widened and a look which Rhu could not quite define came into them—a soft brightness that gave him pause. Despite himself, he felt his pulses begin to throb, nor was this lessened when she swayed toward him ever so slightly.

"How did he happen to get away with you so easily and quickly?" he asked. "Of course, he is a powerful man," he hastened to add.

"No man, even Nord, take Nana if Nana fight hard," she announced quietly, smiling into his face. "Rhu try?" she asked naively, and even Rhu was not so guileless as to mistake her meaning, for there was willing invitation in her tone and in the parted, rather full lips.

Things were not going quite as he had planned, and his embarrassment was not the least bit lessened by the poorly suppressed chuckle from Hut who squatted peering out into the raging storm. Although Rhu understood men and still had much of the prevailing attitude of his people toward women, he suddenly felt very inadequate. Hut's chuckle saved the day for it brought him to his senses. Wisely, he ignored her question, and his face grew rather stern.

"Yes, Nord has good taste," he repeated, "and I am sure you could have made his task a difficult one. Nord is a good man whom I like a great deal. That he is a Forest Dweller makes him no less a man of whom any woman could well be proud should she be of his choice. If Nord will agree to make you his only mate, are you willing?"

Was Rhu wrong, or did Nana's face betray a trace of disappointment? He could not be sure, but there was no mistaking the change in the expression of her eyes.

"Nana only mate, Nana do all work. Nana want man other women want," summing up the philosophy which made women of that time willing to share their husbands with others.

"Then you are willing to be his mate?" Rhu persisted.

"Nord take, Nord keep," she stated flatly. "Nord take, Nord not keep, Nana no want."

"Nord would have kept you, Nana, but did not because I ordered him to release you."

"Why?" the girl demanded.

As Rhu sought for an answer he felt she could understand, Hut stepped to her side.

"Here, Nana, no woman has to mate with any man she does not like. No man may take any woman who is not willing. If you are willing, it is all right with us for Nord to keep you, even though Ku objects."

"Nana willing," she agreed, "but no tell Nord." Even as today, women had a certain pride, although in those times, they may have had little occasion for its expression.

"No," Hut agreed. "Now, Rhu, let's talk to Ku. You may go back to your place," he told Nana who, as she obediently turned away, shot a long and significant look at Rhu who felt his face grow hot.

Old Ku Kut came promptly when Rhu called to him. He had, Rhu observed from the corner of his eye, been watching closely while he and Nana had been talking, but the roar of the storm had made it impossible for him to have heard anything of their conversation. Nevertheless, his icy eyes told Hut and Rhu that he was determined not to be easily swayed from his resolve that none of his family was to be closely associated with the Forest Dwellers. But for his known friendship for both of them, his air could easily have been interpreted as distinctly hostile. To judge from their greeting, however, no one would have suspected that either of them observed this.

"We are sorry your hut was destroyed last night," Rhu began. "We hope you were comfortable up here, although we were not very well prepared for so many visitors."

"Stone hut good," Ku agreed. "Storm bad. Hut not even shake. Hut not leak. No wind." He paused, and then, "When Kut stone hut started?"

"As soon as we have stones for it," Rhu replied. "We believe our fathers will be willing to wait until yours is ready, unless their huts were also destroyed. Storms are usually bad in our end of the Mu Valley, but we never saw such a one."

Ku grunted, eyes questioning. He was not at all misled by this indirect approach to the matter uppermost in the minds of all three.

"If Nord were in your family, he would get some of the Forest Dwellers to help bring in stones for your hut," suggested Hut, precipitating matters.

"Nord not in Kut family!" Ku snapped. "Nord never . . . ."

"Nord is a good man," Rhu interrupted before Ku could finish. He well knew that once Ku had definitely committed himself it would be next to impossible to change him. "Ord is his brother by the same mother, and she was of the Yak family. Next to Ord, he is one of the best of the Forest Dwellers. Ku, Nana is more like you than any of your sons. Not only is she good to look upon, but she is strong, and like you, very determined. Yet, Nord bore no wounds from her strong hands, nor was she struggling to escape when he carried her in last night. Why?"

Ku's jaw dropped. "Nana fool!" he snorted.

"No, Nana knows a good man when she sees one," Rhu disagreed, rather startled at his own temerity, for Ku was not one to submit tamely to disagreement with his ideas. His jaws snapped together and his big hands balled into hairy fists.

"Ku, how did you get Ana (his first wife and the mother of Nana)?"

"Took Ana from . . . . " The astute Rhu had assailed Ku's weakest spot, and for the first time, Ku hesitated.

"*Took her from the family of Gurd, a Forest Dweller,* and she has been a fine wife and mother," Rhu completed for him. "In fact, she is the sister of Gurd, and but for Gurd, your family would twice have been wiped out by the other Forest Dwellers. Her mother was a Plains Dweller."

Ku's mouth dropped open, then snapped shut. "Who told you?" he demanded.

Realizing that at last he had the indomitable Ku on the defensive, Rhu was quick to pursue his advantage before Ku could regain his mental balance.

"Furthermore," he went on, "Gurd, the father of Gurd, could easily have caught and killed you when you took Ana. Twice he restrained his sons to save you, and but for Gurd, the son of Gurd, the Nuds and Wuds would have killed off your family. This the Elders told me, and Ord has told me how his family helped Gurd, the son of Gurd, when the Nuds would have attacked him for helping you. Yet, you, renowned for your fairness and justice, would deny Nord, the son of Kurd, Nana for his mate."

"Nana!" Ku roared to make himself heard above the tempest.

She hastened to his side, her eyes wide with apprehension as they sought those of Rhu for some explanation.

Before Ku could speak, Rhu addressed her. "Nana, if Ku is willing, will you become the mate of Nord?"

"Yes," she answered with a promptness that startled all of them, but she kept well beyond the reach of Ku as she spoke.

"Humph!" Ku snorted. "And you let Nord take you!"

"Nana did not," announced Nord's booming voice as he approached from below. "Nord wrap Nana in fur so Nana have no chance. No woman have chance once Nord grab in arms," he finished.

The sharp glance the girl flung at Rhu made him almost choke with the laughter he was careful to conceal. He had just remembered that Nord was carrying her over his shoulder and that both her hands were free to hold in place the heavy fur in which she was wrapped.

"Then keep her!" Ku snapped, but his grizzled old face was kindly.

"Nord, you will take Nana and join the Kuts," Rhu instructed. "As soon as this storm is over, you are to help Ku build his stone hut. Tell all the Forest Dwellers that from this day, no man is to take for his mate a woman from any one of the families here without first making sure the woman is willing and without getting permission."

It was in this way that the first crude start was made toward the abolishment of a custom as old as any of them had any recollection, and the inauguration of a new one whereby women were given a voice in the choosing of a mate.

LATE in the afternoon, the storm subsided sufficiently for Rhu and Hut to see that the Ku and Dan huts were still standing although damaged so that the women were busy repairing them. In fact, all the huts were still habitable with the exception of that of the Kuts, and Sol and Mai readily agreed that all the workmen give their attention to building the stone house for the Kuts. Nord and Ord lost no time in having the willing Forest Dwellers start bringing in the necessary stones for the purpose.

While watching the long line of perspiring men laboring under their heavy loads, Rhu saw one of the Forest Dwellers slip and fall heavily. A thought suddenly occurred to him, and his eyes brightened.

"Hut!" he exclaimed. "I have an idea! Remember that slider thing you fixed that time? Why can't we make several of them, larger and stronger, and let the men *pull* in loads of stones? The wet ground is slick, and they should slide easily."

Darkness found Rhu and Hut finishing their first rather crude sled, the runners or "sliders" as they called them, made of strong, smooth limbs such as had been gathered for the big bows of the Forest Dwellers. Stripped of their bark, these served admirably.

When it was finished, Ord and Nord could no longer wait to

try it, and persuading four of their companions to mount it, started dragging it over the wet grasses until, reaching the brow of a rather steep incline, it started downward of its own accord. Dropping the vines by which they had been pulling it, Ord and Nord let it slide past them. Gathering momentum, it shot ahead into the gloom, the gleeful shouts of its passengers suddenly turning into yells of excitement as it overturned and spilled them into the slush. It was late that night before the last of the Forest Dwellers had taken his ride down that hill, and muddy, bedraggled, skinned-up and well-shaken, they all pronounced it a monumental success.

The "slider," or sled, more than trebled their progress, for it enabled them to haul more stones each trip than five times their number could have carried. With the addition of more and stronger ones, plus several rains which facilitated their pulling them, they soon had sufficient stones gathered so that the Kut house grew apace.

Introducing the Slider

Unlike the original building, this was only one story in height and had four sides, with square openings in its walls for light, and one great doorway, all of which were closed with skins at night and during inclement weather.

Meanwhile, with that patience so characteristic of him, Dargh and some of the Musons had started cutting the canal in the face of the cliff. A little over a year after it was begun, the first water was brought from the river to the Plain. It had been a monumental task, but the joy and satisfaction of all was ample recompense.

Already the group, which now numbered about five hundred, were becoming more and more closely united. Each member could see that he was having a part in doing those things which contributed to the happiness and well-being of the others, just as the others were contributing to his and his family's well-being and happiness. Each new undertaking was of common interest, for the entire community benefited, while the many accomplishments and advancements made in living conditions gave them all a sense of pride and satisfaction.

For these simple people, life had always been a struggle for survival, both with Nature and against the aggressions of those of their own kind. Through the use of initiative in the gaining of knowledge and through cooperation with man and Nature, they were finding a new way of life which offered them a security and happiness they had never before known. Through actual experience, they were learning the only true and sound basis for community endeavor, the basic democratic principle upon which any lasting civilization must be founded —*cooperation,* one with another.

Naturally, news of this agreeable state of affairs spread rapidly throughout the entire tribe, and before long, Rhu and Hut were besieged with requests from both individuals and entire families to be permitted to join them. It was clearly obvious to the two leaders that all of them believed Rhu and Hut and the families with them had merely "found a good thing." The desire to enjoy the advantages of the Plains and what had been created there was their only idea, and even as they asked admittance, they made specific demands.

Skill and great patience were still required to help those

already there to comprehend each new innovation upon their old customs, and then to accept it. And though proper ideals were being inculcated into their minds and hearts, they must not meet any disturbing element until their understanding was greater and more firmly established. It was plain that the hazy ideas and selfish motives of those seeking admission would result in many conflicts and complexities, and ultimately destroy the satisfaction and harmony now prevailing.

"Yet," puzzled Rhu, "if all people of all tribes are to learn to live together as peaceably and successfully as our people are now doing, they will have to be admitted sometime!"

"And if we do let them in, it will ruin everything!" wailed Hut.

Rhu nodded his head in agreement. "No outsider can possibly realize how much of the good we enjoy results from what the people here have done themselves," he mused. "I don't exactly mean their accomplishments, either, but their willingness to start from nothing, and by initiative and hard work build up something like this! Those who want to come in do not know the first thing about working together; they cannot even realize anything beyond what revolves about themselves or perhaps around their immediate families. All the people here have developed something within themselves that these others can get only by going through the same thing . . . . or so it seems to me. But if all people are to live harmoniously together, there must be some way." He looked questioningly at Hut, who slowly shook his head.

"All I can suggest," he said, "is for us to go see the Elders and get their advice."

"Yes," Rhu agreed. "But how can we do it? Every day, new problems confront us—problems we have to handle quickly, just as in the case of Nord and Nana. I just don't see how we can leave, even for a day, except, perhaps, if just one of us goes."

Before Hut could reply, Ord hurriedly joined them. "Tall stranger at door," he explained. "Wears white dress. Strange stuff. Asks for Rhu."

"An Elder," Hut stated and with Rhu, hastened down to welcome him.

"Well and nobly done, my sons," the Elder greeted them as they bowed respectfully. "It is as Lord Lithargos said."

Emerging upon the Plain, his kindly eyes brightened, and indeed, the view was one to compel admiration. As far as eye could reach lay the fertile green valley, broken here and there by clumps of great trees in whose shade some of the sleek cattle lay, while others grazed contentedly on the luxuriant grasses. The half-completed Dan and Ku buildings and the Kut home in their setting of green, with the beautiful spreading trees forming a fitting background, looked very peaceful and cozy. The simple, sturdy lines of the houses were offset by the variously colored stones with which they had been built, further enhancing the pleasing vista.

In the foreground, Dargh and several of his companions were lining with the same vari-colored stones the upper part of a great basin or reservoir to hold the water now flowing into it from the river—water crystal clear, yet somehow seeming to carry the coloring of the stones in the walls containing it. Women could be seen dipping water with large earthen vessels and carrying them to their homes. Everywhere were laughing, playing children.

Off to the right, several acres of maize almost knee-high showed the regular rows of careful planting—Pflugh's idea, incidentally, for he was an orderly soul—and the Elder's smiling eyes again rested upon Rhu and Hut.

"You have improved upon our work, my sons, for our maize has always been strewn by hand, while yours is uniform and neat. Its cultivation, Lord Hiroto says, will enhance its yield and quality, and this you can now do readily."

"Its cultivation?" Rhu and Hut exclaimed simultaneously, for both were rather at a loss to grasp the meaning of the new word.

"Yes. Keeping it free from weeds and other growth, and keeping the soil about its roots loose so that the water may penetrate better, and the growth be both more rapid and stronger. Your yield will be much greater for it." He paused, and then continued, "Lord Lithargos spoke of a device on which you haul stones. I would see it."

"We have several," Hut commented. "Rhu devised and made them."

"Hut gave me the idea," Rhu disclaimed the credit promptly.

"It works well on wet ground," Hut added, "but is rather hard to pull where there is no grass and when it is dry."

For once, Dargh was embarrassed when, a little later, the Elder congratulated him upon his various achievements, and especially upon the water supply.

"Enclose the pool with a wall and let no one touch the water except to dip it out. Thus it will always be pure and fresh," the Elder advised.

Rhu shot Hut a swift glance. Already they had been planning to use it for bathing.

Evidently catching the thought in both their minds, the Elder smiled understandingly. "It does offer a most inviting place for bathing," he said softly, "so why not construct another one below it and let the overflow keep it filled for that purpose?"

At the Ku hut, which they approached as the noon meal was about ready, the Elder asked to meet Rhu's mother, Meta, who was greatly flustered.

"Meta," he said gently, "you and Mahata should be proud to have borne such sons."

"Not bad boys," Meta conceded, the soft light in her eyes belying her grudging admission, while her wrinkled old face became almost gentle. "Rhu make Meta much work. Always new ideas. Too much wash! No man smell," she snorted finally, glowering at the grinning Rhu.

But a bit later, and after Hut had gone to the Dan family circle to eat, the Elder's eyes grew very tender as he observed the care she used in selecting only the choicest tidbits for Rhu's bowl, rapping sharply the knuckles of one of his brothers who reached for the particular bit she had chosen. It was noticed, also, that the choicest and crispest bits of the maize bread were his. Knowing his people, it was somewhat of a surprise to him, too, that before filling the bowls, Meta had actually washed her hands, although she carefully licked her fingers after each reaching into the succulent stew.

Chapter Fourteen

THE ARRIVAL OF QUE AND NOHR

WITH CHARACTERISTIC patience, the Elder listened to Rhu and Hut's explanation of the difficulties they had encountered since their last visit. Many of his questions indicated that much of it was already known to him, and his chief interest seemed to be in their explanations of how they had arrived at various conclusions.

"And now," Rhu concluded, "we are faced with a problem even greater than all the others, and one about which we were coming to see you."

He and Hut then explained that they had received many requests from those desirous of joining the group on the Plains, but because they feared their lack of understanding and appreciation of what had been done would have a bad effect upon those already there, they had accepted none who applied. They went on to say they felt this was not the proper way to handle the situation, for others should have the opportunity to enjoy what those on the Plains experienced. "Yet, if we admit them, it will not be long before disturbing elements will destroy not only the existing good will, but much of what has already been accomplished on the Plains as well," Rhu concluded.

"It is for this reason that I am here," the Elder began when they had finished. "Of course, it has been a very valuable experience for me to visit you and see for myself all you have accomplished thus far. I am instructed to express the full commendation of Lord Hiroto and Lord Lithargos for the splendid manner in which you have put into operation what we have taught you from time to time. You have been apt pupils, and your work is well done. Because you have arrived at a point where you need further help and instruction in matters not previously taught you, we are empowered to offer our further assistance. Your desire and intention to come and ask for this aid makes it possible for us to give it and to your best advantage.

"As you have said, to bring into your present group those not ready for admission would not only complicate your work unnecessarily, but might easily defeat and set at naught all you have already accomplished. Therefore, you are entirely justified in asking further help with what, to all but Lords Lithargos and Hiroto, is something new in our experience. Your ability to convert the information we have previously given you into actual knowledge through its practical application in your work is most pleasing to the Great Ones. May it ever be so, and we believe it will. Because what you have done is great and noble, and unselfish in that neither of you has sought either glory or special advantage from it, but have ever striven for the good of all, your own advancement will be even greater than we had hoped.

"The Elders have been instructed to institute a system of training for those who would join with you. We shall teach them all what those now here are able to do as well as such other things as your present group will learn in the near future. They will also be trained to work together so that they will fit into the group as well as cooperate in the activities carried on here on the Plains.

"The system we shall inaugurate shall be known as a School. This School shall be established in that portion of the Mu Valley where you killed the great bear when bringing Haitee and Marda to us. Lord Lithargos has pointed out to us that His experience upon another life path proved that to establish it here on the Rhu Hut Plains would result in unnecessary jealousies, and neither the present group nor the ones to be trained would benefit. He states the same reason you have for not *admitting* them—ignorance and inability to grasp the true importance of the work being done here.

"As you have long been taught, there is no such thing as

something for nothing. By that, we mean that no one can receive and benefit permanently from anything for which he has not given an adequate return. Those now here have paid in services to others for all they have received, even to the sharing of their cattle.

"To permit others to come in now would mean they would have the benefit of everything those already here have accomplished by their own efforts while they themselves have done nothing to merit it. Since they have no understanding of what was entailed, and therefore, no appreciation of it, but desire only to benefit from it, to permit their entrance would be a violation of Natural Law. It would not be long before your original group would suffer the consequence. This you have foreseen although you have perhaps forgotten why it should be thus.

"Each applicant for admission to your group, therefore, must give to the School one-half his possessions, be they what they may—cattle or other things of value. Those unwilling to do this shall not be taught until they learn the advantage of so doing."

"Seems rather a big price to pay," Rhu commented. "It would have cost the Kus and Dans dearly."

"Yet, Rhu, they have done as much, if not more, when you consider the division of their great herds among the others, the fact that they supplied more laborers than smaller families, and that they were the first to chance coming here, leaving behind them the best grazing grounds in the Mu Valley."

Smiling, the Elder paused as the two young men reflected upon the truth of his statement. He then continued: "Do you remember, Rhu, that you once gave the Elders your best bull and three heifers of your best stock, all unrelated?"

"Yes, but we owed you far more than that," Rhu answered promptly.

"You are to be commended for that feeling, but the Elders do not see it that way. However, the point is that from this beginning, and with a like gift later from Hut, the Elders began a series of experiments under the direction of Lord Hiroto, and we have developed bulls of such quality as none of your present herds can boast. Also, we have cows of vastly superior grade. The same is true of our sheep.

"When we are given half an aspirant's herd, we shall let him keep the best he has. From the half we take, we shall use such as may be needed for feeding the aspirants. Those which show the greatest promise of development, we shall place in our own herds, breeding the cows to our best bulls. The same will be true of the sheep, and in addition, we shall breed the aspirant's cattle to our best bulls, and the ewes to our best rams.

"Since it will take several Great Suns to train an aspirant, by the time he is ready for admission to your forming civilization, he should have a herd equal in number to his original one and of vastly superior quality, with a surplus of bulls and rams. This surplus he can trade with those already citizens, thus increasing his own herd to equal theirs, and at the same time, permitting the citizens to constantly improve the value and grade of their present ones. Because this breeding process will continue indefinitely, what is true in the beginning will be equally so later."

"But what of the Forest Dwellers who have few possessions and no stock at all?" asked Hut.

"Much the same is true of the Cave Dwellers," the Elder began. "But this problem is less than you may imagine. In the first place, the herds of the School will increase, regardless of how many we use as already indicated, and regardless of those we shall later dispose of in ways yet to be determined. These will require herdsmen and caretakers, for they cannot be permitted to roam at will as was the old custom. Proper feeds must be raised and newer and better pasturage provided. This work will fall largely upon the Forest Dwellers and those of the Cave Dwellers who are less apt as stone workers, and this service shall be the major portion of their payment.

"Furthermore, additional housing will be needed as aspirants for the training are accepted. Eventually, the School itself will require vastly larger buildings than either of you has yet envisioned. The construction of these will be the work of Cave Dwellers while Forest Dwellers will help them. The most skilled of the Cave Dwellers will be taught the manufacture of weapons, tools, and such other implements as will be found of value to the civilization."

"When will this start?" demanded the practical Rhu, all too eager to be about it.

"And who will do the teaching?" Hut asked in almost the same breath, no less eager than Rhu.

The Elder smiled into their intent faces. "And what of yourselves and the part you two are to play?" he suggested. "And what of Dargh, of Ord, and those others who are already demonstrating exceptional ability either as craftsmen or as leaders of their kind?"

Observing the blank expression which had crept into their eyes, his own became tender with compassionate understanding. "It is this very lack of self consideration that so endears you to us," he said, smiling. "The Elders will be the first teachers, while you, together with Dargh and Ord and such others as you may select from time to time will be taught personally by Lords Hiroto and Lithargos with such others of the Great Ones as They may select."

"Whew!" Rhu half whistled, and Hut stared in amazement at this unconscious lack of respect for the Elder. He need not have been concerned, however, for the Elder chuckled softly.

"What a program!" the irrepressible Rhu exclaimed. "Hut, I see where all this is going to lead to even more development here on the Plains!"

"Yes," the Elder agreed, "your responsibilities will grow increasingly heavy so that you will each soon have need of competent helpmates. These, you have provided, and their training for this work is almost completed. On the Short Day, they are to join you here."

"Helpers that *you* have trained?" Rhu asked uncertainly, his facial expression no less puzzled than Hut's. Suddenly, he brightened as understanding burst upon him. "Oh!" he exclaimed. "You mean Haitee and Marda!" And his face reddened slightly.

"Yes, and very apt pupils they have been," said the Elder, smiling gently. "Among other things, they have been taught to prepare wool, to make it into yarn, and to do simple weaving."

"Yarn . . . ? Weaving . . . ?" Hut frowned as he tried to comprehend the meaning of these two entirely unknown words.

"Yarn is like a very slender and fibrous vine," the Elder explained, using terms within the scope of their understanding. "These strands are interwoven as you do with the slender twigs for the making of your huts, although the strands of yarn are much finer and hence more closely woven. This makes what Lord Hiroto calls cloth. This cloth can then be made into heavy garments for cool weather, for coverings for your beds and like purposes, many of which they have also been taught."

The eyes of Hut and Rhu were wide as they listened avidly, their nimble minds already envisioning many crude possibilities.

"Is . . . . is that the manner of making garments such as the Great Ones wear?" asked Rhu.

"Yes, Their garments and those such as Marda and Haitee wear in the warm weather are fashioned from cloth supplied us by Lord Hiroto. It will be some time before the skill required for its weaving can be developed among your people. We have been told, however, that before too long, materials will be grown here on the Plains which will be much lighter than wool, and Lord Hiroto assures us that the simple weaving I have mentioned is the beginning from which the necessary skill will be evolved for the making of lighter fabrics. Haitee and Marda are now able to make the yarn and weave it into cloth, as well as fashion it into garments and such, and they will teach the other women here.

"Seek not to accomplish too much at the beginning," he cautioned. "In this, as in many other things you are to be taught, skill can be acquired only through long and patient practice, just as it has taken you many moons to learn to make and use your bows and arrows, Rhu. No man becomes a good bowman without much practice."

"And good bows and straight arrows," Rhu added, his thoughts racing back to his early attempts at making better weapons.

"Even so," the Elder agreed. "Rhu, let me caution you ever to be patient and to consider well each step before you take it. Be neither too impulsive nor too quick to resort to force. Patience is the great virtue which leads to those of efficiency and precision. They are inseparable, for each requires the other in order to attain its full perfection. The same is true of all twelve principal virtues, and all may be summed up in the one word *love* which is the ultimate perfection of all virtues. It is so all-embracing that it is the supreme attribute of N'Kul, the perfection of all that is good, true, and noble. *Perfect love* is the thirteenth and greatest of all virtues.

"Hut, grow not overly ambitious to rule, to establish laws for others to obey, nor seek too much power. Ever consult with Rhu before you establish any rule or law, even as he should do the same with you, excepting only when you have direct instructions from Those greater than any of us.

"Be loyal. Be sincere.

"Be ever thoughtful of others and never forget that all service should be rewarded, if only by commendation. It is upon those who serve faithfully today that you may depend for like service tomorrow. If one has been faithful today but seemingly fails tomorrow, do not condemn him outright. Seek first to discover the cause of his seeming delinquency. He may be no less sincere today than he was yesterday, yet may lack that understanding which you can and should afford him. Be not deceived by mere appearance. Remember Og. If one previously faithful seems to prove unfaithful today, it may well be that something you have done has created doubt in his mind. Seek always the fault within yourself for it very often explains the seeming fault in another."

Although Hut had been listening courteously to all the Elder was saying, it was becoming increasingly obvious to the observant Rhu that something was disturbing him, so he was not taken wholly by surprise when, as the Elder concluded, Hut broached the subject on his mind.

"You say that the Elders will establish a school and train those who seek admission to our community. I would not question anything you might say or do, but does it not seem reasonable that Rhu and I, who have had so much experience with our people, should make good teachers?

"It is not that we presume to know anything comparable to you Elders, but it seems almost unfair to me for you to assume this heavy task. As you know, Rhu has a great ability when it comes to handling people, so why should he not undertake the

management of those on the Plains while I undertake the training of those seeking to join us here? Rhu and I each have certain special abilities. I seem able to formulate plans and devise
rules while Rhu can make the plans operate practically, and
most assuredly, he is the one best qualified to see that all rules
are enforced with the least friction."

For what seemed to Rhu a long and breathless moment, the
Elder's eyes rested upon Hut as he considered his suggestion.
"Perhaps you do have many of the qualifications you mention,
my son, as is true of the qualities you rightfully assign to Rhu.
But Lords Hiroto and Lithargos have expressed the opinion
and desire that the *Elders* prepare and administer this training
for membership in your community—the training for citizenship, they call it. Therefore, I have stated the decision of the
Elders on this matter. Furthermore, even as it has required the
combined efforts and abilities of both you and Rhu to attain
your present success, it seems best and most reasonable that
you both continue as you now are.

"As to rules, Lords Lithargos and Hiroto are preparing the
basic ones which will be given you and Rhu in due course. My
sons, it is better to have no rules at all than to have those you
cannot always enforce with perfect justice under all conditions.

"Already, you have taken the first important step in the establishment of what will be called the government, and about
which I came to speak. When you had the problem of the
division of your herds, you called in the patriarchs of those
septs already here. You are right in believing that all three
divisions of the tribe should be represented and that Dargh
and Ord be included in this group. We suggest that these
patriarchs, together with Dargh and Ord, comprise what shall
be called your Council.

"Through the Council, you will introduce the laws of which
I spoke and such others as will be given you for the conduct of
the community's affairs. These are to be discussed with the
Council before they are adopted, for the members will then
more willingly and understandingly help you in their enforcement. One of us will be present when you submit them to help
should you need such support in giving the Council the necessary understanding."

As the Elder ceased speaking, the towering Ord entered. "Two strangers stand without. Seek information," his mighty voice boomed. "One is of Chi Yans. The other of Tama Yans."

"We shall see them presently," Rhu answered, reluctant to have the conversation with the Elder interrupted. "I shall call you," he concluded.

"Ord speaks well," the Elder commented after the big fellow left. "I have never known a Forest Dweller, except another Elder, to equal him."

"Ord is exceptional in many ways and learns quickly," Rhu praised. "Next to Dargh, he is our most valuable man."

"I would speak with Dargh," the Elder announced, at the same time nodding his approval of Rhu's remarks. "I see he is back directing the construction of the pool. It is best that you now interview the newcomers. If you so desire, I shall rejoin you later," he added with a kindly smile as he departed.

After Rhu had called to Ord, Hut spoke. "Rhu, I have an odd feeling that we are about to enter into a new phase of our work," he said. "The Elder has given us a lot to think about, but I still feel I am well qualified to do the teaching. It hardly seems fair that I should be denied this great opportunity. Not that I would dare to question their judgment," he hastened to assure Rhu whose face betrayed his astonishment. "Of course, we'll do as the Elders suggest, but it does disappoint me."

Further conversation was impossible, for Ord was coming up the steps followed by two distinctly dissimilar men. Reaching the top, Ord stepped to one side for a moment before departing, making sure that these strangers meant no harm to his friends. As Hut and Rhu knew, he would remain just out of view in order to be immediately available in case of need. This was Ord's own idea. His deep-seated distrust of all strangers was one thing neither Hut nor Rhu had thus far been able to overcome.

"Ord no fool," he had once explained. "Strange man, strange ways. Strange ways, bad ways. Man bad, Ord kill."

There was seemingly no dislodging this from the big fellow's mind, nor was there any question in either Hut's or Rhu's mind but that Ord would do just that, or die trying.

As the oddly matched pair approached, Hut and Rhu got to

their feet, smiling. That the newcomers bore no weapons meant nothing. Ord always saw to that detail. Supremely indifferent to personal danger himself, he was vastly concerned when Rhu and Hut were involved. Despite what he knew of their prowess, Ord took no chances, and if ever two men were carefully guarded, they were Hut and Rhu.

"I am Hut Mai Dan, and this is Rhu Sol Ku," announced Hut. "By what names are you known, and what do you seek?"

"I am Que Ong Lingh, of the Chi Yans," the shorter of the two introduced himself.

"And I am Nohr Phan, of the Tama Yans," the taller one added. "We both have same mission . . . . to learn of your work, the fame of which reaches even to the Tama Valley."

"Be seated," Rhu invited courteously. He was greatly surprised at the culture their unusual manner of speaking revealed. Assuredly, these were no common tribesmen. Glancing at Hut, Rhu saw he recognized this also, for Hut was studying the two intently.

Que was not as tall and of much slighter build than Rhu. His round face and symmetrical torso were smooth and bore no trace of hair, a fact both the Mu Yan lads viewed with astonishment. His dark brown, almost black eyes, were different from any they had ever seen, for they were oblique and slightly almond-shaped, while his cheek bones were more prominent than those of the tribes with which they were familiar. Que had smiled when introducing himself, but now, his face was almost expressionless, conveying nothing of what may have been passing through his mind.

Strange though he appeared to Rhu and Hut, their attention was equally attracted to a yellow band which encircled the Chi Yan's arm just above the elbow.

On the other hand, Nohr was as tall as Hut and much of his general build. His keen and alertly shrewd eyes were blue, his hair golden, and he was equally hairy of chest, shoulders, and back as Hut and Rhu. His rather rugged face and prominent nose bespoke the thinker, while his long and tapering fingers, stubby at their ends, gave promise of great and enduring strength—a man to be reckoned with. About his mouth was an expression of kindliness, and he smiled engagingly as he spoke.

Rhu liked the eyes of this tall bearded man and felt here was one he could trust. But Hut thought the kindly, easy smile a sign of weakness, despite the rugged face. Neither was quite sure about Que for, while the quiet and composed countenance denoted strength, they had been accustomed to reading the expressions on the faces of those they had encountered. Not to be able to do so raised a small doubt in their minds. Still, all in all, they rather liked the newcomers.

Observing that the lips of the visitors were dry and cracked, Rhu called to his sister, Deenah, who served them when they were not at their family huts, asking that she bring water. Turning to the men, he asked if they had eaten. Before they could answer, Deenah hurried up with two earthen cups filled to the brim with water from the perspiring pottery vessel which kept it cool and refreshing.

"Drink," Rhu invited courteously. "I see you are thirsty."

Que's eyes bored into his for a brief instant before lifting the brimming cup to his lips. He sipped lightly, then looked at the now smiling Hut. Evidently reassured by their friendly and considerate attitude, he lifted the cup again to his lips and drank deeply.

Nohr, however, did not hesitate but drained his cup as if long famished. "That was good," he said, wiping his dripping beard with a hairy hand. "More, please?" he asked, smiling as he extended his cup toward Deenah.

Rhu's eyes widened. "Please" was a rare word among the Mu Yans, and except for the Elders, seldom, if ever, used. Assuredly, this man knew more than the average, and his heart warmed toward the stranger.

Taking Nohr's cup, Deenah turned to Que. "More?" she asked.

"Yes," Que answered. "May the blossoms in your cheeks never pale."

Rhu and Hut stared at the speaker in surprise. This, indeed, was something new in their experience, and Hut catalogued the expression in his retentive mind.

After the second cup, Nohr smiled gratefully at Rhu. "Our last meal was yesterday. No game since we entered Mu Valley," he explained.

Deenah's alert ears had heard Rhu's question, and she now approached with two bowls of succulent stew and a supply of maize bread for each.

"What is this?" Que asked, indicating the bread.

"Maize bread," Rhu answered. "You will find it very good when dipped into the stew."

"Maize . . . ? Bread . . . ?" both Nohr and Que asked in the same breath.

"Maize is a grain we raise," explained Rhu. "Ground into fine bits, it is mixed with milk and eggs, then baked."

This was all new to Que and Nohr, and the latter voiced the questions the simple statement evoked.

"Milk? Eggs?" he asked. "And what do you mean by 'raising grain'?"

Because their liking for these strangers was increasing from moment to moment, Rhu and Hut felt a great urge to acquaint them with the work which had been done on the Plains.

"We shall be glad to explain these and many other things, but later," said Hut. "When you have finished eating, we shall tell you of our work here and something of our plans for the future."

"The stew is very fine and the bread excellent," Que commented, licking his lips, while Nohr ate with a gusto that told plainer than words how he felt about it. At last, both were satisfied and Deenah had taken away their bowls.

"And now," Que began, "we would learn more."

"First," countered Hut, "tell us something of yourselves and how you came to learn of what we are doing, as well as how you managed to get here. Suppose you begin, Que, for, as I understand it, you must have crossed both the Thibi and Upa Valleys, and both are none too friendly with strangers."

Chapter Fifteen

QUE AND NOHR

ALREADY IT WAS obvious to Rhu and Hut that the vocabularies of Que and Nohr were far more extensive than was true of any other tribesmen whom they had ever encountered. (Notwithstanding this, for the sake of clarity, their stories are more lucidly given here than they were actually related.)

"Nohr and I have been friends since childhood," Que began. "Our respective clans occupy the grazing lands at each end of a short pass through the mountains dividing the Tama and Chi Valleys. We are of the Plains Dwellers of our respective tribes.

"For more than two Great Suns (years), Nohr has been a most interested observer of happenings here, and we have often spent many consecutive suns (days) together watching and trying to guess what you were doing. Just before the big storm, a Thibi Yan, fleeing his clan, reached our land and was found at the pass as he sought to slip through. He was almost spent and nearly starved, for his weapons were very inferior, and he dared travel only at night. Nohr and I fed him, and he told us of his trouble.

"Two moons (months) before, he had ventured into the Upa Valley where he had overheard much talk about the Mu Yans settling upon the Great Plains here. It seems that the Upa Yans were trying to get two or three of their clans to unite and take this land away from you, but were making little headway because of the fear of your flying arrows which kill at unbelievable distances."

Here, Que paused to eye Rhu and Hut questioningly, obvi-

ously more than half doubting the verity of what he was saying. "At least, if the arrows do not fly, why do they grow
feathers like birds?" he continued. "This is one thing we seek
to learn, if it be true.

"He heard one of the Upa Yan spies say that you also have
great magic because you can make fires simply by striking your
hands together, and this, even more than the flying arrows,
deters them. If you have this power from the fire gods, no
doubt you have other and even greater powers, or so they
think. We would learn of this, although, frankly, we do not
believe it.

"The Thibi Yan told of this to his own clan who chased him
away from their huts as one possessed of bad spirits for daring
to believe in such nonsense. After we had nursed him back to
health, Nohr and I persuaded him to lead us through the Thibi
Valley and the pass into the Upa Valley as we wanted to learn
more about you.

"Unfortunately, we were attacked by some Upa Yans, and
he was killed, but we managed to escape and finally reached
the Mu Valley where we dared travel only by night as there
are so many more Mu Yans than there are Upa Yans. Eventually, we discovered a well-worn trail which took us across
the great river over logs spanning it. It was our intention to try
to slip into this place during the night, but your stone wall
stopped us. Before we could find a place to hide this morning,
we were captured. To our surprise, we were not killed immediately, although our bows and arrows as well as Nohr's zitkern
were taken from us before the big one bade us wait at the
great stone closing the wall."

"Zitkern?" Rhu and Hut exclaimed questioningly.

"It is made of bowstrings so strung that one may sing to their
humming," Nohr attempted to explain.

"Let us see it," Rhu suggested to Hut, who immediately
called to Ord to bring Que's and Nohr's belongings to them.

"What is that upon your arm?" Rhu demanded, pointing to
the yellow band encircling Que's right arm.

"It is my man mark," Que answered. "When a Chi Yan has
killed his first man in a fair fight, one of these is placed upon
his right arm. For each additional victory, we scratch a man

upon it with our war knife." He pointed to the rather well-shaped stone knife which Ord handed Rhu together with the somewhat crude bows and arrows.

"Mine was placed there when I had seen fifteen Great Suns," he continued, rather pridefully extending his arm. "As you will observe, there are eight men upon it." He held up eight fingers as they always did for any numbers.

"Of what is it made?" asked Hut, fingering the band somewhat gingerly.

"Of auer," Que answered. "We find it in the mountains, then hammer it into shape. It is rather soft," he explained.

Although consumed with curiosity, Rhu and Hut were too proud to question further, yet each knew the other was determined to ask the Elders about it.

"And now, the zitkern," said Hut, turning to Nohr.

At Rhu's nod, Ord handed the instrument to Nohr, at the same time stepping close to him, his mighty hands flexed to grab Nohr upon a second's notice. The "thing" was strange to him, and Ord was not one to trust anything he could not understand.

The zitkern was a strong and beautifully finished hardwood stick bent almost V-shape, the heavier end of which was tightly bound to a hollow log about eight inches in diameter and some three feet long. The shell of the log was almost an inch thick, and upon closer examination, they saw that its ends were covered with a hairless skin tightly stretched and sealing the log. (It was not unlike our modern drum.) The skin, they later learned, was the outer covering of a cow's stomach. Between the two ends of the curved stick were strung a number of gut strings of varying sizes, stretched tightly by means of pegs inserted into the stick in much the same manner as modern stringed instruments are fashioned, and forming a crude harp.

Nohr ran his finger lightly across the strings, and Rhu recalled the pleasant sound a bow he was once working upon had given off when one end was held against an upturned bowl. He and Hut watched intently as Nohr twisted the pegs slightly on two or three of the strings, causing a soft, humming sound.

Then ensued the first crude music the two had ever heard

with the exception of the chanting of the Elders and such bits of it as Rhu and Hut had been able to emulate. Resting the log upon his lap, Nohr plucked certain of the strings, cleared his throat, and to the strumming of the weird, but by no means unmusical chords, sang a song concerning the adventures of a mighty hunter.

This was a new and wonderful experience, and Rhu and Hut were enchanted. Observing their rapt faces, Nohr continued, singing of birds and beasts, his imitations of the various creatures being exceedingly realistic. He sang of laughing waters, of storms and of peace. Suspicions lulled, Ord squatted open-mouthed, to listen entranced while all who were within earshot approached the building to hear the better. This was as marvelous to them as the ability of Rhu and Hut to strike fires was to Que and Nohr.

Thus, the first musical instrument was introduced upon the Rhu Hut Plains.

When at last the music ceased, and Nohr lay his zitkern to one side, Rhu asked, "Did you make this zitkern?"

"Yes, but there are many among the Tama Yans."

"But none better," Que supplemented quickly. "He also has made a whistle, and I like it almost as well," he added.

"Do the Chi Yans make zitkerns?" asked Hut.

"I have tried, but Nohr makes them much better than I can."

"I wish we had your whiner," Nohr broke in. "It looks like a gourd with a long neck on it," he explained to his interested audience. "It has one string, and Que plays it with a little bow strung with hairs from a cow's tail on which he rubs the dried gum from a tree. It whines fine," he finished.

"Gourd? What's that?" asked Hut, curious as to what sort of thing would have a long neck and still be used to bring forth pleasant sound.

"A little round, hard-shelled thing that grows on a vine," Que answered.

"Where do you find them?" Rhu wanted to know. "I don't remember ever having seen any such thing in the Mu Valley."

"In the end of the Chi Valley toward the setting sun, there is a great plain where nothing much grows except thorny brush, and there the gourd grows in abundance. It is about the size of Ord's fist. I found one that was dry and was bringing it home hanging on a piece of vine when I discovered that rubbing on the vine when drawn tight, it made an odd noise.

"I remembered Nohr's zitkern and made a bowl like the gourd from wood, fastening a stick to it with a peg at its upper end and a bowstring running to the end of the bowl. I had to put a little block under the lower end of the string to hold it away from the bowl.

"It plunked only one tone and made almost no sound when I tried rubbing my hand along it. I was going to throw it away when Nohr happened to draw his tight bowstring across it, and it made a loud squeaking noise. I wanted to try it, and as I took hold of the neck, the tone changed. Then I tried holding it at different places on the neck and made many sounds, but not very loud. One day, I got some of the gum from a tree on my bowstring and then the sound was much louder. However, it soon got so it was no good, so I put on a finer string and tried some of the gum that was dry. The strings wore out so fast, I tried using hairs from a cow's tail, and thus made a bow especially for it."

"Yes, and he learned to play some of my songs on it," Nohr added. "At first, we called it a squealer, but with the new bow, a whiner."

"And now, let us see your flying arrows," Que requested anxious to fulfill their quest.

Rhu chuckled. "They don't fly," he explained, "but the feathers make them shoot straight. They look like this," he said, handing one of his obsidian-tipped arrows to each of them.

"And here is Rhu's bow," Hut chimed in, passing it to Nohr whose admiration for the fine workmanship was very evident. "You should see Rhu shoot!" Hut boasted pridefully. "I have seen him kill birds on the wing!"

"Nohr is a good shot," Que commented dryly, "but not that good. We have heard many brag of their ability, but few merit it. However, I seek not to question Rhu's skill, though I admit that it was not he who said it. Yet would I like to see him display his skill for it must be great since his weapons surpass anything I have ever seen. First, however, what of the fire?"

Rather nettled that Hut's truthfulness should be questioned, Rhu's tone was gruff as he said, "Hold out your hand. Or, if you prefer, I shall start a small fire."

Que's eyes hardened at this abrupt change in Rhu's manner. Not understanding, he became skeptical and held forth his hand promptly, only to jerk it back precipitately as the fiery sparks from the flint showered into it, raising blisters where they struck.

"It is not well, Que, to question our veracity. I shall shoot at any mark you may suggest, provided it is near enough for your or Nohr's arrows to reach." Rhu's voice had taken on an unaccustomed brittle quality that caused Que to eye him sharply.

"Nay, I had no intent to question your truthfulness. Yet, you must agree that such things seem impossible," he said. Then, somewhat ruefully, "There is no question about the heat from your *magic!*"

"I am vastly more interested in learning of what you are doing here," Nohr stated. "I will admit, however, that I would welcome the opportunity to witness your shooting, for I admire skill in anything where magic is not involved."

"As to the magic," Rhu said, smiling into Nohr's face, "we shall show you how the fire is made though we are unable to supply you with the same materials we use. As to my shooting, what Hut says is true, yet it was more of luck than of skill."

Ord's laugh burst forth from his great chest. "Listen, little one," he boomed at Que, "Ord saw Rhu shoot flying goose, not once, but several times. Ord never see Rhu miss. What Que say now?"

There was no mistaking his truculence, and Que's face, which had displayed some interest, again became utterly expressionless except for the fearlessly glittering eyes.

"Big man, big talk," he remarked tersely, and turning to Rhu, "I, too, would see you shoot, but first would listen as Nohr has suggested."

Before Rhu and Hut finished their story of the work thus far accomplished, and had told something of their plans for the future, the afternoon was well spent, the shooting evidently forgotten for the time being, and the Elder could be seen returning to the three-story building.

"The Elder of whom we spoke is approaching," said Rhu. "Feel free to ask him any questions you like, for you will find him understanding and glad to help anyone who desires it."

He and Hut rose as the Elder climbed the last step into the room, a courtesy Que and Nohr were quick to observe and emulate.

"Welcome to the Rhu Hut Plains, Que and Nohr," the Elder greeted them immediately. "Your coming has been awaited, for you can play important parts in this new society."

"So I have grown to feel," Que said simply as he bowed respectfully. "This day is one both Nohr and I shall long remember."

"The Great Plains are well named," Nohr commented briefly.

The Elder smiled gently. "You may dismiss from your minds all doubts," he said. "Even the marksmanship of Rhu has been understated as you will soon see for yourselves. Both Rhu and Hut have been most unassuming in recounting their work here. Yet, it is ever better so when confidence is to be involved. Only implicit confidence leads to truly great achievements, and it is more readily inspired by understatements of accomplishments than by overstatements. Rhu and Hut, I commend you upon your handling of this situation, and if Que and Nohr have no special questions to ask me, I shall return to our sanctuary."

"There are many," Que answered, "yet so great our confidence in Rhu and Hut after what we have been told and have already seen, we would not detain you, feeling they are entirely competent to give us what we seek at this time."

"It is well," the Elder replied, smilingly. "May it ever be so. Rhu and Hut, to Que and Nohr shall be given the privilege of being the first of their respective tribes to receive proper instruction for citizenship in your group should they so desire. Ere they depart, I shall return to advise them regarding their future work." He then departed, accompanied by Ord who had been a silent listener.

"And now," Hut began, "we shall take you to see what has

been done. For the present, you will be the guests of Rhu and me. Deenah will provide for your accommodation."

Rhu nodded his full approval. Already he and Hut were beginning to feel a real regard for these courteous strangers who had displayed such rare courage and initiative in making their way to the Plains.

From the moment of their introduction, Nohr and Dargh seemed drawn to each other; that many of their ideas and tastes were identical became quickly evident. Que's interest in Dargh's accomplishments was no less than that of Nohr, but it was more impersonal than that of his friend.

As the days passed and the two became more familiar with conditions on the Plains, Que's thirst for information seemed insatiable. The planting and cultivation of the maize; methods of improving and developing better cattle and sheep; the construction of permanent stone buildings and the many problems involved . . . . such matters were ever on his mind. Always, he listened attentively to each explanation, and more often than not, he could be found with Rhu where something was going on, alert to each procedure and the reasons for it.

The basic ideals which actuated Rhu and Hut in all they sought to accomplish and their methods of solving the problems of human behavior held even more interest for him. The story of the conversion of Og was one of which he never seemed to tire, and his questions regarding it were many and varied. With the passing of time, it was apparent that, unlike all the others, even Rhu and Hut to a considerable degree, Que had what may aptly be termed as a philosophical turn of mind.

Although he and Nohr spoke much more fluently than the Mu Yans, it became evident that in some other respects, the Chi Yans and Tama Yans were even less advanced. For example, if there were Elders in their tribes, neither Que nor Nohr knew of them. Neither was there the respect for the holdings of others of their tribe which obtained among the Mu Yan Plains Dwellers. As a result, clan wars were common.

The foregoing understanding of the two new tribe members was acquired, of course, only over a considerable period. It was while the four of them were discussing the Chi Yans and Tama Yans a day or so after Que and Nohr's arrival, however, that an epochal event occurred. The newcomers had mentioned that their family groups were usually larger than those of the Mu Yans because each clan or family was disposed to hold together for mutual protection. Rhu and Hut wondered if this closer family tie might not account for the more extensive vocabularies of Que and Nohr.

"This is probably true," Que agreed. "That I use many unusual expressions is no doubt due to the fact that it is our custom for parents to pass on to their children the family histories," he explained. "Each evening, my father tells his sons of the feats of our ancestors, usually belittling our own. It was because of my complaining of this that I was once sent away from our circle. This gave me the idea of traveling in our Valley where I had many experiences for the Chi Yan clans are not of a friendly nature. Each family, it seems, is totally disinterested in the experiences of other families. From what I have seen here on the Rhu Hut Plains, I feel this has retarded our advancement."

"Most Tama Yans speak but little," Nohr commented. "It is only through tribal chants that they have any records of the past. The zitkern is a tribal instrument, though very crude, for few have much skill in their making. Que helped me with my present one, being very skillful with his hands.

"As with the Mu Yans, the Cave Dwellers of the Tama Yans make almost all our stone tools, but I have never before seen arrowheads made of stone. The Forest Dwellers are utterly savage and but for the constant fighting among themselves would probably have killed off all the Plains Dwellers. I cannot understand how you were able to tame those of the Mu Tribe."

Hut shook his head. "Ours are not much better," he said. "Only Rhu is able to get them to do anything. Those who are here are the best from among them.

"The Mu Yan Plains Dwellers have regular grazing lands for each clan, but the clans try to keep on a friendly basis among themselves because of the Forest Dwellers. In this way, we seldom have much trouble with one family trying to take the lands of another. However, only the Ku and Dan families have ever *worked together*. This has made Rhu's family and mine so powerful that we have helped to maintain peace, especially for our end of the valley."

"The Chi Yans cling to established customs and find it hard to change," Que volunteered. "I believe they would make very good members of your society, however, for once they get an idea firmly implanted in their minds, they hold fast to it. I have the acquaintance of one or two who, like myself, are interested in matters not usual to the Chi Yans. Perhaps, in time, they could be trained in the principles of working together for the common good."

"At least three families of the Tama Yans have watched your work here," Nohr declared. "I believe curiosity alone would make them consider it. As a whole, the Tama Plains Dwellers are not unfriendly, but they are inclined to oppose anything new to them. My father, to my surprise, encouraged me to come on this trip, but whether he would consider giving up anything he has for something new to him, I cannot help doubting. He will never believe a Forest Dweller can be trusted . . . ." Here, he stopped abruptly, for Ord approached them on the run.

"Rhu!" his great voice roared. "Big force comes down canyon. Nord saw. Cari Yans!"

Chapter Sixteen

THE BATTLE IN THE PASS

WITHOUT COMMENT, Rhu picked up and strung his bow, hung two quivers of arrows over his shoulders, and started for the roof.

Slinging his own quiver over his shoulder, Hut, too, was about to leave when Que spoke.

"If permissible, Nohr and I would be glad to help," he suggested.

"By all means," Hut agreed readily. "If you need additional arrows, you will find an ample supply here," indicating several quivers which were always kept filled for possible emergencies. "There are also extra bows. Take any you desire." With no further ado, he hurried after Rhu.

"They trust us," Nohr commented softly. "It would be an ill return for their kindness were we to fail them."

"Yes," agreed Que, selecting one of the more slender of the beautifully fashioned bows. "These are truly fine weapons," he pronounced, drawing forth one of the feathered and flint-tipped arrows.

"I never saw such bows," Nohr agreed. "I see that the arrow fits at the exact center, and their pull and balance are perfect! The arrows, too, are much longer than ours, and perfectly straight! Somehow, I feel very confident of the outcome no matter how many are the attackers. Perhaps now we shall see Rhu shoot in earnest!"

Well equipped, the newcomers hastened to the roof where they found Rhu and Hut at the end of the wall nearest the cliff from which position they commanded the incoming trail for a good two hundred yards. Nohr stepped into the space between the two, his eyes widening as he watched the powerful Forest Dwellers testing their great bows, many of which were a good seven feet long, while their arrows measured at least four feet in length.

Que took his place beside Hut and he, too, observed these enormous men as they prepared for action. From this vantage point, a good thirty or more feet above the trail, he could also see how ideally the building was placed for defense. A steep and towering cliff abutted it on the left, while on the right, it was flush with the Hatamukulian River gorge. The cleared space before it was barely twenty feet wide, and the great boulders beyond this afforded ample protection from any mass frontal attack. Que's pulses quickened as he saw that the cleared space ended abruptly at the chasm from which the steady roar of the raging river far below seemed much louder than he remembered. Since no barrier had been placed here, any massing of men outside the great door was extremely hazardous.

His approval changed to wonder as Nord arrived on the run, immediately instructing fourteen of the Forest Dwellers to lay aside their bows and arrows and take positions beside great piles of jagged stones. Hurriedly, Hut explained that they would hurl these down upon any of the enemy who approached too near the wall, and Que nodded his understanding.

"I do not see Ord," Nohr remarked.

Rhu chuckled. "If you watch carefully beyond those great boulders below us, you will see him and fifty more armed Forest Dwellers. When the Cari Yans attack, they will fall upon them unexpectedly. All the Forest Dwellers who are up here, except the stone throwers, will join them just as soon as expert bowmen from among the Plains Dwellers arrive to take their places."

"What of Dargh and the Musons, as I believe you call them? Do they not fight also?"

"Yes, Nohr, the Musons are wonderful fighters and willing. But there are not so many of them, and they are very valuable men, so we do not call upon them unless absolutely necessary. We rarely use any but the Forest Dwellers. However, this must be an exceptionally large attacking force, for I see that Ord has summoned the Plains Dwellers to help."

"I never saw anything like this!" Nohr exclaimed. "It surely proves your statements about the advantages of unified effort. With the Tama Yans and the Chi Yans, it is each family for itself, as a rule, and I understand the same is true of the Upa Yans."

"Yes, that is the way it is with the Cari Yans, too. That is why I cannot quite understand the numbers attacking us. It must be an unusually large force for Ord to consider it necessary to assemble all our fighting men. The Forest Dwellers have been able to handle all attacks since we completed this building although we always have all men prepare to be called. Every man in the entire group is trained as to his place and what he is to do until hand-to-hand fighting begins. Each group of twelve is under the command of one trained leader, and the leaders get their orders from Ord. Should Ord be killed or seriously hurt, Nord takes command. Ord takes his orders from me, then from Hut. Thus, we have a well-organized company which the Elders call our army."

Nohr's eyes were bright with appreciation. This was all new to his experience, but he was quick to realize the advantages of such foresight and careful planning. All that now remained was to see how it would work in practice. However, his air of steadily increasing confidence was all too apparent as he emulated Rhu and laid out a supply of arrows upon the stone ledge provided for this purpose.

"Here they come!" Rhu cried as the first of the attackers came charging along the trail, followed by what seemed a never ending stream of yelling savages.

Although sorely tempted to start shooting, Nohr wisely waited for Rhu to begin. Easily a hundred of the enemy were in sight before Rhu's bow twanged, and a brief second later, the leading warrior sprang high into the air, Rhu's arrow transfixing his chest.

"Aim low," he cautioned. "Shooting from this height tends to make one overshoot." His second arrow claimed its victim, a good hundred yards distant, and Nohr's eyes proclaimed his admiration.

Rhu's next arrow was companioned by Nohr's, and both struck the same man.

"I'll take those to the right," Nohr grunted, then almost wept as his next arrow missed, although it found its mark in the abdomen of the man behind the one at whom he had shot.

"Good shooting!" Rhu complimented.

And then began a rain of arrows into the oncoming horde. At the same time, the arrows of the enemy commenced their weaving flight toward the defenders, most of them falling short of their mark, although an occasional one flew harmlessly overhead as some more powerful bowman shot. The savage war cries continued, but now they were mingled with the screams of the mortally wounded. It seemed as though flesh and blood could not stand against the hail of well-directed arrows, very few of which did not leave death or a screeching wounded man in its wake.

But still the aggressors came pouring around the bend and into the trail, until by sheer weight of numbers, some reached the stone wall barring the passage. It was then that the great Forest Dwellers by their stone piles went into action. Hurling their mighty weapons down upon the unsuspecting enemy, the slaughter became grim and awful, the screeches of the wounded drowning out the war cries.

A big Forest Dweller beside Que grunted savagely, then tore from his shoulder the arrow which had gone completely through the fleshy part, bringing with it a stream of crimson blood. Another Forest Dweller dropped in his tracks with an arrow through his neck. Courageously but vainly, he strove to jerk it free, at the same time struggling to his feet. He was too weak and his knees sagged, but before he collapsed completely, two women grabbed and carried him to the room below. Their places were taken immediately by two others.

Still another woman was striving to bind the wounded shoulder of the first man hurt. He was a difficult patient and sought to evade her ministrations until Rhu ordered him to hold still. The seemingly berserk man complied immediately, standing patiently until his wound was covered with a strip of soft doeskin, after which he lost no time in returning to his task.

Que observed all this and marveled.

IN HIS desire to help, Nohr stepped forward to shoot down upon the milling enemy below, but Rhu seized his arm.

"Don't expose yourself," he commanded. Then addressing his warriors, he shouted, "Shoot those far up the trail!"

They hastened to obey and so effective was their shooting that a gap was cut into the approaching host. Under the direction of Nord, they proceeded to hold it open, permitting none of the enemy to cross, while at the same time, greatly decreasing their number.

Observing this, Rhu clapped a cow's horn to his lips and blew a blast upon it. From the rocks where they had been safely hidden until then, twenty big Forest Dwellers sprang into the fray before the building, their war axes and clubs making short work of those still able to fight, and to be perfectly frank, most of the seriously wounded. Since the surgery of these early people was crude and none too effective, this was rather a mercy.

Still, there were those beyond the gap, who, unable to proceed, started to retreat. Again Rhu blew a mighty blast upon his horn, and from their concealment far up the trail, another force of yelling Forest Dwellers, led by Ord, swung into action, cutting off the retreat of the enemy and forcing them down the trail toward the clearing. Here, they were met by the Forest Dwellers from below who, by now, had disposed of those who had come before them. Reinforced by Nord and the men he brought from the building, they had charged up the trail to help fight the remnants of the enemy and so complete the victory.

Reaching for his quiver, Rhu drew forth several of the longer arrows and quietly notching one of them, he mounted the parapet that his view might be unimpeded. As he watched Nord and his men charge toward the now demoralized remnants of their attackers, his alert eye caught the stealthy movement of an enemy archer far up the trail as he rose to his feet and drew his bow, his arrow directed toward Ord.

With a grunt, the muscles of his powerful torso writhing from the effort, Rhu drew the long arrow to his ear and launched it with such speed as to appear almost careless. The shaft described a beautiful arc, striking below the armpit of the

enemy archer just as he released his own missile . . . . but too
late to save Ord!

For a long moment, Nohr stood staring his unbelief that such
a shot should have been made at a good hundred-and-fifty-
yard distance! Quickly he turned to Rhu, but Rhu had disappeared! Up the trail, Nohr saw two of Ord's men preparing to
pick up his inert body. And then, Rhu appeared upon the trail
below the hut, racing toward the men now carrying Ord between them.

With a groan, Nohr selected one of Rhu's longer arrows. "It
would be useless for me to try such a shot," he moaned, half
aloud. But he stepped to the spot were Rhu had stood, arrow
notched and eyes elert for the slightest movement among the
crags beside the trail. As he watched, another groan left his
lips. How could he know friend from foe? At that distance, all
men, aside from size, looked much alike, but even had they
been closer, he did not know any of the Mu Yans by sight.

Then, as though he had guessed his predicament, Hut's
voice came to him. "Mu Yans all wear their skins over the left
shoulder that the arrow arm may be free," he said. "My bow is
not powerful enough for such long shooting," he added softly
as he notched an arrow. "Yet shall I try. But no man has Rhu's
skill, though I fear it was too late."

"I would it had been I," Nohr mourned. "Ord was beloved
of Rhu."

"And for good cause," Hut added. "There was but one Ord
and we shall miss him sadly."

"Grieve not too soon," Que said quietly. "It comes to me that
Ord will not die this day. See," he exclaimed excitedly, his
usually rather expressionless face alight. "Ord stirs."

Sure enough, just as Rhu reached the two men carrying the
stricken Ord, the big fellow stirred, and as they started to lay
him down, struggled to his feet. He stood weaving and uncertain as they held him, and Rhu saw there was an arrow in his
head. Reaching up, he snapped it in two and carefully withdrew the slender shaft from the wound. His hands were very
gentle as he bound about the nasty, bleeding wound a strip of
doeskin all warriors carried for such purposes.

With a grunt, Ord collected his swirling senses and grinned

down into Rhu's anxious face. "You should not have left the safety of the hut," he growled. "Ord's skull too thick and hard for wooden arrow. How did it happen?" he asked as his head cleared.

"This did it," growled a big Forest Dweller, dropping the limp body of the man Rhu had shot. "See," he continued, "only Rhu could have done this!" He pointed to the stone tip of the arrow just showing through the skin on the side opposite from which it had entered.

"Save arrow," Ord commanded. "Ord would keep it."

Most of the Mu Yans had now joined them with some twenty-five wounded prisoners.

"Where are the others?" asked Rhu, glad for the chance to hide the feelings which raged through his heart.

"Dead!" came the prompt and terse reply.

Rhu did not press the question. Knowing the regard in which Ord was held by his men, he was surprised that *any* were left alive. As a matter of fact, had those bringing in these prisoners known of Ord's plight, it is doubtful whether they would have been spared.

Upon their arrival at the hut, Que, who came from the building to meet them, inquired of Rhu as to the disposal of the fallen foe.

With a rather grim smile, Rhu pointed to the laughing, boasting Forest Dwellers, each of whom carried two or more bodies which he unceremoniously tossed over the bluff into the river below before returning for more. A little later, such Tama Yans as were gathered along the precipitous walls of the river marveled and speculated excitedly about the many bodies seen tossing in the roaring waters as they swept past.

Although many of the Mu Yans bore ugly wounds, few were so seriously wounded as to prevent their being present that evening when Rhu and Hut questioned the sullen prisoners. The hardihood of these big fellows in making light of hurts that would have incapacitated most men proved to be far less surprising than what the questioning disclosed, to say nothing of the subsequently resulting events.

Chapter Seventeen

THEDO

UPON THEIR RETURN to Hut and Rhu's big room, Que remarked, "I observe you use no aid to healing other than binding the wounds. The Chi Yans have discovered that the leaves of certain plants are very helpful. So far, I have seen none of these on the Plains, but I have a small supply with me. If Ord may join us, I would show you how to use them. I shall need hot water and a small bowl, if you will have Deenah bring them."

Rhu immediately summoned Ord while Deenah hastened to have ready the required water.

Que then drew from his bag some carefully wrapped leaves which he placed in the bowl. Pouring a portion of the hot water over them, he allowed them to soak while with infinite pains, he removed the leather bandage from Ord's throbbing head and examined the wound. Carefully, he washed it with some of the water in which the leaves were soaking, after which, he made two poultices of the leaves and with a fresh strip of doeskin, bound them in place.

"Feel good," Ord grunted, studying one of the dry leaves which had dropped upon the stone floor. "Look like blooming weed."

Que smiled. "That is what it is," he answered. "We call it the yellow bloomer, but use only the leaves."

"I shall ask the Elders regarding this and such other plants as might be equally useful," remarked Hut who had been a most interested spectator and listener. "Each day, Rhu, we learn something new."

"If only there were more for the other men," Rhu said regretfully. "Some are badly hurt, and but for the protection of the Great Ones, we should have had many dead."

"I regret I have no more," Que responded with deep concern. "The Chi Yans use a number of leaves, roots, and blossoms for healing various things."

"Yes," interjected Nohr, "and Que is among the best of them in this learning. I have seen him . . . ."

"What little I know," Que interrupted hastily, "I learned from my mother. Yet shall I gladly contribute what knowledge I possess. Having seen what you call seeds and how you plant them, perhaps I may be able to get some from the plants in the Chi Valley and bring them here for your use."

"That will be wonderful," Rhu agreed enthusiastically. "Perhaps the Elders may be able to aid us, too, and if not them, Lord Hiroto surely can.

"And now, Hut, do you not think it would be well to have the captives brought to us? I would also like Nohr and Que to be present while we talk to them, on the condition, of course, that you are interested in joining with us eventually," he said addressing the two.

"For one, I shall be delighted," Nohr answered.

Que nodded his full agreement. "It has been in my mind ever since our first talk to express my desire to become one of your group," he stated.

"The Elders are preparing to give special instruction to those desirous of living on the Plains," Rhu informed them, "and as the Elder stated when you came, you two are to be given the opportunity to avail yourselves of it."

Hut smiled approvingly as he departed to summon the captives.

As Rhu was speaking, he observed Nohr painstakingly examining the bow he had been using. "If you would like it, you may keep that bow," he volunteered.

Nohr's face beamed. "I shall give you my zitkern for some of your stone-tipped arrows to go with it," he countered.

"Agreed," Rhu answered. "Take what you consider a fair exchange." Turning to the Chi Yan, he said, "Would you like a bow and some arrows, Que?"

"I have with me little to offer in exchange," Que replied, "though I would like nothing better. The craftsmanship is wonderful, and I have never used their equal . . . . nor even seen them," he hastened to add.

"It was not my intention to ask anything in return, although the Elders teach that sooner or later, we must compensate in some form or another for all that is given to us. In your case, Que, your service to Ord is worth the bow and many arrows. Besides, your readiness in standing by when we were attacked is appreciated. Nor would I belittle your fine work, Nohr. I do not ask the zitkern in return. I cannot play upon it, and you can."

"I will teach you how to play in return for your teaching me how to shoot as you do!" Nohr proposed with a laugh from where he was already selecting a supply of arrows.

Rhu smiled as he picked out a rather slender but beautifully balanced bow, handing it to Que that he might try its pull.

"This is admirable!" the Chi Yan exclaimed. "I like it even better than the one I was using. I can now draw the arrow to its head!"

"Yes," commented Rhu. "It is a somewhat lighter bow, but you will find it almost as powerful as the one Nohr uses. At least, that has been my experience, although the stiffer bows will shoot farther. However, it takes unusual skill to shoot accurately beyond eighty paces, while below this distance, the lighter bow is equally as deadly."

"In the hands of a competent bowman!" Que commented dryly. "I would prefer to face the average Chi Yan armed with this bow than you, Rhu, armed with my old one."

"Perhaps," the embarrassed Rhu agreed diffidently. "But do not forget the arrows. The best bows are of little worth with poor arrows. Up to fifty steps, with these arrows of ours, I will shoot almost as accurately *without* a bow as with crooked and unfeathered arrows and my best bow."

Que's and Nohr's eyes grew wide at this seemingly impossible statement.

"I will show you," Rhu exclaimed quickly. From a special quiver, he took an arrow, notched about one-third the distance from its flint tip to the feathered end, and a three-foot stick, one end of which was tapered like the end of a bow. In fact, it was half a broken bow with the knotted gut string still attached.

Grasping the stick in his left hand, Rhu placed the knotted end of the string in the notch, stepped to the front of the room and stood scanning the sky as though waiting for something. Que and Nohr stepped nearer.

Presently, a large buzzard-like bird came soaring past. With the feathered end of the arrow at his ear, Rhu quickly extended his left hand holding the stick. A quick thrust forward and downward with the stick and the arrow was launched. True to its aim, it sped, transfixing the bird which turned end over end as it plummeted to the earth below.

Folding his arms solemnly, Que turned and bowed to Rhu. "Thus are the doubters humbled to the dust," he said simply.

"Only in seeing can one believe the seemingly impossible," Nohr announced quietly. "Yet, Rhu, after seeing you shoot during the fight, it is not in me to question any statement of yours regarding marksmanship, or anything else, for that matter."

Abashed by this unexpected praise, Rhu turned to gaze out across the Plains where Hut was returning with the captives, accompanied by Dargh and Nord.

Seeing them, and with a quick glance at Ord who was quietly regarding all that was going on, Que remarked, "I observe that you seem always to include Ord and Dargh whenever you have anything serious to consider, such as talking with these approaching prisoners."

"Hut and I regard them as the most important men in our organization," Rhu answered simply. "Also, they represent the Cave Dwellers and the Forest Dwellers. It is my hope that you two will each be to your tribes as Hut and I are to the Mu Yans, once you have been instructed by the Elders."

"I, for one, await that time," said Que, "although I confess I hardly see how they can offer more than you and Hut."

"As compared with them, we are as mere children," Rhu replied. "It is to them that Hut and I owe all we know."

Thoughtfully, Que picked up and examined his new bow . and arrows. "Yet, Rhu, it is to you that Nohr and I owe the possession of such craftsmanship as these represent. I would not seem to belittle those who stand so high in your estimation, but no matter how great the wisdom of those who teach, it is the aptness of the pupil to use and apply what is taught that finally determines its usefulness.

"Despite your modesty, I am sure the Elders will agree with me that you and Hut represent qualities that neither they nor anyone else can inculcate by mere teaching alone. It is one thing to listen to words of wisdom, but quite another to have the rare ability to profit from them. Otherwise, why have you two been selected for the truly magnificent and imposing task before you?" Que concluded with an air of finality.

Rhu's embarrassment had been mounting steadily ever since the conversation began, and he was grateful that Hut and the others chose this moment for their arrival.

Nevertheless, Que was to have his answer, for the rumble of Ord's voice rose above even the clatter caused by the entrance of the newcomers. "Elders noble. Elders wise. Rhu and Hut *great!* Ord die for Rhu and Hut!" he asserted stoutly, thus summing up his entire philosophy of life and loyalty.

"And it is said that Forest Dwellers may not be trusted," Nohr murmured, smiling warmly at the speaker. "May N'Kul surround *me* with such men as you, Ord."

The big fellow's face reddened. "Be as Rhu, and N'Kul will," he answered gruffly, rising to his feet and directing that the prisoners stand before Rhu, Hut, Dargh, and Nord, who were now seated.

Que shrewdly noted that the wounds of each captive had been carefully bound. Well knowing the usual treatment of such prisoners as were spared being killed outright, his heart warmed toward the people of the Plains who had progressed so far in humanitarian principles.

Eying the assembled captives, Rhu asked, "Who is, or was, your leader?"

"Thedo!" growled a great, hulking red-haired giant, fully seven feet tall, deep of chest and mighty of muscle. "Thedo lead *all* fighters," he stated boldly.

Both Rhu and Hut's eyes flew wide with astonishment. "Are you Marda's father?" demanded Hut.

"Yes!" the big man snapped. "Thedo come. Take Marda and Haitee."

Before the lads could recover from their astonishment, Ord bounced to his feet with a snarl. "Thedo try, Ord tear apart!"

"Sit down, Ord," Rhu said quietly.

While the hair along his back still stood rigidly erect, Ord complied, but his eyes were bleak. "No man touch what Rhu or Hut take and live long," he stated, and there was no mistaking that he meant exactly what he said.

"Come closer, Thedo, and sit down here," said Rhu, indicating a stone over which a great hoogwar skin was draped. "You others sit where you are while we talk with Thedo."

"Thedo stand!" snarled the big Cari Yan.

"Thedo sit!" Ord snapped.

And Thedo sat, speaking well for his discretion.

(Because much of the following conversation was carried on by means of signs, due to limited vocabularies, liberties have been taken and the dialogue given far more freely than was actually true. This is for the sake of both clarity and greater ease of reading.)

"Thedo," Rhu began as the lowering-browed man sat down, "were you the one who organized and led this force against us?"

"Yes," Thedo replied tersely.

"Was it only to rescue Marda and Haitee?" Rhu continued.

"No." Thedo's eyes brightened, and his heavy jaws clamped as if he were steeling himself for what he believed would be the next and most natural question. But as many another has done, he misjudged his questioner.

"How did you do it?" asked Rhu.

Thedo's slow working mind strove to fathom the reason why he had not been asked for the other reason or reasons. Too startled to fabricate an answer to suit him, his reply was a truthful one. "Hahn agree easily. Hahn Haitee's father. Bring many fighting men. Hahn get friends Zoho and Gulho families. I get Wardu. He live on Chiata Plain, and he get Harco of Hata Yans who live across Telha River from Wardu and who friendly."

"How many fighting men did you have?" Rhu continued his questioning.

"Almost five hundred," Thedo replied, eyes glittering as he counted off the number with his hands. "Only Hahn, Zoho, Wardu, Harco, and captives of Harco family now live. Harco family last in force to enter Chiata Pass."

Rhu's eyes rested upon the group which had been listening silently. "Harco, stand up," he ordered.

A tall, black-haired and rather heavy-faced man of about forty arose. Of all the men present, including Ord and Nord, he was by far the hairiest, his heavy beard cut squarely across just below a jutting jaw.

"Why did *you* join in this attack upon us?" Rhu demanded. "The Mu Yans have no quarrel with you."

"Wardu Harco's friend," the other answered slowly, and there was no mistaking his simple sincerity.

"I admire one who stands by his friends, even against me," Rhu said impulsively.

The big Hata Yan's face brightened. "Friends few, enemies many. Hata Yans stand by friends."

"Come over here and sit down," Rhu invited, indicating a pile of folded skins close beside him. "I would talk with you later. Wardu, stand up," he ordered, again addressing the group.

About the man who now stood was an air of alertness quite different from the slow and stolid bearing of Harco and Thedo. His forehead was high and his jaw quite as determined as Harco's.

Hut, who had remained silent thus far, observed the Cari Yan carefully studying the building. "Why do you study our hut?" he asked.

"Work new. Interesting," Wardu answered. "Wardu would learn how build."

"That you shall do, in time," Hut assured him, "provided only you decide to join us. We shall talk of this later."

"Thedo, what was your other reason for attacking us," Rhu demanded.

Again the big Cari Yan was caught off balance, but this time, he set his jaw stubbornly and refused to answer.

Silently, Ord got to his feet, his glittering eyes boring into those of Thedo whose alert ears had detected Ord's movement, causing him to look at the giant.

"When Rhu ask question, Thedo answer," Ord snarled, baring his teeth in the wolfish grin which Rhu knew only too well would be followed with quick and drastic action.

Thedo reconsidered. "We would take the Great Plains for our own," he said sullenly.

"With these few men?" asked Rhu.

A gleam of cunning crept into Thedo's eyes, seeing which the observant Rhu spoke. "Ord, immediately assemble all our fighting men and prepare to fight. Better send to the Plains for additional forces of Mu Yans to attack from the rear when the fight starts," he ordered.

"Ord already send," the big fellow grinned. "Og gone to get them. Ord not fooled. Thedo no good."

"On the contrary, Thedo may be a good man, Ord," Rhu contradicted. "It is only that he has made himself an enemy, not knowing just what he was undertaking. To be an enemy does not necessarily mean that a man is no good, though I do not like his trying to deceive us." Turning to Thedo, he said, "We had not started to fight. Not all the Cari Yans could take this Valley from us, Thedo."

"So Harco knows," that individual spoke up unexpectedly. "Since Harco friend only of Wardu, may Harco send word to Hata Yans not join in foolish attempt?" he asked.

"Certainly," Rhu agreed readily. "I trust you."

"Harco not lie," the Hata Yan stated bluntly. "Harco like Rhu."

Thedo's great chest filled as if he were about to speak, but one glance at Ord, and it deflated suddenly.

Ord laughed harshly. "Have care, little one," he snorted.

"May Hahn send word?" asked Haitee's father.

"By whom, if only Hata Yans are left?" Rhu demanded.

"Thedo lie. Two prisoners Hahn's sons. Hahn warn Cari Yans not be fools. Hahn no fool. Hahn would learn about Mu Yan work." With a flirt of his hand, he wiped the sweat from his brow.

"So would Wardu," that worthy agreed promptly. "Wardu's father say this fight no good."

"Your father?" Hut asked in surprise. "I thought you were head of your clan."

"No. Only friend of Thedo and Hahn. Only part Wardu clan come."

"Gulho would learn of work here," announced another of the Cari Yans, a man about the size of Thedo, but kindlier of face.

"Zoho bring only younger men," another of the Cari Yans interpolated, rising to his feet with a pantherish ease surprising in one of his bulk and age. Rhu and Hut regarded him with surprise. He looked much like Hut's father and except for his auburn hair, could have passed as his brother.

Thus deserted by his principal followers, Thedo seemed daunted for the first time. With his surrounding neighbors seemingly going over to the enemy, what chance did he have for taking over the Plains? He sighed heavily, but deep in his eyes there still lurked a gleam of cunning which did not escape the astute Rhu who was studying him thoughtfully.

"All right. Select your men. Ord, see that they are allowed to leave when Hahn, Wardu, and Harco have indicated them. Harco, what of the men who are left? May they be trusted to obey you?"

"Good men," Harco answered. "They mind Harco or die. All single. Harco bring no married brothers or clansmen."

"May I speak?" Que asked quietly.

"By all means," Rhu agreed readily. "We shall be glad to hear what you have to say."

Chapter Eighteen

A NEW PROBLEM

I AM QUE ONG LINGH of the Chi Yan Tribe," Que said slowly and distinctly. "Thirty Great Suns have I lived. During the last ten of these, I have traveled from one end of the Chi Valley to the other, and with Nohr Phan, over much of the Tama Valley. Together, we have seen and learned much. Yet, until we came to the Rhu Hut Plains, all we have witnessed is of too little consequence to be worthy of mention, but I would have each of you know that we are not without some learning beyond the confines of our own clans.

"With only curiosity did we come, none too certain of our welcome and without thought of doing more than see for ourselves what is being done here. Today, we seek the privilege of remaining to learn more of the great wisdom which lies back of the accomplishments of Rhu and Hut who have started something that is so big and far-reaching as to take away one's breath.

"Here we find Plains Dwellers, Forest Dwellers, and Cave Dwellers living together peaceably and happily. Only seeing could have made us believe this possible. Under the leadership of Rhu and Hut, we find here the beginning of a type of living so wonderfully different from all we have ever seen that our greatest of all desires is to become worthy of being a part of it. In time, we hope to see all the Chi Yans and Tama Yans participating in it. Even this vision has grown until now we would see both the Cari Yans and the Hata Yans become a part of it.

"The extent of the Rhu Hut Plains is beyond the knowledge of any of us. It takes one Great Sun for a man to travel from the point where the Tama Valley joins the Chi Valley to where the mighty Hatamukulian River enters the great water far to the north. Nohr has made this journey, and since the Tama Valley is high, could see enough land to support several tribes, and we have no way of knowing how far toward the rising sun it extends."

As Que spoke, Rhu and Hut studied the faces of Wardu and Harco especially. There was no denying the growing interest of each, yet it was plain that of the two, Wardu was grasping the most of what Que said. Nevertheless, the occasional lighting up of his rather somber eyes showed that Harco was slowly but surely piecing together the various points. The other Hata Yan prisoners watched him closely, smiling when he smiled and becoming uneasy as he frowned in his concentration.

Thedo, on the other hand, appeared to be growing increasing sullen. "Whole idea no good," he growled. "Forest Dwellers soon try take all. Forest Dwellers no good."

With a grunt, Ord was on his feet. So swift was his movement that before Rhu or Hut could speak to restrain him, one mighty hand encircled Thedo's bull neck, and the big Cari Yan was lifted clear of the floor and shaken like a rat.

"Ord!" Rhu snapped.

The shaking subsided, but Ord stood holding Thedo whose protruding tongue and bulging eyes bespoke his rapidly approaching strangulation. His herculean efforts to free himself proved utterly ineffectual, for neither did they serve to break Ord's grip or cause the Mu Yan to use his other hand. Then, with another grunt, Ord tossed Thedo aside with as little effort as if the mighty Cari Yan were but a small sack of wool.

"Thedo speak one word more about Forest Dwellers and Ord snap neck like rotten stick," he snarled and sat down again.

Struggling to regain his breath, Thedo got to his hands and knees and finally managed to reach his seat where he sat, bleary-eyed and panting, rubbing his aching neck.

"You have looked death in the eye, Thedo," Rhu announced quietly when he saw the big fellow's eyes begin to clear as he regained something of his normal breathing. "Let this be a lesson to you. Ord is no man with whom to trifle. I would sooner trust any Forest Dweller in our group than you who still think in terms of treachery."

Still far from appeased, Ord growled, "Thedo no good."

"Perhaps Thedo does not fully understand," said Hut.

"Thedo hears without comprehending," quietly commented Que.

"Maybe," Rhu replied uncertainly. "Yet I like not his shifting eyes. Still I would not misjudge him. We shall hold him for a time and see what we can do to help him. After all, he is the father of Marda who is beloved of Hut," he explained to Que.

"Yet we cannot endanger our work because of personal feelings," Hut said a bit sadly.

"Let me talk with Thedo later," Nohr requested.

"May I be with you when you do?" asked Dargh, speaking for the first time.

"Certainly. I shall be happy to have you," Nohr agreed promptly. "No doubt you can tell him much I do not know."

"That will be fine," Rhu acquiesced, only too glad to have help with what bade fair to be a knotty problem with which to cope.

"Harco would talk more with Que and Rhu or Hut," the big Hata Yan announced. "Harco has Hata Yan friends."

"THIS has been a day long to be remembered," commented Hut that evening as he and Rhu were preparing to retire.

Rhu nodded gravely. "Do you realize, Hut, that if all these undertake the training of the Elders, we shall have Tama Yans, Chi Yans, Cari Yans, and Hata Yans in our group?" he asked.

Hut frowned, as he always did when pondering deeply. "Yes, I realize too well. It will certainly justify my wanting to establish a set of rules."

Rhu hesitated before replying. Then, "Of course, we shall have to establish something of the sort, but I cannot forget the words of the Elder about that. I certainly would like to talk with Lord Lithargos before I ever agreed to any rules."

"Do you not think the Elders competent?" Hut asked, eying his friend quizzically.

"Certainly. But do not forget that the Elder said most of their advice concerning this work was coming through Lords

Lithargos and Hiroto. I am sure the Elders would understand why I would like to talk with Lord Lithargos."

"What do you think of Que and Nohr?" Hut asked.

"I like and trust them," Rhu answered simply.

"I like them, too," Hut agreed readily, "but Que is clever. Like his face, his words do not always convey exactly what he thinks. Not that I think he is not to be trusted, Rhu. It is only that he is not as blunt as *we* sometimes are. His words should be weighed."

Rhu eyed Hut questioningly. "Well," he said, somewhat hesitantly as he chose his own words carefully, "it may be something we should try to acquire, this thing of being careful how we speak to others. In some respects, he reminds me of the Elders. They have the ability to render a rebuke or to teach a lesson without hurting a fellow. Remember the pool?" Rhu chuckled whole-heartedly.

"I was just about to mention using it for bathing!" cried Hut, bursting into laughter. "We are always doing something, aren't we?"

NOHR approached Rhu late in the afternoon. "I have talked at length with Thedo," he announced, "and Dargh has explained to us both many things about which I have wondered much. My enthusiasm grows daily. However, Thedo still gives me the impression that he has no intention of joining with us although he seems to like everything. I am sorry to say that I do not trust him."

"What do you recommend?" Rhu asked as Hut joined them.

"To allow him to return to his clan would be to court further trouble," Nohr stated positively. "He will assuredly try again to assemble a body of men to attack us and even though Wardu's father did not agree with him, his clan is not large enough to resist Thedo's force should they try to cross Wardu's lands. I see no way out except to hold Thedo. I do not believe he should mingle with those already here, either. He will try to influence them against you, and although I do not believe he would succeed, he could create dissension if he did not get killed. Your people are very loyal. On the other hand, if you were to try to hold him, where and how would you do it?"

"We could turn him over to Ord," suggested Hut.

"He would probably be dead before night if we did." Rhu's eyes twinkled as he spoke. "Ord distrusts him and whom Ord distrusts, he hates. No, I would hesitate to do that, yet I do not believe he should be allowed to return to his clan. What would you advise beyond Ord?" he asked.

"Que may have a plan," Nohr suggested.

"Then get him," Rhu stated promptly. As Nohr left, Rhu turned to Hut. "We have made no provision for holding prisoners. I have never thought of such a thing. Neither do I like the idea of killing them as has been the usual Mu Yan custom."

"That we cannot do," Hut declared rather sharply. "It is not because of Marda, either. I think we should never kill a prisoner simply because he cannot be trusted."

"Neither do I," Rhu agreed readily. "I do not believe in killing, any more than you do, except in defense. Still, having no place in which to hold him apart from others, I confess that I am puzzled as to what is best to do."

"I hear them coming," Hut announced. "I surely hope Que has a suggestion."

Que did not speak until he was seated, and while his face, as usual, was expressionless, his eyes were very tender as he looked into Hut's anxious ones. "Among the Chi Yans," he began with unusual abruptness, "we never take prisoners for any purposes beyond questioning them. Then we either kill them outright or return them to their own people. I am sorry to say that sometimes we use quite drastic measures to make them talk so that death is often preferable, and when administered, comes as a relief to the prisoner, Personally, I prefer never to attend a questioning. Your way is best, I am convinced, unless the case be exceptional.

"You are doing many things so far from the usual that it is well for us to seek a solution which does not involve torture, for my judgment tells me that, sooner or later, situations will arise in which your own people will be involved. If you never have among your people those who offend against the common good, indeed I shall be forced to agree that powers beyond the human are helping you.

"Here, however, we have a different situation. One not of our own people is involved." He paused to ponder.

Rhu chuckled inwardly. For the first time, Que had referred to himself as one of the group. Only his twinkling eyes betrayed Rhu's thought to the observing Hut who nodded his understanding.

"Yes, Thedo is not of our people," Que continued, apparently unaware of Rhu and Hut's observation, "so we must consider the eventuality of Thedo's never becoming one of us. If this be the case, then what? We must either kill him or else turn loose a potential enemy who will have the added advantage of knowing much about us and our defenses and therefore be better able to scheme against us.

"In the meantime, as Nohr has explained, we must not turn him loose among our own people lest his truculence create disturbances. Neither will it be well to turn him over to the Forest Dwellers who are fighting men and short-tempered. Now, if we had a stone hut of proper size, we could place him in it while he is here."

"According to Dargh," said Nohr, "that you do not have, and Thedo would escape from anything less strong."

For some moments there was a puzzled silence and then, once more, Que spoke. "Rhu, your brother Grut is a large and powerful man. Why not place Thedo in his care?"

"Grut could handle him," Hut agreed before Rhu could speak, "but where and how could he keep Thedo? Grut lives with Sol, Rhu's father, and in their hut."

"I'll send for Grut and see what he has to say," Rhu announced. "Grut thinks slowly, but he is no fool," and he dispatched a Forest Dweller for his brother. "However," he continued as he returned to his seat, "this is only a temporary solution, for, like Que, I believe we shall have other cases, and we seek a solution that will be permanent."

"Dargh tells me that he can build a stone hut of the right sort within a single moon by putting all Musons to work upon it," Nohr stated. "I recommend his doing so and making it large enough to hold several prisoners."

"That is a good idea," Rhu agreed, and Hut nodded his approval. "Grut would be a good man to place in charge of this place, too, and the experience he will gain with Thedo should help him. I shall ask him about it. But," and Rhu frowned heavily, "what shall we do with Thedo if he does not improve? We cannot hold him or other prisoners there indefinitely. Neither can we simply kill those whom we cannot influence. The Elders say we may not kill another except in self defense, or when killing is the lesser of two unavoidable ills."

Suddenly, Que's face brightened. "Why not enclose a large space with a high wall topped with sharp crystals over which no man may climb without serious injury? Inside this, start crops that require much care and let the prisoners do the work. It is not well, according to what you teach, that anyone be allowed to receive without earning. In this way, they would earn their keep."

Hut's eyes shone. "Yes, and that would also help with such of our own people as might have to be placed there," he exclaimed.

Rhu, however, frowned heavily. "I like it not," he half growled. "I would put no man of ours in a place where he would be ever a prisoner."

"That is not the idea," Hut protested, warming to his subject. "He would be placed there for a period governed by the nature of his refusal to abide by the law."

"Who is there among us to justify this passing of judgment?" Rhu demanded.

Again it was Que who presented the answer. "Why not have several men engaged in the same type of work as the one on trial? In this way, he would be judged by those who understand the nature of his work, his temptations, and his way of thinking. This should be fair and insure justice with understanding," he concluded.

Rhu's face lit up with a wide smile. "You have thought of what seems to me to be a very good solution," he said. "If the Elders agree, then I am willing. Here comes Grut," as that big and hairy fellow came up the steps.

To explain to the slow-thinking and puzzled Grut that they wanted to hold a prisoner captive rather than kill him outright took quite some time. Once he grasped the idea that it was he who had been elected to guard the prisoner, however, he worked out what was to him a most gratifying procedure.

"Grut guard Thedo," he said, grinning with satisfaction. "Night, Grut fasten Thedo's thumbs behind back and big toes together with bow string. Thedo stay where put. If try escape, Grut break leg."

"Do you mind doing this?" Rhu asked, for despite all else, his affection for his big and truculent brother was deep and sincere.

Grut grinned at him a bit wolfishly. "Rhu ask, Grut like do," and his grin widened. "Grut like anyhow," he finished emphatically.

Getting to his feet, Rhu slapped his grinning brother on the back. "Good! Watch Thedo carefully. He is sly and determined." As Grut looked a bit mystified, he made it clear. "Thedo smart and mean."

"Grut not smart," he growled, "Grut strong. Grut mean too."

"Grut smart as Thedo," Hut spoke up, "and stronger. Grut take no chances," he added thoughtfully.

However, none among them so much as suspected what the coming night was to bring forth from this arrangement.

Chapter Nineteen

FURTHER DEVELOPMENTS

PERHAPS IT WAS an inadvertent grunt which awakened Grut about midnight to discover Thedo with his hands to his mouth and gnawing at the thong binding his thumbs together. Since Grut had bound the thumbs behind Thedo's back, it was plain that despite his bulk, Thedo had managed to double up sufficiently to draw his feet between his hands.

Grut's teeth bared in a snarl of rage as the tough thong gave way and Thedo's hands parted. Before he could move, however, Grut was upon him and with a blow, stretched the big Cari Yan upon the earth more than half unconscious. Quickly stringing a running noose about Thedo's neck, Grut again fastened his hands behind him. This time, however, he tied the end of the noose to the thong binding the thumbs together, grinning happily as he did so. For Thedo to try getting his hands in front again would surely result in his being strangled.

"How Thedo sleep?" the Cari Yan growled.

"*Grut* sleep!" was Grut's only reply.

There followed a long silence broken only by the heavy breathing betokening Grut's easy slumber.

With infinite care, Thedo rolled to where Grut's great, obsidian-headed war axe lay beside the doorway. Silently and patiently, he labored until he finally managed to get his hands on each side of the sharp edge, then sawed away until they were free. Next, he hacked his feet apart, and with the axe, rose silently to his feet. His eyes glued upon the shadowy form of Grut, he took a step toward him, axe raised and ready for immediate action.

The steady rhythm of Grut's breathing varied not a hair, but his half-shut eyes took in the situation even as his alert ears caught the almost imperceptible rustle of Thedo's movement.

Silently, Thedo advanced another step, then paused and inhaled softly as he made ready for the forthcoming death stroke. Apparently deciding he was still a bit too far away for an effective blow, Thedo took another step. A split second later, he struck the earth with a tooth-jarring thud as Grut's hairy, powerful hand shot out and grasped his ankle, jerking his feet from under him. With the same lithe motion, Grut rose to his own feet and hurled himself upon the now snarling Cari Yan.

With the skill of long practice, Thedo struck with the axe, cutting a nasty gash in Grut's hairy back just as he grasped Thedo's wrist. Blood spurting from the gaping wound, Grut summoned all his immense strength, swinging Thedo's heavy body into the air and coming down with bent knees in Thedo's unguarded and straining stomach.

Even before Grut was injured, it is doubtful whether he was any stronger than Thedo, but he had the advantage of the many tricks he had learned from Rhu. Now he brought them all into play as he literally swarmed over the Cari Yan. In a perfect frenzy of almost insensate rage, clawing, tearing, twisting, and tossing his enemy around until, gaining the hold he sought, with an Herculean effort, he swung the struggling Thedo high above his head and dashed him to earth with bone-breaking force. His fury not yet exhausted and with seemingly replenished strength despite his serious hurt, Grut again lifted the roaring Thedo above his head, this time twisting the Cari Yan so that when he swung him to earth, his head struck first, smashing the skull with a sickening crunch.

Exhausted, Grut stood swaying upon his rapidly weakening legs, then collapsed beside his dead prisoner just as Sol Ku, awakened by the commotion, reached him.

Sol's eyes lit instantly upon the bleeding gash, and he gave forth a roar which brought the already awakened family streaming into the room. One of his big sons carefully lifted the stricken Grut, carrying him out into the open where, according to custom, the family fire was kept burning under a shelter. The entire family followed him to watch while, with tender care, the big fellow laid Grut beside it. Immediately, some of the women went to work to treat the injury in the only way they knew while Sol dispatched another son for Rhu.

Accompanied by Hut, Que, Nohr, and Ord, Rhu arrived on the run, and his was the first face Grut saw as he recovered from his swoon.

"What happened?" Rhu asked, his concerned face showing how deeply he was affected by Grut's plight.

"Thedo . . . . got . . . . loose. Grut . . . . kill," Grut gasped between clenched teeth.

Without a word, Ord left the group to enter the house, returning with the body which he tossed down beside the fire. "Ord *say* no good," he growled. "Nord," as his scarcely smaller brother joined the group, "throw in river!" he ordered.

Quickly taking in the situation, Nord grasped the body by the wide belt about its middle and walked away with it as if he were carrying a child in his great hand.

"I'm sorry, Hut," Rhu said simply, turning to his friend. "I do not understand how Thedo could have gotten free after Grut tied him up."

Hut shrugged his shoulders. "He would have killed Grut. Grut acted only in self-defense. It cannot be helped," he stated flatly and turning, started back to their room.

Rhu stared after his retreating form. "Hut is sorely troubled," he said to Que.

"Why should he be?" Que asked. "Thedo was an implacable enemy and a dangerous man."

"Yet, he was the father of Marda," Rhu answered.

"Physically, perhaps, but it ended there according to what you have told me concerning her," Que stated tersely. "What of her mother?"

"I do not know," Rhu replied. "I have never seen her, nor have I ever heard Marda mention her."

"Then give the matter no further thought," Que counseled. "It is with the present and the future that we are concerned that this may never again happen."

"Perhaps," Rhu said uneasily. "But I like it not and wish it might have been different."

"Yet the Elders have said to choose the lesser of two unavoidable ills, you have told us. Has not that been done?" Feeling the matter was disposed of, Que turned his attention to Grut who was again conscious.

Slowly, Rhu returned to the great stone hut where he found Hut sitting staring toward the graying east. Silently, he placed his hand on his friend's shoulder.

Hut patted it in recognition of Rhu's attempt to console him. "Do not be troubled, Rhu," he said. "There was no other way. I do not blame Grut who but did his duty as he saw it."

"I wish it were otherwise, Hut. What will Marda say?" asked Rhu, dropping down to sit beside his friend.

"What *is* there to say? I was not thinking of that but of how to prevent the repetition of such a thing. After our talk yesterday, I got to thinking and rather lost my liking for Que's suggestion of a place of confinement. Such should never be needed for a people working together for the common good. Neither does it seem likely that we shall have many more like situations. To be preparing for such contingencies seems to me to be wrong. It indicates that we *expect* such things, and the Elders teach that to expect things to happen is to cause them to happen."

"I often ponder that," commented Rhu. "Still, what would have happened to us if we had not had a carefully planned method of defense? We have done nothing to warrant such attacks, yet this is our second one since we have been here."

"That is true, and even Lord Lithargos thought our plan a wise one. As you have often said, only a fool would approach a hoogwar without being armed." Hut was plainly puzzled.

"Yes, but why approach him in the first place? Does not that invite attack? Is it not putting into operation a cause?" Rhu shook his shaggy head in perplexity.

Hut had a fresh idea. "Might not our taking Haitee and Marda be a cause?" he asked.

"Would you leave them behind to be killed or worse were it to do over again?" Rhu asked. "Of course, we might never have gone into the Cari Valley in the first place. But I cannot find it in my heart to regret it, nor did the Elders have any objection to our bringing the girls to them. Would they not have done so had we been in the wrong?"

"Perhaps they, too, chose the lesser of two evils, Rhu."

"Then why did they not forbid our going over there on our last trip to get them?"

"Because, my sons, there is a tie from a previous life of which you have no recollection."

Rhu and Hut bounded to their feet and turned quickly to face Lord Lithargos who stood directly behind them.

"Have not the Elders spoken to you of karma, of those things from previous lifetimes which you have brought forward in uncompleted states?"

"Indeed they have!" Rhu exclaimed, his face lighting up as comprehension dawned upon him.

"My sons, you cannot be blamed for failing to remember at all times all you have been taught and which has been so new to you. It is to your credit that you have been trying to reason it out. Be not concerned about the effect the manner of Thedo's passing has upon your mates. The Elders have explained to them for you.

"At one time, without provocation he who was Thedo killed him who is Grut today. That karma has been discharged and because this killing was in the line of duty to his own people, Grut will not have to face repercussions in another and future life because of it.

"Rhu, one need not necessarily approach a hoogwar to be in danger from its attack, so your philosophy was sound though poorly stated. When duty takes one into places of danger, he must be prepared to meet it. If he *fear* that danger, then will he draw it to him, but this is vastly different from being prepared to meet it courageously. It is the *fear* that is wrong, NOT *the forethought that makes him safe against unprovoked attack.*

"As you roof your homes against the storms that are inevitable, so are your preparations to repel unprovoked attack. However, *let not your preparations for defense grow into preparations for attack against another.* That, my sons, is to invite disaster. Those who would seek to profit from aggression—and this, you will learn in time includes forms other than the physical aggression with which you recently have been beset—must expect to suffer from the aggressions of others. You cannot take from another by unprovoked attack without suffering from a like cause. To defend what you have created is vastly different from trying to take away the creations of another, whether by insinuation, by force, by trickery, or by stealth."

"What about our taking Marda and Haitee?" Hut asked.

"Did you take them, or did they come with you of their own free will?" The gentle voice was very firm.

"Yet, we went into the Cari Valley by stealth," Rhu asserted, coming to Hut's defense.

Lord Lithargos smiled into their concerned faces. "Yes, you did. Each time. However, your first trip was not inspired by the desire either to harm or to spy with a view to future attack. Your mission was in itself harmless and inspired by a sincere desire to learn. You had no thought of taking anything not your own, did you?"

"No," Hut and Rhu answered in unison. "As you have said, we went because we were curious to see what lay beyond the mountains," Hut continued.

"How may one hope to learn if he seek not? Your trip was no different from the first one you made to the Cave Dwellers of your own tribe, Rhu. Remember ever the lesson I have come to give you. To take by force is to lose by force. Que approaches. He is destined to be of vast help to you both. Hiroto and I shall teach him. However, say nothing of this until I bid you do so. See, he comes with Nohr and Dargh."

At His suggestion, Hut and Rhu turned to look below, and when they turned back to speak to the Great One, He was gone.

Hardly had they recovered from this startling disappearance when their approaching friends joined them.

"We have been discussing the building for housing prisoners," Que began. "Dargh says he can build it, but that the enclosure will take several moons because it will have to be too high for one to climb over. If we are to include much land, it will be a big undertaking."

"Why build such an enclosure?" Nohr asked. "Not only would it take a long time and great labor but, at best, it will be unsightly and probably most disagreeable inside, for no one would be able to see through it."

"That is true," agreed Rhu. "But how else can we hope to keep the prisoners safely?"

"I found some thorny bushes near the mountains, much like

those in the Chi Valley," replied Nohr. "These, I happen to know, grow rapidly. They are not tall, but very thick so that one cannot get through it without cutting his way, and the vines are tough. Suppose we were to enclose the grounds with a wall of this by planting small bushes as you do with some of your present flowering shrubs. In a short time, this would make a wall through which one would have great difficulty in passing, yet not be too tall to see over. By planting some of those other thorny, flowering shrubs I have seen near some of your houses along the outside of the wall, it would soon be very pretty. I notice the flowering shrubs develop long branches and these would also help to make the wall even more impenetrable."

Warming to his subject, Nohr became almost enthusiastic. "The less dangerous prisoners could be given the task of caring for these flowering thorn bushes. Besides, when we have no prisoners, might not some of the cows you keep for milking be placed inside, especially at night, where they would be safer? By planting some of your best grasses, they would also be both safe and well fed without someone having to care for them by day."

Rhu and Hut were quick to grasp the import of what Nohr was suggesting and immediately, new ideas of still further uses for such walls came to mind.

"Why could we not utilize the same method for enclosing some of our fields of maize?" Rhu exclaimed. "That would keep out the cattle with which we have had so much trouble."

"It might even be possible to enclose great areas in which a family could keep its best breeding stock," added Hut. "The Elders have promised us some of their best bulls as soon as we are prepared to handle them properly."

Thus began the first fencing of lands and the start of many specialized agricultural industries. Within the next two years, the plains in the immediate vicinity began to take on an ordered appearance, adding greatly to the general beauty of the landscape. In addition to the hedge, the colorful roses around the prison enclosure appealed so much to the forming citizenry that before long, almost every home had a hedge of them somewhere on the premises. The ever inquisitive and observing Que soon discovered that short strong branches of the roses would take root and grow when carefully tended for a time, thus overcoming any lack of the plant that might have been experienced.

TOWARD the close of the summer, Hut mentioned a subject about which he had been thinking for some time. "The Elders say Haitee and Marda are to join us this coming Short Day, Rhu," he said. "Should we not have huts of our own for them? True, we would no longer live together, but we can keep our place in the big stone hut for conferences and interviews. We should have places of our own." His eyes were bright with the pleasing thought.

"I would like them close together," he continued. "There is that nice hill just beyond the pool, where the trees will afford shade, and the view is excellent. We can see all over the valley from there."

For a moment, Rhu hesitated, then seemed to reconsider. "Let us get Dargh and see what he can do in such a short time," he said.

Dargh was of the same mind as Hut. If he and the other Musons could stop work on the prison, and he could have plenty of help with bringing in the necessary stones, he would have both places ready in time.

"I don't like the idea of starting them before our other job is finished," Rhu remarked, although somewhat uncertainly for the idea of sharing a place of his own with only Haitee was very appealing.

"Oh, that's all right," Hut reassured him. "After all, I think we are entitled to this much for ourselves."

"That's just the reason I hesitate," Rhu demurred. "I don't like the idea of building for ourselves while entire families are still living in huts. Besides, I'm afraid of getting too many things started rather than finishing each one as we go along."

"Dargh think should build homes," stated that individual. "Rhu and Hut leaders. Rhu and Hut should have fine huts. Dargh use colored stones. Make pretty," he concluded enthusiastically.

"And think how surprised and pleased the girls will be!" Hut added.

Here, he struck the right chord, for the thought served to

overcome Rhu's scruples, and together with Que and Nohr, they went to look over the prospective site of their new homes.

From the top of the hill beyond the pool, it was possible to see not only the valley, but the river, and even into the Chi and Tama Valleys where they ended upon the precipitous banks of the Hatamukulian River. Since Hut preferred it, it was decided that his house should be the southern one while Rhu's would be to the north, both facing the east and overlooking the valley.

Rhu expressed no preference. Seated beneath one of the enormous oak trees, he appeared to be absolutely content. Many times, he and Hut had come here, but today, with the thought of a home and mate, everything seemed very different. Although sentiment was to be a product of many, many centuries of life and experience, he felt its faint stirring within as the beauty of the surrounding scene and the promise of the future soothed and rested him.

Nohr it was who came to him as he sat there so quietly. "Hut says he has an idea of his own as to how he wants to build his house. Would you mind, Rhu, if I were to make a plan for your house?" he asked.

"That would please me very much," Rhu assured him. "Hut always has had more skill at such things, and I am not surprised at his having very pronounced ideas as to what he would like. I have no doubt that his home will be beautiful, so I shall more than welcome your ideas. A room is a room to me, I am afraid, but I like beauty no less than does Hut."

"I have spoken to Dargh and he, too, has some ideas gleaned from his experience. He wants to work with me in the planning. Which shall we start first?"

"Hut's," Rhu stated without hesitation. "He probably has his plan in mind already while I haven't a single idea on the subject."

Nohr smiled warmly. "It is as Dargh said it would be," he said. "Tomorrow, Dargh will send men to begin gathering the stones for Hut's house and as soon as we have them all here, we can get those he has in mind for your house." With a knowing smile, he hastened away to join Dargh, and Rhu's heart grew warm as he saw them talking and smiling, and glancing in his direction as they did so.

Chapter Twenty

THE MARRIAGES OF RHU AND HUT

AN INTERESTED GROUP gathered about a small fire, all eyes intent upon a flat, thin slab of white limestone. Rhu, Hut, and Que were seated on skin-covered stones while Nohr and Dargh lay upon their stomachs. Beneath the brilliant, full moon, the lines Dargh was making with a charred stick upon the flat stone were plainly discernible. The designs for the two new houses were being laid out.

Heretofore, Dargh had planned as he built, and this was simple enough since all buildings thus far had been rectangular structures varying only in size and location, and built solely as a means of protection. Now, something beyond a four-walled building was being considered. Plans were being made to introduce many innovations, not the least startling of which was to be the family fire inside the house.

"But the smoke!" Hut demurred. "How can one stay inside when the smoke will soon make it impossible to remain in the place?"

"And a hole in the roof will let in the rain," Rhu added, not so sure he was going to like this idea.

"In our caves," Dargh said thoughtfully, "smoke pass out through hole in roof. Keep out water by building little room above, like this." From his prone position, he outlined what he designated as a cave, drawing a little stone chimney on the ground above it.

Scrutinizing the sketch intently, Nohr's eyes suddenly brightened as an idea occurred to him. "Why not build small room with opening walled in to hold fire?" he asked, making a crude drawing of the first fireplace known to man.

Hut frowned as he tried to visualize it as it would be built. "How could we cook in there?" he asked.

Pointing to his picture of the open fireplace, Nohr explained. "Make the fire room large enough to hold cooking pots." He looked at Rhu who nodded his understanding.

"Why not make a small one and try it?" he suggested. "Make it of sticky earth first and of stone later."

With a grunt, Dargh was on his feet and hurrying away, to return presently with a big pot of soft clay, such as was used in making their cooking vessels. Enthusiastically, he and Nohr set to work. Against one of the stone pillars supporting the roof of the big stone hut at the front, they built a fireplace such as Nohr had drawn, making it about two feet square and the flue a good four or five feet high. Carefully, they then laid a small fire in it, and to the amazement of Rhu and Hut, the smoke began to pour out the top, practically none escaping from the opening where the fire burned brightly until the wet clay began to crack from the heat.

"To build a large one," mused Rhu, "we must use stones. Perhaps the sticky earth could be used to fill in between them and make them stay piled up. But sticky earth could not hold the stones across the top of the fire room. They will fall in," recalling to mind his many attempts to build roofed stone huts. This seemed to present a similar problem.

But Dargh was competent to handle the situation. "Put long stone across front," he explained. "Long stone hold rocks."

Having worked out the idea of an indoor fire to their satisfaction, the group turned its attention to the houses themselves. Simple though it was to be, Dargh labored painstakingly on the plan of a house in conformance with Hut's ideas. In all he did, Dargh was meticulous, and drawing such a plan was an unaccustomed exercise.

Nohr eyed the drawing with knotted brow. "Is it to have two rooms?" he asked.

"Houses and huts are now divided by skins. Why not by walls?" Hut answered.

"What for?" persisted Nohr. "Only one family." Despite his

words, his frown indicated that he was seriously weighing the idea nevertheless.

Rhu's eyes brightened as comprehension dawned. "Very good. One room for sleeping. One for cooking and eating in bad weather," he reasoned, still adhering to the age-old custom of cooking out-of-doors.

Here, indeed, was a departure from the ordinary, and certainly, two rooms were a great luxury. This and the proposed fireplace were outstanding innovations. But when the idea of a porch was finally developed and agreed upon in order that the weather might not beat in at the doorway, thus permitting it to be open for additional air during the hot season, Hut's pride was without bounds.

When Nohr and Dargh worked out designs to be built into the structures by means of colored stones, even Rhu was inspired to unheard of flights of fancy. Que advanced the idea that a bow and feathered arrow be worked into a design above the door of Rhu's house, a suggestion to which all readily agreed. In all other respects, the two buildings were to be identical. This was all very pleasing to Rhu, and Hut was delighted that his ideas were to be followed.

Under Dargh's competent direction, Hut's house grew apace and both Rhu and Hut watched with great interest. But as the little house neared completion, other matters so filled Rhu's days that he had little time to visit the laboring Musons while they worked upon his own. Furthermore, Grut suddenly developed an interest in so many things he wanted to show him that the time was fully occupied even when Que or Nohr did not make equal demands. Anyway, its construction was in competent hands, and having watched every detail of Hut's building and knowing his was to be its duplicate, Rhu was not as intrigued as would otherwise have been the case. And although he may have observed the air seemed charged with pleased expectancy, he little suspected that he might be the victim of a pleasant conspiracy.

A day or so before the all-important Short Day which was to witness the arrival of Marda and Haitee to occupy them, the houses were completed. Compared with those of the other families, they were very small, but seen upon their knoll and surrounded by beautiful trees, they were the most outstanding in the valley.

"OH, OH!" exclaimed Haitee, clinging close to Rhu's sinewy arm as the four of them and twelve of the Elders arrived at the bridge Rhu and Hut had engineered less than four years before. "How did you ever do it?"

"It wasn't so bad after we found out how to go about it," Hut assured her, and proceeded to explain to the entranced girls how they had contrived it while the Elders listened, their kindly eyes taking in the heavy, rugged structure.

In the middle of a sentence, Hut stopped abruptly, startled at the expression on Rhu's face as he disengaged Haitee's arm and strung his bow with practiced speed and skill. Almost automatically, Hut unslung his own bow, then laughed, although somewhat nervously, as the presence which Rhu's sharp eyes had detected stepped into view. It was Ord.

"Whew!" Rhu whistled, returning his arrow to its quiver and unstringing his long bow. "I thought we were in for something," he explained to Haitee whose eyes were round with surprise. Glancing down at her, Rhu chuckled softly as she swiftly returned to her girdle the obsidian knife he had once given her and then drew the soft, white robe back into place.

Following them, the Elder who had last visited the Plains remarked to his companions, "Have I not told you of Rhu's shrewd perception? Truly was our judgment sound," and the others nodded silently as they smiled their agreement.

"Marda, this is Ord," Hut explained to the staring girl who afterwards admitted that she had never before seen such a big man.

Ord gave Marda one swift glance, then strode past her to beam down into Rhu's smiling face. "Ord come out quick," the big fellow chuckled. "Rhu's eyes sharp. Ord no want to be target for Rhu." His wide smile reassured the startled Haitee. "Ord like Haitee," he finished, and turning, strode back past Hut and Marda to disappear an instant later around the sharp bend in the trail.

"Why! He's a giant!" Haitee exclaimed softly. "So that's the famous Ord you have talked so much about." Looking up at

Rhu, her eyes shone with pride. "How did you ever . . . ." she began. But whatever she was about to say was never completed as before her startled eyes a company of mighty Forest Dwellers lined up on each side of the road with a precision worthy of today's most modern, highly trained troops. As the little party walked between these big, proud warriors, their beaming faces reflected a warm welcome strangely at variance with their otherwise grim efficiency.

"Imagine Rhu going out among such men as these and bluffing them into following him," Hut bragged to Marda. "Most of these were in the original group he brought back on his first trip to recruit them."

As he spoke, some twenty immediately ahead of them wheeled into a double line with mechanical precision and marched onward as their advance guard.

"I'll bet this is Ord's idea," Hut concluded, looking back just in time to see the warriors behind the advancing Elders fall in as their rear guard. Then Ord strode past them all to take his place at the head of the force.

The First Building

"Well, *you* secured the *most* men, didn't you?" Marda asked.

"He certainly did," Rhu answered before Hut could speak. "And don't forget that it was just as hard as what little I did."

"You think a lot of Hut, don't you?" Haitee asked, smiling rather pridefully up into Rhu's face.

"He is my best friend," Rhu answered simply, and for a time, they marched silently ahead.

"The Elders have told us about the big stone building," Haitee remarked a few minutes later. "I am anxious to see it and to meet Dargh who built it."

As she finished, they turned a bend in the trail and the building came into view.

"It isn't nearly as big as I expected," Marda commented, and as seen nestling against the towering cliff, it did seem small and almost insignificant.

"Just wait until you get closer to it!" Hut remonstrated. "Remember it was built one stone at a time and every stone in it was carried far before it was put in place. It may not look so big from here, Marda, but it represents a monumental task!"

"Oh, it isn't that," Marda disclaimed promptly. "It was just that I expected it to be so much larger. Yes," as they drew closer, "it does look larger now. You certainly did a wonderful thing, Hut, in bringing these people here and doing all this."

"Not I," Hut said, a bit sharply, Rhu thought, "but Rhu and I. And we could never have done it without the help of Dargh and the others."

"Don't let him fool you," Rhu chipped in. "Hut had as much to do with it as any of us."

Haitee squeezed his arm. "That is not as I gathered from the Elders," she said softly, "but, of course, Marda and I each see things through her own eyes, you know."

Then as they reached the building and she gained a true idea of the size of the stones used in its building, she cried excitedly, "O-o-oh! Do you mean that they carried each of those great stones!" Such a thing as several men carrying a stone upon what we would call a crude litter never entered her head for she never dreamed of doing such things by other than sheer brute strength.

They passed through the big doorway and were in the build-

ing and through it when such a spectacle greeted their eyes
that Rhu and Hut stopped in amazement. Lined up before them
was every man, woman and child on the Plains, most of them
carrying wild flowers which they had painstakingly gathered
for this great occasion, and which they began strewing before
the advancing party so that they actually walked upon a carpet
of fragrant and colorful blossoms.

Never before had either Hut or Rhu realized the esteem in
which they were held. Glancing up at Rhu, Haitee was
astonished to see a tear trickle down his darkly tanned face.
With a quick flirt, he swept his hairy hand across his nose,
then rubbed it with an air of nonchalance that in nowise fooled
Haitee, and again, her heart swelled with pride.

Before the building, the throng now numbering more than
five hundred, gathered in a great semi-circle and seated themselves, while Ord led the Elders to the piles of soft furs used
for seats, and they, too, sat down. Only Hut, Marda, Rhu, and
Haitee remained standing.

It was clearly evident to Rhu and Hut that this was all the
working out of some carefully prepared program, for such a
performance was an entirely new departure from established
custom. In fact, from some of the comments of the assembled
folk, it was all too plain that even they did not entirely comprehend what it was all about.

To his surprise, Rhu discovered that Lord Hiroto was among
the Elders, although He had not been with them during their
trip homeward. Then his gaze encountered the smiling face of
Que, and a moment later, that of Nohr, and he began to suspect
that these two had much to do with the arrangement. Somehow, the matter of the flowers was quite in line with many
things characteristic of the Chi Yan.

Suddenly, Rhu was conscious that the murmurs of the assembly had ceased and all was very still. Then came the deep,
rich tones of Lord Hiroto.

"People of the Rhu Hut Plains," He began, "you have assembled to witness a most impressive ceremony that will soon
become the common practice." His manner of speaking was
slow and deliberate so that while some of His words may have
been more or less unintelligible to many of His listeners, still

the majority were able to grasp most of His meaning. Those having the greatest difficulty were later informed by those who did understand.

"Until now, it has been the custom in all tribes for a man to take to his hut, by force or otherwise, the woman of his choice, after which she was considered as his own. It also has been quite common for a man to have as many such women as he could support, those bearing him children being considered wives.

"Already, I am happy to say, one phase of this practice has been changed here. No longer may any woman be so taken without her consent. This is as it should be. The next step is one being taken by your leaders, Rhu and Hut, whereby no woman may be taken to a man's hut without the ceremony about to be enacted—that of marriage.

"No such ceremony may be performed until both the man and the woman involved have consented to it before the one authorized to marry them, and this ceremony once performed, the woman gains and retains the status of wife regardless of whether she bears children.

"Heretofore, when a man desired to rid himself of a wife, he had only to return her to her parents. He could retain the children or not as he desired. Following the marriage ceremony, this may no longer be done as you will better understand when this first marriage is completed. They may not separate without the consent of your Council which will also decide who shall retain the children.

"In the case of all those who are now married according to the old custom, there will be no change except that no longer may they separate without the consent of the Council who will also decide about the custody of the children. Certain rules will be given to you whereby all such matters shall be governed. You are now parts of a forming society which shall soon become known as a civilization wherein *all* shall be assured of equal justice and all given equal opportunity to present his or her side of any question.

"Should the Council be unable to arrive at a decision, the matter may be referred to the Elders until such time as certain other arrangements have been completed. The manner in which this shall be brought to pass will be given to the Council who will see that each of you is fully informed about it. In due course, all these and many other matters will be revealed to you by your leaders, Rhu and Hut, who shall be regarded during their lifetimes as the emissaries of the Elders.

"While the marriages of Rhu and Hut with their respective choices must be performed separately, as will all future ones, these two will be considered as one that none may later claim one or the other as having been given preference.

"Hut, because you are nearest, will you and Marda stand before me?" As they did so, He placed Hut to His left and Marda to His right.

Haitee's trembling hand clasped Rhu's arm and he pressed it to his side reassuringly.

"Marda, do you, of your own free will, take this man beside you to be your lawful wedded husband, to love, to honor, and to obey until death do you part?"

For a long moment, Marda seemed to hesitate, then flicked her tongue across her dry lips. "Yes," she said softly.

"Hut, do you take this girl beside you to be your lawful wedded wife, to love, to honor, to cherish, and to protect until death do you part?"

"Yes," Hut answered promptly.

"Take her right hand in your right hand," Lord Hiroto requested, and as they complied, "Hut and Marda, by virtue of the power vested in me this day by Those far greater than I, I pronounce you man and wife. May only happiness and contentment reign in your lives from this day hence." Smiling gently, He motioned them aside and with Haitee and Rhu before him, repeated the ceremony.

Next, requesting both couples to stand before Him, Lord Hiroto handed both Marda and Haitee each a tightly woven silken bag holding about a pint. "In these bags are golden grains of wheat which I have brought from a distant planet. From these seeds will come many times their number, and after the second harvest, I shall explain their use, for wheat shall become the most important of all crops raised for the nourishment of mankind.

"To you, Haitee and Marda, am I giving gladly this very

precious gift, something I promised you when you first came to the Elders. To you both, therefore, is the honor of giving to mankind a priceless possession. May each seed produce an hundredfold. And now," he concluded, "the Elders would bless you four."

Silently, the Elders surrounded the couples and began a simple chant extolling the virtues of each of the four and asking N'Kul's blessing upon them. Despite his excitement, Rhu looked about and observed that Lord Hiroto was no longer in their midst.

The Elders having completed their chant, Nohr stepped to the front, zitkern in hand. "Follow me," he said softly. Lustily singing to his own accompaniment, he led the way to the new homes, followed by all but the Elders who remained seated.

"Where are we going?" Haitee asked timorously, her radiant face upturned to Rhu.

"To our homes," he said simply.

"Our homes?" she demanded.

"Yes. Wait until you see them!" he said with a chuckle for, thus far, neither he nor Hut had mentioned them, even casually.

"Hut!" Marda exclaimed, her eyes very bright. "What does Rhu mean, 'homes'?"

"Wait until you see them," he repeated Rhu's statement, winking over her head at the grinning Rhu.

But the girls were not the only ones destined to be surprised at the end of this trip.

Chapter Twenty-one

AN ELDER SPEAKS

NOHR HAD STOPPED SINGING and everyone now stood still as the buildings became visible through the trees.

"What beautiful huts!" exclaimed Haitee as she caught sight of them.

"They are our homes," Rhu stated simply.

Haitee grasped his arm tightly. "Homes!" she cried breathlessly. "Oh, they are perfectly beautiful! Which is ours?"

"The farther one," Rhu explained. "The one with the bow and arrow over the door." Then he started. His and Haitee's house had two windows in the front! Hut's had only one!

"Marda! Marda! Aren't they wonderful?" Haitee's voice rose excitedly as she called to her friend.

"Indeed they are!" and there was no mistaking Marda's pleasure. "They are beautiful even though small compared with the usual family huts of our tribe." Suddenly, her eyes widened, and alarm leaped into her voice. "Why . . . . why, they are on fire!"

"Oh Rhu!" Haitee cried in an agony of fear.

"Sh-h-h!" he cautioned her, his eyes dancing. "This is something new. Our fires are inside, but they are all right. The houses are of stone and cannot possibly burn."

"Did you ever see stones burn?" Hut teased, grasping Marda's arm as she would have started to run ahead. "The houses have 'fire places' in them. At least that is what Que calls them."

"Who is Que?" asked Marda a bit irritably, somewhat upset over her unfounded fear, natural though it was.

"A Chi Yan and a good friend of Rhu's and mine," Hut explained. "He stands beside Nohr, a Tama Yan, who plays and sings as he walks."

All this talk was too much for Haitee. "Let's hurry," she exclaimed impatiently. "I am simply dying to see inside!"

"What is it like inside?" Marda demanded, no less impatient. "Why don't you tell me about it?"

The Homes of Hut and Rhu

"Wait and see for yourself," Hut admonished, grinning happily. Had he and Rhu suspected what lay ahead, however, they would probably not have been so calm or proceeded so deliberately.

Essentially an out-of-doors man to whom his hut was but a place to sleep and store things from inclement weather, it had never occurred to Rhu that his home would be much more, except that it was a permanent affair and far safer than any hut could possibly be. Therefore, when Haitee stopped short at the door to stare open-mouthed, Rhu caught his breath in astonishment and almost unbelief as he looked over her head and into the room. Never in the wildest flights of fancy had he ever envisioned anything comparable to what lay before them.

The floor, which had been simply packed, hard earth the only time he had seen it was now paved with smooth white limestone slabs, flat greenish stones forming a crude border. A great hoogwar skin lay in the center of the room, and upon it stood a table, probably five feet long and three feet wide, the top a single slab of limestone, and the legs of wood, bound to a wooden frame supporting the stone top. Four crude wooden stools stood around the table.

Nohr and Que had labored patiently upon these furnishings and those in Hut's home even while the houses were being built, but by no word or action had they ever betrayed their secret.

Yet, it was not these things alone which surprised Rhu. From where he stood, it was plain to see that instead of the two rooms in Hut's house, this one had three!

Haitee fairly danced into the room to the left and again stopped to stare in surprise and delight. This floor, too, was of spotless white limestone. A great bearskin lay before the low stone couch piled high with fur coverings, some of which, of course, were always used to lie upon. Before the window, upon a low frame, was a shallow vessel containing clear water, but too little of it to be of practical value. Wonderingly, Haitee leaned over to find her own image reflected from it. Examining the basin, she found it, too, was carved from the same white stone. Several times, she found herself peering into it. Did Marda, she wondered, have one like it? It was odd. Yet, she had often peered into placid pools for the same purpose.

Following her excited movements, Rhu saw that the remaining room was a duplicate of their sleeping room except that it contained no "gazing pool," as he quickly dubbed it after seeing its purpose and the frequent use Haitee made of it. The reason for this third room, he could only surmise, finally deciding it would afford excellent accommodation for any visiting Elder who might remain overnight. Not once did it occur to him that Dargh had insisted upon it as a mark of personal distinction and of the outstanding regard in which he held Rhu.

As the two stood before the cheerful fire in the central room,

Haitee's eyes were round with wonder that the blaze should be so controlled. Plying Rhu with questions, she had no rest until he told her the entire story of how this great discovery had come about.

Above the fireplace was a wide slab of stone upon which were many eating and cooking bowls of various sizes which Rhu promptly recognized as the handicraft of his mother. He chuckled softly, for with the realization of the love that prompted these gifts came another thought . . . . how, he wondered, would his forthright mother and the impulsive Haitee get along?

By now, Haitee was examining the pots before and upon the fire, discovering even a clay oven. To be sure, it was small but amply large for the making of a supply of maize bread for four people, and in it was hot bread ready for the eating.

Suddenly aware that he had not thought of his friends outside during the excitement, Rhu belatedly hastened out to invite them to enter, but not a person was in sight. Thoughtful consideration was already being born, and Rhu shrewdly suspected that the astute Que was largely responsible for it.

"Shall we go to see Hut and Marda?" he asked.

"After we eat," answered Haitee, who was already busily engaged in getting their first meal since morning upon the table. "What ever is this?" she demanded suddenly.

Rhu immediately recognized the leg and thigh of a fowl, his favorite food, and knew beyond all question that his mother must have left but scant minutes before their arrival.

Supper over, they hurried to make their first call upon Hut and Marda, arriving just as those two were about to depart for their first visit to Rhu and Haitee. Their home was a duplication of what Rhu and Haitee had found except, of course, this had but the two rooms. Since Hut's mother had prepared their first meal in the new home, the girls had great fun comparing notes.

"Did you ever dream things could be so wonderful!" Haitee exclaimed as she and Marda examined everything.

Rhu and Hut sat at the table and exchanged knowing comments and glances at the varied exclamations from the excited girls.

"This is certainly unlike anything I have ever seen," Marda agreed readily. "Even the caves of the Elders are no better. They do not have those things to eat upon nor seats that one may move about."

"I'll miss our time guides, though," Haitee commented, referring to the sundials used by the Elders.

"Even the large jars were filled with water," Marda mentioned. "Hut says he will have our water carried up here by one of the men."

"Do the men carry the water for the other women here on the Plains?" Haitee asked. "It hardly seems fair for us to have it done if the others do not."

"Well, I had not thought of it in that light," said Marda. "But it must be all right if Hut suggested it. What is your place like?" she asked eagerly, for the question had been uppermost in her mind.

"Come on over and see for yourself," Haitee invited. "I'm sure you will like it as much as this one. It's wonderful!"

Arm in arm, Haitee and Marda preceded Hut and Rhu as the four arrived at the other home.

"Oh!" exclaimed Marda as they entered. "You have three rooms!"

"Yes, though I don't know what the third one is for."

"I think I like two best," said Marda. "Ours are larger, and I like plenty of room. I believe the view from our porch is better, too, although I do like the tree in front of your home, and you can see more of the plains to the north."

After carefully inspecting everything, the girls joined Rhu and Hut before the fireplace.

"How do you like our homes, Marda?" asked Rhu.

"I was just telling Haitee that I am in love with both of them. But why the third room here?"

"That was Nohr and Que's idea. They thought the two homes should be a little different," Hut explained, his eyes twinkling as he glanced at Rhu. "The third room will serve for any of the Elders who may come to discuss things with Rhu and me."

As Hut finished speaking, a startled expression flitted over

Rhu's face. "What has become of the Elders who came with us?" he asked, turning to Hut.

"Hm-m-m!" Hut muttered, frowning. "I confess I had forgotten everything else except what has been happening to us and the excitement of getting into our own homes. I suppose we should go to see about it."

Rhu's keen ears detected almost inaudible footsteps, however, and a moment later, Grut appeared, his heavy, homely face alight with smiles. "Que send Grut. Elders use your old room. Nobody else come. Grut go."

"Not before you meet Haitee and Marda," Rhu stopped the big fellow.

"Grut see. Grut like. Haitee . . . ." He hesitated, evidently groping for some word. "Haitee like blooming weed!" he announced, his sweat-bedewed brow showing the strain the thought had exerted upon his slow-working mind. "Marda good, too," he finished, dimly sensing that she should be included.

Hut chuckled softly. He knew Grut, realizing that, in his eyes, the sun rose and set for Rhu, and that he was ready and willing to die for anything or anyone who was important to Rhu. "That is a very real compliment," he assured the smiling Marda. "Grut is not given to praise, and I'd like to bet he is the one who brought us the wood and water."

Grut's heavy face flushed beneath its bushy whiskers, and he hung his head in an agony of embarrassment.

Impulsively, Haitee stepped in front of him, and reaching up, pulled his head down by the simple expedient of grasping his wiry whiskers, then kissed him.

Grut turned and fled into the gathering darkness.

Rhu and Hut laughed happily. "I'll bet his face is red enough to light up the trail," Hut almost shouted.

"Yes, and I'll bet he won't wash it for a month, especially where Haitee's lips touched him," Rhu agreed. "Poor old Grut! He always was afraid of women, but once he selects one, I'll bet he'll never look at another. Of all my brothers, he is the only one who ever does anything for my mother. Hm-m-m! I'm beginning to wonder just how much of what was done here today is Grut's work."

AS RHU emerged from the door the following morning, he discovered a neat pile of firewood, an earthen jar of milk, a goodly supply of eggs, a leg of fresh venison, and a great jar of fresh water. In the soft earth before the porch his sharp eyes detected the tracks of a man's big feet where he had tiptoed up to the porch several times, and then where he had hurried away, evidently running. One particular print showed plainly the outline of a scar upon the right foot.

"Grut!" he muttered, grinning softly. "I'm betting he has undertaken this, and if he has, Haitee will never have to carry wood or water. Now, I wonder . . . ." and he looked over toward Hut's house.

There was nothing on the porch. Either it had already been taken in or nothing had been left there.

Rhu shook his shaggy head. "Grut has only one idea at a time," he mumbled, but his eyes were very soft. Should he mention this discovery to Grut? Wisely, he decided to leave that to Haitee. Nor did he mention it to Hut.

As he turned to enter his house where Haitee was already placing the cooking pots over the fire he had started when he first arose, he saw the smoke begin to emerge from Hut's chimney, and his smile widened. It was good to be alive.

IT WAS later than usual when Hut and Rhu arrived at their old quarters which were to serve as a meeting place for the discussion of all matters concerning the integrating civilization. If any of the Elders took note of this, however, no mention of it was made. After the customary greetings were exchanged, the Elder who had previously visited Hut and Rhu spoke.

"My sons," he began, "for the first time, the Elders have had the opportunity of seeing for themselves all that you have accomplished here. To say that we are well pleased is very mild praise. Better still, Lords Lithargos and Hiroto are equally pleased.

"As mentioned upon my last visit, Que is destined to become a very important factor in this forming civilization together with Dargh, Ord, and others who will later join with you. Your growing confidence in Que is well placed. We shall take him with us upon our departure in order that we may give him such special instructions as may be essential to his deeper understanding. Dargh and Ord will be taken later, and you will both be fully advised of what all three are taught, which will be principally that which will bring their understanding up to your own. This is in conformance with our talk on this subject and will constitute a part of the schooling for citizenship which has already been started.

"Now, we would take up the matter of the establishment of certain general and basic rules for the successful management of the forming civilization.

"As you well know, there are certain great Natural Laws which govern all things from the growing of the grass to the movements of the stars. These Laws are universal, self-executing and completely impersonal, governing all creation in the same manner. Laws or rules made by man which are not in strict conformance with these Universal Laws are foredoomed to failure, for man-made laws are fallible and depend upon the uncertainties and interpretations of man who is far from being without error. Neither are man-made laws self-executing, but dependent upon man-created action for their administration. Consider thoughtfully, therefore, the establishment of any rule or law for the governing of the civilization.

"No group of people, regardless of how well intentioned or willing, can work together with the greatest efficiency without proper supervision and competent guidance. There must always be those who coordinate all efforts.

"Thus far, the people of the Plains have worked under your guidance. However, you have always come to the Elders for supervision and direction when you were uncertain or needed help beyond your knowledge. So do the Elders turn to the Lords of Venus and Mercury for that which is beyond *them.* Thus does all our work in the formation of this society or civilization come under the supervision and direction of Lords Lithargos and Hiroto who, in turn, work under the guidance of N'Kul. This plan is called organization.

"In time, you will delegate certain authority to others, but they will still come under your supervision just as those whom they direct come under theirs. In selecting these, bear in mind that many who have the ability to coordinate and direct the

efforts of others may have less skill than those whom they are
to direct, while those who possess the skill, unfortunately,
often lack those qualities which make for the most efficient cooperation. And cooperation, it must always be remembered, is
absolutely essential to the success of the new society.

"At the same time, never discount the value of the dreamers
—those who have vision but lack the ability to give the visions
reality. Nothing great can ever be accomplished except where
there is vision. Still, one must not become visionary and impractical in his dreaming. You both have that rare combination
of ability to envision and to execute, to plan and to work your
plans. Without this ability, you would not have been chosen
for the work you are doing. It is this ability which all must, in
time, acquire.

"No man has the right to delegate responsibility to another
without granting commensurate authority or power to discharge it properly, yet lust for power presents an ever present
danger for those to whom it is granted. Therefore power, no
matter how small, should never be lightly assumed, sought, or
exercised except with extreme care. That which is definitely assigned is all that mortal man should ever undertake, especially
power or authority over others. Think well of this lesson, my
sons, for in this direction lies your greatest danger.

"Between now and the beginning of the next Great Sun, or
year, as it shall henceforth be known, you will both be given
certain basic laws and commensurate power to enforce their
execution. Establish no others in which kindliness, tolerance,
and justice to all in equal measure are not outstanding.

"With this power will come responsibilities greater than any
you have thus far been called upon to assume. Discharge them
well and with wisdom. Humility, my sons, is the most godlike
of the virtues. Cultivate it diligently. Power is never safe except in the hands of the truly humble.

"And now, my sons, we would speak with Que, and in your
presence. You two are our chosen emissaries. In your hands we
would place great powers and upon your shoulders, heavy responsibilities. Forget not that as the homes, so the civilization
of which they are a part."

For a long moment, he stood looking at Rhu and Hut. Twice,

he appeared to be about to speak, and an expression of sadness and compassion came into his kindly eyes. Gently, he laid his hand upon Rhu's shoulder. "My son . . . . my son!" he said softly.

Glancing swiftly toward the other Elders, a chill shot up Rhu's spine. The eyes of all were upon him, and all reflected the same emotion as the one who had spoken.

His eyes upon the floor and a slight frown of deep concentration upon his forehead, Hut apparently was unaware of this. "I shall summon Que," he announced, departing upon his mission.

HAITEE skipped quickly through her chores and ran over to see her friend. "Marda," she cried, "don't you think we should go over to see our new mothers? Rhu says it was they who prepared our suppers last night, and I would like to thank Meta for being so kind."

"Hut says we will probably find them both rather blunt and frank in their opinions, Haitee, and I rather planned to wait until Hut could go with me," Marda demurred.

"According to Rhu, Mahata is not quite as outspoken as Meta, and Rhu and Hut will be too busy to take the time for a few days, especially with the Elders being here. It's such a beautiful morning, and I am anxious to begin getting acquainted."

"I am too, Haitee. Besides, if we are to do the many things the Elders planned for us we should get started. Do you know which places are theirs?"

"No, but we can ask. I wish Grut were here. I know he'd help us."

"Maybe we'll be lucky enough to see him," Marda suggested. "We can ask for him, can't we?"

Following the trail worn by all those who had contributed to their welfare and happiness in the new homes, the girls found themselves approaching a big stone building. Nearby was the low, rambling structure housing the birds which supplied the eggs now being used more and more.

"What in the world do you suppose they are?" Marda asked excitedly, pointing to the pens. "Surely, they are not the old frames of the family hut! I never saw anything like them, and besides, they seem to be full of birds or something!"

"I'll bet that is where they are raising birds! Rhu told me about how they came to be built. Meta and Mahata were the ones to think of it, and they had the first ones erected. Rhu says they are big and have woven roofs so the birds can't escape. And there's Grut! Yoohoo! Hello there, Grut!" Haitee hailed the shaggy man whose wide smiles showed how very welcome they were.

"Hello, Grut," Haitee greeted him as they neared each other. "We came over to thank Meta and Mahata for all they did for us yesterday."

"Meta glad see Haitee and Marda," Grut assured them. "Grut say Haitee like food. We live here," he added.

As they rounded the corner to approach the front of the house, Sol Ku emerged, his shrewd old eyes lighting up as they rested on the girls. "Sol glad see Haitee and Marda," he welcomed them. "Grut, find Meta," he ordered, and taking Haitee by the hand, led them into the house where he seated the girls on a great pile of soft furs.

Although roughly partitioned with large skin curtains, still, both girls were astonished at the size of the big room. The many pillars supporting the heavy stone roof enhanced the spaciousness of the cool but rather gloomy interior—or so it seemed to Marda and Haitee whose eyes had not yet readjusted themselves from the outside brightness. This is why they did not at first see the many curious eyes peering at them from the curtained cubicles.

Hardly were they seated when Grut entered with Meta, whose kindly but penetrating eyes brightened as they rested upon Haitee.

"Meta glad see Haitee and Marda," she greeted them. "Rhu and Grut tell Meta many things about Haitee and Marda."

Impulsively, Haitee kissed Meta's weathered and lined cheek as she squeezed the toil-hardened fingers. Had it been lighter, the girls would have seen Meta's kindly old face darken as the blood rushed to it, for, as a rule, Mu Yan women were undemonstrative. Had Haitee but known it, that one simple gesture won for her a most powerful ally.

Sol chuckled softly.

"Grut gone get Mahata," Meta explained as Haitee would have thanked him for getting Meta. "Mahata anxious meet Marda. Mahata good woman. Mai come soon. Sit beside Meta, Haitee," she invited, and Sol observed that she still clung to Haitee's hand which seemed very small in her big, gnarled one.

"Grut is so sweet," Haitee said a bit breathlessly, for she had only just begun to realize something of the strain this meeting was engendering.

"Grut good boy, but fresh," Meta commented.

As Haitee was soon to learn, whenever Meta spoke of one of her sons, she invariably tempered any praise with some pertinent criticism. Haitee was also to learn that this latter prerogative Meta reserved exclusively for herself, and woe unto anyone else who criticized one of her brood, especially Grut or Rhu.

"He has certainly been kind to me," Haitee defended Grut.

"Grut better be good to Haitee," Meta replied sharply.

Recalling some of Rhu's comments regarding this indomitable brother of his, Haitee was hard pressed to repress a smile as she wondered just what Meta would do if her ideas and Grut's happened to clash.

"Grut bring Mahata," announced that worthy as he entered the building closely followed by Hut's mother who went immediately to Marda.

Not quite as impulsive as Haitee, Marda was less expressive in her greeting although there was no lack of cordiality. Mahata, too, was more retiring than the forthright Meta, and what might easily have resulted in a rather awkward silence was broken by the arrival of Mai Dan who promptly kissed Marda and had her sit between him and Mahata.

"What is this?" Mahata asked, fingering the cloth garment Marda wore.

"The Elders call it cloth," Marda explained.

"How make?" asked Meta as she also examined the garment worn by Haitee.

"Cloth is woven of threads made from certain blossoms as well as fibers of certain plants," Marda continued. "It is also made from sheep wool. We have been taught how to do this, and have been instructed to teach you and the other women here how to make the yarn and then how to weave it into cloth. Frames must be made on which the weaving is to be done."

"Rhu make frames," Meta announced confidently.

"Yes, and so can Grut," Haitee declared, and the sudden brightening of Grut's face made her glad she had included him.

"Rhu do better. Grut too clumsy," disagreed Meta promptly.

Haitee smiled up into Meta's face. "Grut will make mine," she stated quite positively. Already she was developing a great confidence in this gruff but gentle brother of Rhu's, and the pride that glowed in his eyes was ample reward for her temerity in thus disagreeing with Meta.

"Maybe so," Meta agreed surprisingly.

Sol was almost startled, for he had fully expected a totally different reaction. Meta was not one to have her statements questioned.

"Grut clumsy—but patient," she further astonished Grut by complimenting him. "If not good, Rhu fix." For Meta, the matter was closed. "Need frame to make yarn?" she asked.

"Only a stick to hold wool and one on which to wind the yarn," said Haitee. "If you will get a supply of wool, tomorrow we'll begin. I think you and Mahata should learn first. When you two do it, others will be willing to follow."

"Any who not follow Haitee will hear from Meta. Meta say, better do," Meta announced grimly. "Mahata and Meta get wool. Learn make thread."

"Fine," Haitee agreed enthusiastically. "And I want to thank you for all the nice food you sent us. The Elders have taught us how to prepare other foods as good as maize bread. Marda and I will teach you and Mahata all we know, while you will teach us much *we* don't know. Rhu thinks he has a wonderful mother," she concluded, smiling into Meta's face.

"Rhu good boy. Haitee good girl. But Rhu make big talk sometimes. Rhu like, Rhu praise. Rhu no like, Rhu bash face. Meta once spank Rhu. Rhu bite leg. Humph!" However, the undisguised pride in her eyes belied the snort.

Haitee giggled as she envisioned the spanking episode.

"Rhu good boy," Sol interjected, rather hastily Haitee thought.

"Humph!" Meta snorted again, glaring at Sol. "Meta have own idea. Grut!" she snapped suddenly as she observed his broad grin, "Go hide ugly face before scare Haitee!"

Afterwards, when Haitee related the morning's events, she was inclined to be somewhat miffed at Rhu's unrestrained laughter. "If anybody but you had dared to giggle at something Mother said, she would likely have slapped her face. No wonder Father interrupted. Mother is very sensitive in some ways, but she surely loves you, Haitee. I've never known our folks to display such feeling and consideration for anyone before. It certainly shows the high regard in which they hold you and Marda."

During the weeks and months of patient labor as the art of hand weaving was laboriously and painstakingly taught, Haitee came more fully to realize the truth of this. She held an unusual place in Meta's rugged old heart while Marda was no less loved by the more patient Mahata. But when it came to the instruction of the women, Meta's supply of biting comments because they were so slow of comprehension kept them at their tasks as nothing else could have done. In her own way, Meta was a character with whom to reckon, but in all the years of their association, never once had she anything but kindly consideration for Haitee, nor was any task ever too onerous to perform if it was for the wife of her beloved Rhu.

Chapter Twenty-two

THE LUST FOR POWER

FROM THE TIME Rhu and Hut had been children, they had been close friends, sharing all their ideas and most of their experiences. Since coming to the Rhu Hut Plains, their many activities prevented them from being as inseparable as previously, but when night fell and they were alone, each acquainted the other with all that had taken place while they were apart. Long and serious were the discussions and many the plans for the future that were made during these evenings, all too often, the first faint signs of dawn appearing before they dropped off to well-earned slumber.

With their marriages, however, fixed habits of life were altered to meet the new conditions, and a gradual change in the relationship took place. Days filled with activity, and evenings equally full of the delights afforded by home life, Rhu and Hut spent less and less time together discussing the day's events, and more and more in the company of their wives.

At first, each would sit quietly mulling over in his mind the things he previously would have talked over with his partner, missing the close association which made such discussions possible. Gradually, an almost imperceptible drawing apart developed. Although they never failed to act in perfect harmony, nevertheless, there grew in the heart of each a feeling of separativeness. Both were painfully aware that things were not as they should be, but the more they tried to overcome it, the more pronounced did the separation become.

Instead of taking the other into his confidence and thus straightening out the incipient misunderstanding, Hut and Rhu were silent, striving to make it appear as though nothing were wrong. Then, as countless millions of others have done to their sorrow, each began to seek the cause in the other and thus observed characteristics of which he had never before been aware.

On their part, Marda and Haitee were naturally curious as to the reasons for the long periods of silence which so absorbed their husbands. In fact, they spent a great deal of their time speculating upon the probable cause, most of which they attributed to themselves, and with no small degree of apprehension. Were they failing in their wifely duties? Were they losing the love of Rhu and Hut? Were their husbands deliberately withholding from them things they should know and understand?

It was Marda who finally suggested that perhaps things were not going smoothly between Hut and Rhu. This thought found fertile field in their imaginations, and each feeling that her first loyalty was to her husband, their conversations became less intimate, for each girl unconsciously began to withhold some of her thoughts from the other. At first, they were all unaware of what was occurring, but before long, they, too, developed the same sense of separativeness as was growing between Hut and Rhu.

Deprived of the former close companionship, Rhu and Hut began to talk to their all too willing and sympathetic wives about the events of the day. Since the girls were inclined to agree whole-heartedly with their mates, it was not long before Rhu and Hut discussed their plans for future undertakings with them, so that, while husbands and wives became more closely bound, the separation between the two friends widened.

Rhu and Hut's work on the Plains had always been more or less supervisory, and for some time when engaged in common undertakings, each continued to augment the suggestions and ideas of the other in directing those who were doing the actual work. However, Ord and Dargh, together with many of the others were now becoming so adept that they required little direct supervision once they understood the end to be accomplished. On the other hand, and as the Elders had explained, competent guidance by those who had a greater vision of what was to be accomplished was always necessary in order that all the work be properly coordinated.

Always deeply interested in everything his people were doing, the intensely practical Rhu was ever ready with suggestions and ideas for shortcuts and greater efficiency, so things proceeded rapidly and with steadily mounting satisfaction and pleasure when he was about.

Hut, who had always before devoted his efforts and abilities to suggesting new plans to Rhu and in helping put them into effect was now gradually spending more and more of his time cultivating the good will of those whom he was selecting and inculcating with his ideas for the administrative work to be undertaken by an enlarged Council. This, he planned to form by adding to the present one new members of his selection. Encouraged by the ideas and suggestions of Marda, he found his interests leaning more and more toward the governing angle of their great venture.

Immersed in his own steadily increasing activities with the inventive Dargh and Ord's rapidly expanding ideas for the greater perfection of the army, Rhu was slow in realizing Hut's more infrequent visitations to the various enterprises so steadily growing in number and importance.

Under such circumstances, Rhu's astonishment was understandable when Hut eventually launched into a detailed explanation of what he had been doing. His face gradually hardened as Hut proceeded, becoming almost grim as the selected Council was named and the long list of rules enumerated. Not until then did he awaken to the extent of the separation which had developed between them.

That Hut should not only have selected new members for the Council without consulting him, but had already discussed the matter with them was so unexpected as to be a complete shock to Rhu. But that Hut should compile rules for Council procedures which would affect all their people after all Lord Hiroto and the Elder had said seemed to him nothing less than sacrilegious. Furthermore, as he listened he realized that the rules which were set forth would subordinate even him to Hut's dictation!

It was all so unlike the Hut whom he had always loved that his first feeling of utter amazement quickly changed to one of resentment. Stung to the quick, a hot flush rose in his face. Then, more calmly, he reflected that it was so completely at variance with their usual custom that undoubtedly, Hut was merely joking and would admit as much. But as Hut continued to elaborate upon his ideas, Rhu was forced into the realization that he was not only in deadly earnest, but was fully determined to act, with or without Rhu's sanction!

The entire affair seemed preposterous, especially coming from one who had always held the Elders in such high regard. Refraining from giving expression to the conflicting emotions which beset him, Rhu tried to determine what he could say which would adequately meet the situation and wished fervently that one of the Elders were there to advise him.

As if in answer to his unspoken plea for help, the deep and resonant voice of Lord Lithargos interrupted Hut's dissertation. "Hut, my son," He said, and in His tone there was a quality neither had ever heard before, "by what authority have you taken upon yourself the pronouncements of edicts, not only without consulting Rhu, but at variance with what both Lord Hiroto and the Elders have previously stated?"

Rhu and Hut came to their feet with a start and turned to face the Great Being. Before either could recover from his surprise, Lord Lithargos continued, and His voice was cold and stern.

"Forget not that the assumption of such power imposes responsibilities far beyond your present understanding. Without the experience essential to the wisdom required, by what standard do you measure your *fitness* to judge what is best for all concerned? Can it be possible that Lord Hiroto was right in feeling that a lust for power may result in your undoing? The forming of this civilization no one man may defeat. Place not yourself in a position where your ambition for control may crush you.

"Rhu, it is not in my heart to condemn the feeling which, but a few moments ago, welled up in your heart. It is not easy to cast off resentment under such circumstances and where you have every right to feel the sting of disappointment in a friend.

Yet, this is not good. True humility comes not easily when one has had so much to do with the building as you have, then finds his dearest friend would relegate him to a position of inferiority."

"But—but," Hut stammered, face crimson and beads of cold sweat standing out upon his brow, "I had neither the desire nor the intention of doing any such thing to Rhu! He has been so immersed in the practical aspects of the work that he has seemed to neglect what appears to me to be the most important of all!"

"Then why did you not consult him? Appearances, my son, can be devastatingly deceptive. Besides, did not Lord Hiroto say that I should enunciate the basic laws to be followed?"

Long habit and affection caused Rhu to come to Hut's aid. "Was he not consulting me just now?" he asked.

Lord Lithargos' cold eyes never left Hut at whose heart clutched the clammy fingers of doubt while his nimble brain sought to grasp the opening Rhu had afforded. His heart warmed at the undeserved loyalty. Still, his mouth felt dry as ashes, and cold chills crept up his spine as the coldly impersonal eyes of the Great Being remained fixed upon him with disconcerting directness. Just how much had He heard?

"I—I am sure it did not sound as I intended," he stammered. "I certainly did not mean that Rhu was to play an inferior part, or even to intimate such a thing. I sought only to have things well organized before I talked it over with him."

But even as the words left his mouth, Hut knew they were inadequate for Lord Lithargos for the level eyes of the Great One continued to bore into his as if waiting and expecting him to proceed further. No trace of the customary warmth was in them—only cold appraisal.

Hut's tongue flicked across his dry lips. "I—I was undoubtedly wrong in undertaking to formulate any laws, but I had no remote intention of doing anything contrary to your wishes," he tried to explain. "These are but ideas I have long had, and saw no wrong in giving them expression."

"Even to selecting and informing those you chose for the new Council?" Lord Lithargos asked softly. "Was it not agreed that your patriarchs, together with Ord and Dargh, form the

Council under you and Rhu? Why have you selected several from your own sept? And why did you appoint yourself as the head of the Council?"

"It—it was not intentional," Hut demurred. "I was merely trying to make it a Council of Twelve."

"With yourself as the thirteenth," Lord Lithargos concluded dryly, "while Rhu was given no official status."

Hut's face brightened. "Rhu and I were to be as one on the Council," he said, heaving a long sigh.

"Then why was not Rhu mentioned as one of the Council?" Lord Lithargos asked crisply. "Think well, my son, ere you state intentions which are not backed by concrete facts. Had this been accepted, Rhu would have been one of the leaders only by your sufferance, and that is far from good. Let this be a lasting lesson to you, my son, lest you should further disappoint the Elders.

"As for you, Rhu, your willingness to defend Hut more than offsets your original resentment. Therefore, you have thus far created nothing that could become negatively karmic. My sons, this day must see you both reunited in your common endeavor, and it were best that this incident never again be mentioned between you. Unfortunately, you, Hut, already having talked to your proposed new Council members, must explain to them that the old Council is to remain as is. Let it be as of your own volition."

Rhu felt sorry for the perspiring Hut for he well knew it was going to be far from easy for him to have to pacify those who must now be eliminated. Secretly, he determined that never would he allow *himself* to be placed in such a position through ill-advised haste in announcing any decision of his own.

After a brief pause, Lord Lithargos again spoke. "For the time being and as has been stated, the Council shall be composed of Sol Ku, Mai Dan, Ku Kut, Gar Yak, Dorg Mauk, Ord, Dargh, and the two of you as its head. No Council meeting is to be held at which you both are not present," and His eyes swung to Hut.

"Today," He continued, "I shall state the ten basic laws so that you may think them over carefully until the arrival of the Elder who will discuss them with you at length.

"The first law is that no man shall seek to profit at the expense of another. To be Cosmically sound, both parties to any transaction must profit equally.

"The second law is that no man singly, nor the commonwealth collectively, may take anything away from another by force.

"The third is that all natural resources shall remain the property of the state or commonwealth and may not be claimed as personal possessions by any individual, or any group of individuals not constituting the entire citizenry.

"The fourth: Every citizen, and every child thereof, shall be entitled to, and receive, equal education, equal opportunity for the expression of his ability, and equality of standing before the laws of the land.

"The fifth: All advancement in position shall be based upon merit and the performance of service alone.

"The sixth: No individual shall be entitled to retain as a personal possession anything for which he has not personally compensated in equal value.

"The seventh: No individual shall have the right to operate in the environment or personal affairs of another unless asked to do so by that person, and only where criminal or treasonable intent can be proved or the civil rights of another have been violated may the State or commonwealth as a whole operate or interfere in the personal affairs of an individual.

"The eighth law is that no one may intentionally kill or injure another person except in the defense of life or State.

"The ninth is that the sanctity of the home shall be kept inviolate, and no woman may be taken in marriage without her consent.

"The tenth and last is that in all matters affecting the common good, when no violation of Natural Law is implied or involved, the opinion of the majority shall rule, subject only to the consent of the Elders whose decisions shall be final.

"These, my sons, are the ten fundamental laws by which the Council shall be governed in all matters. When the Elder has explained in detail all the many points involved in them, you will better understand their vital importance to the ultimate success of the Great Work in which you have started. In time, there will be many variations of them, but only as they are kept inviolate can there be permanent success and security.

"Weigh them well. Consider each point thoughtfully so that all questions concerning them may be well formulated. The Elder will thus be enabled to make clear any and all possible points of confusion, for you must be able to explain them fully and completely to the Council who will adopt them.

"I shall now repeat them in order to fix them in your minds," and Lord Lithargos proceeded to do so. Nor was it remarkable that His words were remembered. It must not be forgotten that having no written word, these people had developed highly retentive memories.

"And now, Hut, my son, you will visit those to whom you talked about the formation of a new Council. It is best, always, to admit an error rather than to try to justify the unjustifiable —to attempt to rationalize the inexcusable. Cultivate humility. Thirst not for temporal power which can all too easily crush you as did the great serpent which the man would have tamed and made a pet. Like fire, power can consume as readily as it can bring comfort. Seek not to create what you cannot control," and Lord Lithargos was gone.

"Rhu," Hut began hesitatingly as if unsure of his ground, "I would not have you think I do not appreciate what you tried to do for me this morning. I did not realize how it must have seemed to you, for I really had no intention of hurting you or usurping any power."

"Forget it," Rhu answered gruffly. It was characteristic of Rhu that he bore no grudge even though the hurt was deep, but the fact that Hut's eyes did not meet his and that he seemed ill at ease did not escape him.

Long after Hut had departed upon the mission Lord Lithargos had assigned to him, Rhu sat thoughtfully considering the many little things Hut had recently said and done and which he had to admit should have forewarned him. His heart was heavy as the forebodings which he could not dispel kept creeping into his thoughts. At last and with a heavy sigh, he departed to join Ord and so get his mind upon other matters.

All during the ensuing afternoon as he drilled a group of Forest Dwellers, Ord eyed him shrewdly, his black eyes unusually somber, and no sooner had Rhu departed than he dismissed his men and hastened in search of Dargh.

"Rhu troubled. He say nothing, but his heart heavy," he rumbled in his great chest.

For a long moment, Dargh sat silently staring into the darkness. "Dargh saw. Something on Rhu's mind. When Hut's name is mentioned, Rhu's mouth tighten. He sigh often. Only yesterday, Pflugh tell Dargh Hut forming new Council. He say no mention of Rhu on Hut's Council."

"Ord hear same thing. Maybe Rhu learn of this today."

"Where *is* Hut?" Dargh asked abruptly.

"Ord not know, but Ord find," that mighty man stated grimly. "If Hut . . . . "

"No," said Dargh, laying a restraining hand upon the great, hairy fist of his friend. "Rhu not like. Hut his friend," he added quietly.

"Any man hurt Rhu, Ord kill!"

Dargh realized only too well just how much Ord meant exactly what he said. "We are only guessing. We do not know," he reassured him, although he failed to feel the confidence he wanted to convey. Ord had but expressed aloud the very feeling that lay deep within his own loyal heart. "Maybe Rhu not know about new Council. Maybe Rhu feel sick," he said hopefully, trying to assuage his own apprehension and at the same time lead Ord's thought away from the terrible situation the big man's words had pictured.

"Huh!" Ord snorted. But he smiled into Dargh's concerned face. "You good man, Dargh," he stated simply, and rising, strode away, shoulders sagging and the usual elasticity seemingly gone from his hairy legs.

Dargh shook his head, running great, gnarled hands through his matted hair. Then he chuckled as he thought of how the night before, while he was sleeping in a carefully selected spot in the brush within earshot of Rhu's home, the catlike tread of Ord twice had passed within inches of his retreat.

"Well," he muttered as he rose to leave for home, "it will be a smart man who gets the best of Rhu."

HUT SPENT much of the afternoon sadly mulling over the morning's events in a secluded spot where he was safe from chance discovery. Just how could he carry out Lord Lithargos' instructions with the least possible embarrassment to himself? When he and Marda had discussed his plans, everything had seemed very simple. It had been no part of his intention to be false to Rhu, but just why did such a clear thinking man as Rhu allow himself to be so immersed in purely material things that he gave little thought to the finer, more essential ones? Was it not far more important to consider the matter of a properly organized governing body than to be so concerned about houses, crops, armies, and the like?

To him and Marda it had appeared clearly evident that with his interest so deeply rooted in these material affairs, Rhu had little taste for the orderly conduct of governmental activities and would be only too glad to have Hut take them over. And if he, Hut, were to be the governmental leader, he must have enough of his own people on the new Council to assure having his ideas carried out.

Many times during the afternoon, he assured himself that he had no intention of even *trying* to take anything away from Rhu. He had merely wanted to relieve him of the duties of ruling so that Rhu would be perfectly free to work with and direct the craftsmen and soldiers.

But excuse himself as he would, the realization that he had been reprimanded by Lord Lithargos for his failure to uphold his best friend pressed heavily upon Hut. More bitter still was this matter of having to go to those whom he had selected to be on the new Council after he had pledged them to his support! Once again the icy sweat beaded his wrinkled forehead.

Then he had a great inspiration! He would enlist the aid of his father! Why had he not thought of this before? With Mai's backing, he could easily devise acceptable excuses for the change of plans regarding the personnel of the Council. With lighter heart, Hut hastened away to put his plan into effect. He knew how to handle Mai!

Nearing the home of his father, he was startled at the change which had occurred since his last visit some five days ago. Extending about ten feet from the front wall of the stone house was a smaller structure consisting of four upright posts set some eight feet apart covered with the familiar thatch and sod roof so long used for their huts. In its cool shade and watching his approach was his father. Looking closer, Hut saw that he sat on a wooden seat not unlike those in his and Rhu's homes.

"When was this built?" Hut asked as he came within speaking distance.

"Nohr built it at Rhu's suggestion," old Mai replied. "He is finishing one before the home of Sol today. Later, Dargh will make them of stone."

Hut frowned. Rhu had not mentioned this innovation, and for the first time, Hut experienced a tinge of jealousy. Why had not HE thought of this? The evident enjoyment it was affording Mai was all too apparent! However, Hut's face betrayed nothing of the new emotion of which he was the unwilling victim, but he knew his father well enough to realize that Rhu's consideration for his comfort would loom large in his eyes.

He went straight to the point. "Father," he said, "I have been thinking about this new Council of which I spoke the last time I was here."

"So has Mai," his father answered eying Hut levelly.

Hut swallowed—hard. "Yes, it is a very important step," he began the carefully thought out explanation he had formulated before coming. "I've given it much thought, and I want to make some changes. I think I should keep only the original members, and add Ord of the Forest Dwellers, and Dargh of the Musons. This means . . . . "

He stopped short as Mai demanded with disconcerting directness, "What *Rhu* think?"

"He agrees, of course," Hut replied, puzzled at Mai's rather abrupt interruption.

"Then why so much Hut and so little Rhu?" Mai pursued his own line of thought. "Mai and Sol always act together. Too much Hut. Too little Rhu in what Hut say."

"Why—why, of course Rhu and I always do all things together, Father."

"Rhu not one of Hut's Council. If Rhu not in Council, Mai not in Council."

Hut frowned. This conversation was not at all as he had planned it, and there was something in Mai's attitude that startled Hut, something he did not quite understand. "Of course Rhu is to be one of the Council," he stated.

"But Hut want to be head." Mai stuck to the point he had in mind. "Not good. Hut tell Mai Rhu discover this place. Hut said Rhu had idea. *Hut* now want rule. Not good. Mai would hear what Rhu say."

"I have already talked with Rhu, and he agrees with my plan," Hut stated flatly.

"Old plan or new plan?" demanded Mai. "Old plan sound more like Rhu."

"Rhu made no objection to the new plan," Hut defended.

"Then why change back to old?" his father quickly demanded.

Hut well knew that for him to admit that Lord Lithargos had objected to the new plan and had insisted upon the original Council remaining intact would discredit him in the eyes of his father. Why had he not included Rhu in his previous talks with his father regarding it? He would then have spared himself this awkward discussion. He was getting into a bad spot, yet if he did not mention Lord Lithargos, he would have to admit that he had not consulted Rhu when naming the new Council.

Then his nimble brain suggested a solution. "Rhu and I talked the matter over with Lord Lithargos, and it was Lord Lithargos who suggested this change in my plan." In a way, this was very true.

Mai's shrewd old eyes bored into Hut's, but he said nothing.

"I want you to help me explain to Hun and Mar Yak, Tun and Sol Kut, and Yaug why they will not be on the Council," Hut explained, coming at last to the point he had in mind when first approaching his father.

But old Mai Dan did not accede so readily. "Why Hut select them in first place?" he asked bluntly.

"Because they are my closest friends. Except, of course, Yaug, who is my brother."

Mai had pondered this subject many times since Hut had first approached him concerning the additional members to the Council. He had tried to fathom just what was Hut's reasoning in the matter and had drawn his own conclusions which, given the occasion, he now expressed.

"So you figure Mai your father, and Sol do as Mai do. Ku Kut do what Mai and Sol do, and maybe Gar Yak! Hut then want five friends his own on Council! Rhu have Ord and Dargh and maybe Dorg Mauk." Holding up his hairy hands, fingers spread, Mai snorted derisively. "Rhu have three to Hut's nine!

"Hut build fire. Hut burn own fingers putting out fire. Mai do what *Sol* do, and Sol do what *Rhu* want. Hut tell Hun and Mar Yak, Tun and Sol Kut, and Yaug be on Council. *Hut* now tell them *not* on Council. Mai do nothing!"

Rising from his stool, Mai entered his house, leaving the sweating and nonplused Hut outside to realize his father's decision was unalterable and that he, Hut, need not expect his backing on any controversial matter unless Sol himself first went against the wishes of Rhu—a very remote possibility, as Hut knew only too well. For the first time, the full nature of the penance Lord Lithargos had placed upon him became clear, and his heart grew heavy.

WHILE HUT was greatly disturbed and disappointed at Mai's reaction to his request for help, it was to his credit that no thought of resentment crept into his heart. He was fair enough to realize that he had brought this about by his own thoughtlessness and lack of consideration for Rhu.

It is exceedingly doubtful whether Hut had even considered taking unfair advantage of Rhu, but there had been times when he regarded the quick-acting Rhu as rather impulsive. It was easily conceivable, therefore, for him to believe there might come times when Rhu would have to be restrained, and it was for this possible, though highly improbable, situation that he had planned. Besides, if anything untoward were to happen to the adventurous Rhu, then the definite control of the Council might become of paramount importance to the welfare of the community. For that matter, neither of them could hope to live forever and, sooner or later, others would inevitably have to replace them. It was for this contingency, Hut assured himself, that he had selected the younger men for the Council.

What Hut had failed to realize was that this undertaking in which he and Rhu were engaged was far greater than any personality or personalities. He had forgotten the part the Elders were playing—and the Lords of Venus and Mercury! Blinded by the fact that he and Rhu had had such important roles thus far, he failed to reason that they were but part of the working out of a Great Plan and that should anything happen to them, the Lords of Venus and Mercury were fully competent to find others to take their places.

WHEN HUT finally reached home, Marda was quick to recognize that something unpleasant was on his mind, but she said nothing as she placed their evening meal upon the table. After he had satisfied his first natural hunger, however, she could restrain herself no longer.

"Did you have a hard day, dear?" she asked quietly.

Hut sighed heavily, but made no answer.

"I am anxious to know whether you got Rhu to agree to our plan for the new Council," she persisted.

Staring gloomily into space, Hut spoke slowly. "Oh, it was not difficult to persuade Rhu. He is ever ready to support any ideas of mine, and I think I presented our plan very aptly. Unfortunately, Lord Lithargos arrived before Rhu had an opportunity to express his own ideas and thus enable us to present a united front."

"Do you mean that Lord Lithargos did not agree to our plan?" There was now a slight edge in Marda's voice.

"W-e-l-l," Hut drawled slowly as she had long since discovered to be his custom when he had unpleasant news to relate, "I would not say that exactly, but He thought the Council should remain as it is with Rhu and me as its head on equal footing."

"That isn't so bad," Marda commented rather relieved. "You can always depend upon your father's support of your ideas, and as *he* does, so will Sol, Ku Kut, and Gar Yak. That gives you control as you will have at least four of the seven on your side, and while not as good as having the others we selected,

from what you say, this will be sufficient. Ord and Dargh do
not reason. They will simply do whatever Rhu says, but if a
problem is submitted to all the community, the clan votes will
be mostly on your side. The Yaks, Kuts, and the Kus, since
Sol and Mai always agree, will all side with Mai. I wouldn't
bother about it. Besides, Rhu will never fail you," she finished
with deep conviction, unconsciously paying Rhu a very great
tribute.

"But I have to tell Yaug and the others they are not to be
on the Council, and that isn't going to be an easy thing to
do. They were greatly elated over being selected for that
honor."

"Oh, that's easy," Marda commented quickly. "Get Rhu to do
it. They will blame it on him, and you can explain it away later
after the first shock of their disappointment is over."

"But Lord Lithargos said that *I* was to do it," Hut stated
flatly. His face flamed with resentment that Marda should always be referring to Rhu's ability to handle disagreeable situations so efficiently.

"He *didn't!*" Marda exclaimed incredulously. "Why should
He do that?"

This was the very point Hut had sought to avoid. "I'm not
entirely sure," he said evasively. "It seemed as if he felt that I
should have taken Rhu into my confidence before the appoint-
ments were made and had him with me when it was done."

"No!" Marda's surprise was very evident. "What did Rhu
say?"

Hut's face darkened with embarrassment. "W-e-l-l," he
drawled, "Rhu pointed out that I was consulting with him just
before we observed Lord Lithargos was there. There is no use
trying to deceive the Great Ones, Marda. You should know
that. I do not know how much of what I had said He overheard, but He was not fooled, although I did not mean to
take any unfair advantage of Rhu."

"Of course you didn't," Marda said appeasingly. "But did you
not remind Him that the Elders have always said every group
requires a directive head?" She smiled a trifle sarcastically although her voice betrayed no such feeling.

"And have Him think I *meant* to supplant Rhu or did not

want to share the direction of the work here with him!" It was plain Hut considered her idea rather a stupid one.

Marda stiffened and a glint appeared briefly in her eyes, but if Hut observed this, he made no comment.

"No, I simply agreed to see Yaug and the others as He requested." Hut hesitated as if uncertain whether to proceed, then his mouth tightened. Sooner or later Marda would have to know. "I thought it all over this afternoon and decided to see my father and get his help. That would have made it possible for me to escape having to admit I had made a mistake, but . . . . " Again, he hesitated.

Should he go on? *Could* he do it and not disappoint Marda too much? After all, had they not planned this thing together? Drawing a long breath, he plunged into the account of his interview with Mai.

Food untouched, Marda listened, her expression changing from utter amazement to one of hot-tempered rage. Her face grew brick red, then whitened as she slowly got to her feet. Startled, Hut stopped talking to stare at her in stunned surprise, cowed by the bitterness in her blazing eyes.

"You—you," she cried, almost choking over her words. "You," she repeated, "you blunderer! Why did you not include Rhu in your talk? 'I, I, I'," she stormed. "Can't you ever learn to say 'we' once in awhile? Now we shall have to make all our plans anew, and everybody will be watching every word we say, everything we try to do, and every single step we take. I'll bet *Rhu* would never have been caught in any such predicament!" she cried accusingly, shrewdly choosing the most stinging thing she could possibly have said.

Grimly, Hut got to his feet. There was but one way to handle such a situation.

Chapter Twenty-three

HOME DISCIPLINE

ALL THE AFTERNOON Rhu tried to fight down the sense of depression which weighed upon him, but even Ord's new idea of organizing his army into companies according to the men's height did not arouse his interest. It was as his two loyal friends had surmised; Rhu was sick at heart from the knowledge of Hut's failure to keep his trust. The very bottom seemed to have fallen out of everything. Nothing, he felt, could have been more unexpected or disheartening than to find his lifelong and beloved friend so weak and unreliable. He could not seem to quite understand it.

Strive as he would to hide his dejection, as we now know, Rhu deceived no one, least of all Haitee who, as was her custom, met him that evening as he came through the trees near the house. Quietly, she slipped her small hand into his and silently they entered the house where Rhu sank down heavily upon his stool.

"You are tired," she said solicitously, placing the hot food upon the table. But for all her simulated air of unconcern, Rhu was keenly aware that she was also very conscious of his mental depression.

They ate in silence and when they were finished, Haitee set things to rights, knowing full well that in due time, Rhu would relieve himself of the burden which was preying upon him. Finally, he spoke.

"Lord Lithargos was here today," he stated, deciding to begin his explanation from that point.

"What did He think of Hut's selection for the Council?" Haitee asked, so unexpectedly that Rhu was startled.

"How did *you* know about that?" he demanded, and before she could reply, "Why didn't you tell me before?"

"I learned it only this morning when Grut was here with some vegetables from his garden and the two birds for our evening meal. He said Yaug had told him that Hut had selected Yaug to be one of the Council. You have never mentioned anything about doing this, so I felt sure he was doing it without having consulted you. After Grut left, I went over to see Marda to make sure. I did not ask her directly, except to ask how Hut was progressing with the selection of members for the Council.

"Rhu, I have never before known Marda to try to deceive me, but she looked so guilty and was so evasive in her attempts to make me feel she knew nothing about it that I just *knew* she was mixed up in it. I did not press the matter because her attitude was anything but friendly or frank, so I changed the subject and talked about how thoughtful Grut is in bringing us water and wood and other things. Then she became angrier than I have ever seen Marda and demanded to know why he was doing so much for us and nothing for her and Hut. It wasn't until then that I realized he had never done these things for them and the depth of her resentment because of it. I tried to tell her that Grut was doing it of his own volition as I know you would have included them in any such plan. I know now that I should never have mentioned it, but I never dreamed that Grut was not doing the same for her and Hut."

"It is Grut's own idea," Rhu admitted. "It never occurred to me to mention it, but knowing Grut, and that he had undertaken this the very first day after we were married, I knew he would keep right on doing it unless I told him not to. Who does get their wood and water?" he asked.

"Marda says *she* has always had to bring their water, but that Hut had instructed one of the Forest Dwellers to bring them their wood. Our wood is always uniform in size and easily handled, but Marda's looks as if the Forest Dweller grabbed whatever brush and chunks that came handy, and some of the pieces are so big I doubt whether I could lift them. I'm glad I didn't mention that Grut also brings our food for she has often complained that she has a lot of trouble in getting the sort of things Hut likes best. I only hope she does not say anything to Grut about it."

"Grut can take care of himself," Rhu said with a chuckle, his spirits rising as he pictured what would probably happen if Marda undertook to chide his blunt and stubborn brother.

"Well, what did Lord Lithargos say?" asked Haitee, impatient to know the entire story of what had been troubling Rhu.

"He did not like Hut's selecting new members for the Council and asked him why he had done it without consulting me. Hut said he thought I was so busy with other things that he did not want to bother me. But Lord Lithargos said that for the present the Council was to remain as it is. Then he told Hut to tell those he had selected that they were not to be on the Council. I felt sorry for Hut and would gladly have done it for him."

"*You would!*" Haitee almost snorted. "Let him do his own explaining! You would have taken all the blame, and Hut would later have wormed his way out of it."

"Hut wouldn't do anything like that," Rhu defended. "At least, he is always fair."

"Then, why did he try to put so many of his own friends on the Council? And incidentally, Rhu, Grut says that both Dargh and Ord kept watch over our house last night. He saw them from where he was hiding where he could watch our door."

"Huh?" Rhu exclaimed. "I'm not surprised at Grut, but why would Ord and Dargh do that?"

Haitee giggled over Rhu's all too evident amazement. "Neither one knew the other was doing it, unless it was Dargh who had hidden where Ord almost stepped on him without knowing he was there. Grut told me he had seen that himself, and he considered it a huge joke on them."

"He would!" Rhu chuckled softly, his eyes very tender. "That would be just his idea of a perfect joke. But why would they do it?" He frowned. "Surely, if Ord and Dargh knew of this Council thing, they would have told me about it. Besides, why should they think we should be guarded?"

"Maybe they have seen the tracks of some animal around here and thought to capture it," Haitee ventured.

"Humph!" Rhu snorted skeptically. "Ord would not seek to catch any wild animal by walking around or pacing up and down where he hoped to get a chance at it. Their actions indicate they were guarding against man! But that is absurd!" He paused for a moment and then exclaimed sharply, "What more do you know about this, Haitee?"

"I know nothing else, but there is *something* about all of it that isn't right. Rhu, I don't like to say this, but do you think Hut and Marda might have some idea of assuming control of our people? With a Council composed of relatives and friends, and knowing that Mai and your father always act together, might they not have thought it possible that Hut could influence his father so that nearly all the people would be on their side?"

"I don't believe it!" Rhu stated so positively that Haitee knew better than to pursue her line of reasoning. However, she could see from his air of preoccupation that her idea was being given serious consideration. None knew better than she what such a situation would mean to Rhu; still, she felt she must voice her suspicion.

After a long silence, Rhu sighed heavily and his face brightened. "Hut and I have always worked together, and we each know the other is ever ready to work out any difficulties in his ideas," he said as though thinking aloud. "Besides, Ord and Dargh are to be on the Council, and I am not without influence with both my father and Mai. So I see no possibility of any such trouble, Haitee, even though it was intentionally planned, which I cannot believe. Hut does seem to like to lead and to exercise power. Lord Lithargos cautioned him against it. But he is no snake to bite without reason. . . . Just what do you mean by 'taking sides'? I can understand how the Plains Dwellers, for example, would join together against the Forest Dwellers in the old times, but there is no such situation here. What gave you such an idea?"

"In her anger against Grut, Marda referred to him as having favorites and siding against her and Hut. You see, Rhu, among the Cari Yans, families often split up when one of the sons gets the idea of gaining control. He persuades others of the family to join with him—to take sides, as we expressed it. Quite often the son influences his brothers to form a family council of which the father is supposed to be the head. But he, too, has to abide by what the council decides, and sooner or later, the son who wants control gets the council to agree to his ideas. In this way, and without destroying the family, he gains the control he wants.

"This plan of increasing the Council here looks to me as if Marda has influenced Hut to follow a similar course, even though, like you, he may have had no idea as to the direction in which it was leading. Marda is very jealous because our house has three rooms. This afternoon, she even said that a three-room house did not make us any better than her and Hut, but that Grut's serving us only went to show that we *felt* superior to them.

"I don't know where she gets such ideas. I never intimated any such thing, nor did I ever think about it at all. I pointed out that their rooms are larger, and because you had wanted Hut to have the first home, it had been built first, and this added room was but a new idea that Nohr and Dargh had evolved. She had to admit there was something to that, but she says she is going to have Hut build them a house with *four* rooms as *she* intends to have a large family. Humph!" she snorted rather inelegantly, "I guess we can have just as . . . . " She stopped short, mouth open and eyes distended for, from the direction of Hut's home, a piercing scream stabbed through the night!

Rhu hurriedly grabbed his war axe, and emerging quickly from the house, he immediately saw the mighty bulk of Dargh outlined against Hut's lighted doorway. Before he could take another step in that direction, however, two powerful, yet strangely gentle, hairy hands grasped his arms, lifted him from his feet, and carried him back into his own home.

Still speechless, Haitee now stared in wild-eyed amazement at the towering man who was gently and easily placing Rhu upon his feet.

Ord's bewhiskered face wore a wide grin. "Rhu not blame Ord," the big fellow said uneasily as his friend spun about. "Rhu cannot help. Hut teach Marda wife's place in family hut. Dargh see no real harm come." He smiled at the startled Haitee.

Rhu studied Ord's face with wide eyes, then relaxed. "You

do not mean that Hut is beating Marda?" he asked in utter astonishment.

"Marda mad. Try tell Hut Hut fool. Hut teach Marda Marda mind Hut and not call Hut fool. Hut mad too! *Marda* fool." Ord nodded his great, shaggy head vigorously.

"Oh, oh!" Haitee gasped. "Oh, Rhu!"

Rhu tossed aside his razor-edged war axe and grinned at Ord. "I don't think I'd want to fight *you*," he said with a chuckle. "I was perfectly helpless in your hands."

The heavy rumble in Ord's hair-matted chest was his idea of an echoing chuckle. "Ord grab before Rhu have chance!" he boomed. "Rhu have chance, Ord run," and his laugh bellowed into the night. "Ord strong; Rhu quick like stag!"

"Oh, Ord!" Haitee said tremulously, her eyes very bright at the compliment he had paid Rhu. She well knew that Ord feared no man, and the idea of the gigantic fellow fleeing from one as small as Rhu did much to relieve her tension and bring a happy smile to her face.

"I wonder whether I should go over," Rhu asked Haitee.

"No. Marda will love him all the more. I think she deserved it," she said sincerely. "I didn't think Hut had it in him, but I once saw him fight a bear." She smiled happily over the memory.

"Hut kill bear?" demanded Ord.

To Rhu's great embarrassment, Haitee proceeded to relate the story of Rhu and Hut's epochal fight with the bear. Nor would either she or Ord permit him to interrupt to correct some of her very definitely biased description. "And here is the knife Rhu used to kill the bear," she concluded, handing the perspiring Ord the blade which she had always treasured. "Hut wound another rawhide grip on it," she added.

Almost tenderly, the big man turned the blade over and over in his great, hairy hand that made the knife seem small and inadequate by contrast. "Ord give leg to see," he rumbled. "No man but Rhu could do." He eyed the sheathed knife suspended from Rhu's waist and without which he was never seen and added, "Ord glad grabbed both arms!"

No amount of explanation or denial by Rhu was ever successful in convincing Ord that Rhu alone had not killed the bear, and many and many a night, Ord could be heard retelling the story with many fanciful additions he evolved in his own mind, each of which but served to enhance the credit of Rhu. And never did Ord start to tell of it when there was not a concerted rush among the Forest Dwellers to hear it. They never seemed to tire of listening and eventually, it became an heroic legend.

But on this night, Ord confined the telling to Dargh who, in his turn, again writhed and sweated copiously as Ord elaborated upon the gory struggle. This tale was quite unlike Rhu's original and more modest description as told to Waugh and the Cave Dwellers. Already, Ord was adding many intimate details which, in his eyes, enhanced Rhu's indomitable skill and bravery, and which Dargh accepted without question. He finally climaxed the story by telling of Rhu's grabbing the bear by the ear with his teeth and dragging the foaming brute from the prostrate Hut, while he hammered in its skull with his war club.

THE FOLLOWING morning proved to be one long to be remembered by all concerned. Hut left his house long before Rhu started his own family fire. Ord and Dargh were busily regaling both the Forest Dwellers and the Musons with the story of Rhu's battle with the bear. Haitee was consumed with curiosity as to what had happened to Marda. Marda was determined to have it out with Grut and was going to insist that he no longer discriminate between her and Haitee, while Rhu was deeply concerned over the nature of his coming talk with Hut. Hut, in turn, was no less concerned about the same thing.

Up much earlier than usual, Marda was in time to see Grut steal up to Rhu's house and deposit two brimming jars of water on the door step. Hurrying outside, she waylaid him as he departed for his next load. "Grut," she called.

The big fellow stopped and turned toward her as she hastened to his side. "Huh!" he grunted as she neared him. "Marda have accident? Eye black, face bruised."

Marda's face flamed and her anger mounted. How dare he question her! Not stopping to think that perhaps his question was well intentioned, she ignored it and made the mistake of venting her rage upon him. "Grut!" she snapped. "Don't you know that you are supposed to bring me water and wood, just as you do for Haitee?"

"Huh?" he grunted in some surprise, and with a tightening of the mouth that should have warned her.

"You heard me!" she snipped. "I order you to do for me exactly what you have been doing for Haitee."

Grut glowered down at her. "Grut do what Grut want do."

"Then you'd better want to do as I say," she stormed, almost beside herself as she thought of the probability of the sharp-eared Haitee overhearing her conversation, if it may be so called—not realizing that Haitee was still asleep and missing it all.

Grut's eyes brightened as an idea came into his slow-moving mind. "Hut better beat Marda more," he grunted. "Marda no good. Grut do as want. Nobody order Grut. Marda get own wood and water like other women. Haitee *Rhu's* wife." Turning his back upon the nonplused girl, he strode away, dismissing the entire matter from his mind as definitely settled. And so far as Grut was concerned, it was. She was not HIS wife, so why should he be bothered about what she wanted?

"Some day," Marda stormed to herself, "some day I'll make that hulking brute regret his words!" Weeping with rage, she returned to her house to sit crying beside the slowly dying fire.

Suddenly she realized that Hut had left without touching his breakfast, and a great fear welled up in her heart. Presently she smiled and her eyes grew tender. "He really loves me!" she exclaimed softly, and began happily attending to her morning chores. For the time being, she even forgot her rebuff by the indomitable Grut. With meticulous care, she began preparations for the evening meal. She would have for Hut everything he liked most, even though she would have to go to his mother for a supply of some of them.

Then she went into her bedroom, glanced into her gazing pool, and gasped. No wonder Grut had asked what had happened! How could she ever face Hut's mother looking like this? Wisely, she decided not to go. She would ask Haitee for some suggestions. Maybe she could persuade her to go to Hut's mother for her!

It was quite some time after she had seen Rhu leave that Marda finally summoned up sufficient courage to face Haitee.

Since she had dismissed their conversation of yesterday from her own mind, it did not occur to her that Haitee might not have done likewise. It was what she had seen in the gazing pool which deterred her. How was she ever to explain her bruised face! But if Hut were to have the delicacy she had in mind, she would have to approach Haitee.

Standing in the doorway of Haitee and Rhu's home, she greeted her friend in the customary manner.

"Oh, come in, Marda," Haitee invited. "I'll be there shortly. I'm making up our bed," she explained. A little later as she entered the main room where Marda sat facing the door, she caught her breath, for the side of Marda's face toward her was bruised, and her eye swollen almost shut. What could she say?

Then her impulsive heart softened. "Oh, you poor thing!" she exclaimed gently. "Come here by the fire and let me bathe that face. Before he left, Que gave me some leaves that are fine for bruises and hurts. I'll have to soak them in hot water first, then tie them over the hurt. I fell over a stool and bruised my shin, but this stuff cured it almost at once." She dropped some of the now dry leaves into a small bowl of hot water from the fire, stirring it from time to time as the two talked about everything they could think of except what was uppermost in both their minds.

"That surely feels good," Marda said gratefully as the soothing poultice began taking almost immediate effect. "Que didn't leave *me* any," she announced.

"Oh, he said he was able to find only a few," Haitee explained. "He's going to search again when he comes next time, when I am sure he'll give you a good supply."

"Haitee, I wonder whether you would go over to the Dan home and ask Hut's mother for some of those green things he likes so well. I look so terrible I hate to go myself."

"Of course I will," Haitee agreed readily. "I wanted to see her and Rhu's mother anyhow, so I can do both at once. Have a drink?" offering Marda some of the sweet, cool water Grut had brought fresh that morning. As Marda gratefully drank, Haitee wondered whether this could possibly be the same girl she had visited yesterday. Well, she would try to emulate Rhu and act as if nothing at all had happened.

The morning grew steadily hotter, and before she was halfway to the Dan home, Haitee was almost sorry she had started. Then she met Grut carrying a great load of wood she knew was destined for her. "Hello, Grut," she called to him, and he dropped his burden to come grinning to her side.

"Sun hot," Grut rumbled. "Haitee want something?"

"I was going over to Mai Dan's to get from Hut's mother some of those green things Hut likes so well. Marda asked me to get them for her."

Grut's deepset eyes glowed. "Grut get for Haitee. Haitee go back. Stay inside. Big storm come. Grut bring weeds for Hut to Haitee. Haitee no tell Marda Grut get," he said gruffly.

His bewhiskered and usually dour face was now positively glum, and Haitee shrewdly suspected that Marda had made good her threat to speak to him. She well knew, however, that Grut would mention it only when he was good and ready to do so.

"Grut, you are a perfect dear," she said softly, for after Rhu, this hulking fellow came next in her affections. "I would not have asked this of you, but I will surely appreciate it if you will get the stuff for me. I don't like storms."

Grut's face softened and his smile was warm and friendly. "Grut *glad* do anything for Haitee." He paused for a moment and then went on, "Hut tell Yaug Yaug not on Council. Yaug mad. Say like Rhu best. Hut like woman. Woman don't know own mind. Change all time. Haitee good. Not like Marda. Marda just woman." And leaving Haitee to digest his words as she saw fit, Grut started for the Dan home on the run. Heat meant little to him.

AT ABOUT the usual time, Rhu climbed the steps to his old quarters which he and Hut now used for their personal conferences and meetings. He found a distraught Hut had arrived before him, eyes encircled by dark rings, and two parallel scratches reaching from his temple to his chin. However, his cheery "Hello, Hut," gave no indication of his having observed anything out of the ordinary.

Hut's face softened and his eyes brightened for he knew that not a thing about his appearance had escaped Rhu's sharp eyes. How good it was to have such a friend! Then his face darkened as the matter of the Council came to mind with its

intimation of falsity. Why had he ever listened to Marda! Could
he make Rhu understand he really meant no betrayal of
friendship? He must try, and the longer he waited, the harder
it was going to be. So, smiling wanly into Rhu's face, he
plunged into his confession.

"Rhu, no matter how it may seem, and no matter what I have
done that was wrong, I want you to know that I never had any
intention or even thought of trying to supplant you in anything. I can see now that what I was doing could have given
me just that power, but I can only tell you that I never would
have used it. You are my best friend. You always have been
and always shall be.

"Yesterday, I thought I could escape the humiliation of having to explain to the others that they are not to be on the Council. I felt sure my father would help me, so I went to get him
instead of following Lord Lithargos' instructions. Some day I
hope I'll learn that when one seeks to evade tasks suggested
by the Great Ones, he only makes bad situations worse.

"Father denounced me for what I had done, said he would
do only as Sol directs, and that I could burn my own fingers
pulling the embers from the fire I had built. I want you to
know this because it places the entire power of direction in
your hands and without your having stirred so much as one
finger to gain it. I am so ashamed of myself that I dread to go
about my task of telling Yaug and the others, but of course, I
must do it."

Rhu's warm heart ached for his friend in his predicament,
and he said impulsively, "Aw, Hut, why not let me go along and
help? I'm even willing to go and do it for you!"

"No, Rhu. I may have been acting like a fool in this thing
thus far, but I'm not so foolish as to think I can escape meeting
my own tests. No, I'm going to do this thing myself, come what
may." He sighed dismally and continued, "There is something
else, Rhu, which I should not have done. Last night . . . ."
he began and Rhu would have stopped him. "No," he insisted,
"I am going to make a clean breast of it. You have the right
to know the worst. Marda made me angry, then made matters
worse by making me jealous because of her continual references
to how much more efficient and dependable you are than I am.

"She even stood up in my own house and defied me, even to clawing my face when I approached to assert myself. Then I saw red and knocked her down. I picked her up, but I was still so angry that I slapped her face so hard it knocked her across the room. I don't know what got into me. I am so ashamed that I don't see how I can face the Elders, let alone Lord Lithargos."

Coming to Hut's side, Rhu slapped him on the back, then placed his arm around his shoulders. "You do just what I am going to do . . . . forget it. Every man must maintain discipline in his own home, and Haitee says Marda will love you all the more for it."

"Haitee!" exclaimed Hut, his face crimson.

"Don't let it bother you, Hut. We heard Marda scream, and I started for your house. Ord stopped me, but Dargh was standing by at your door to see that nobody got really hurt. Don't worry about those two either, for they will say nothing. At present, Ord is so full of Haitee's biased version of our fight with the bear that he will think of little else for some time to come. Anyway, he thought you were doing exactly the right thing, and what either Ord or Dargh thinks, you can be pretty sure the other will agree.

"Do you know, Hut, I've been thinking you and I should go to the grove and pray to N'Kul. We've rather neglected this ceremony lately. How about meeting me here early tomorrow and greeting His arising?"

"All right. Like you, I think we should observe this oftener," Hut agreed enthusiastically. "I'll meet you in plenty of time."

At this point, Dargh came rushing up the steps. "Rhu," he cried, almost breathlessly, "I would speak with you alone . . . . soon," he added after a brief pause, and he seemed to be struggling for something further to say.

Feeling much more like his old self since Rhu's arrival, Hut shrewdly guessed that Dargh was trying to excuse himself for excluding him. He knew how hard it was for their people to excuse anything they did and not seem weak in so doing, so he quickly put him at ease. "That's all right, Dargh," he said, "I was just getting ready to leave, so you can go right ahead with Rhu."

Chapter Twenty-four

"WATER ROCKS"

D ARGH'S PERTURBATION was quite apparent, and seeing that the big fellow was evidently laboring under
some strong emotion, or else was having trouble in stating his
errand, Rhu invited him to sit down. "What troubles you?" he
asked.

Still Dargh hesitated as if experiencing difficulty in finding
the right words to express what was on his mind. Then he drew
a long breath and his eyes brightened. "Rhu know Dargh value
Rhu's friendship more than anything," he began. As Rhu
nodded his assent, he continued. "Wardu say Hut and Rhu not
agree." Here Dargh's jaw set. "Dargh know Hut make Council
without Rhu. Dargh and Ord back Rhu no matter what come.
Wardu think whole scheme fail if Rhu and Hut not agree.
Wardu want to return to tribe. Ord say no unless Rhu say yes."

"Tell Ord to bring Wardu here," Rhu ordered, frowning that
such a situation should have come so quickly, and wished
fervently that Hut were back.

Stepping to the front of the room, Dargh called his message
to Ord, who, judging from the brief time before he arrived
with Wardu, evidently had been below awaiting the summons.

"Sit down," Rhu invited the three. Then addressing Wardu,
he went directly to the point. "What leads you to believe there
is any disagreement between Hut and me?" he asked.

Uneasily, Wardu glanced from Ord to Dargh, then back to
Rhu as if uncertain whether to be frank.

"You may speak freely, Wardu," Rhu reassured him. "Ord
and Dargh are my confidants."

"Hut form Council without Rhu," Wardu began. "Wardu believe present plan not succeed if Rhu and Hut not work together. Wardu like Rhu and think Rhu make best leader. Many in valley think Hut want rule. No like. Want Rhu." Here he hesitated as if pondering what to say next.

Rhu remained silent, sensing what was to come, his nimble brain already formulating his reply.

"Wardu get many Cari Yans. Ord get many Forest Dwellers, and Dargh many Musons. Why not divide Rhu Hut Plains. Rhu start new group. Rhu control. Let Hut have those who like Hut."

Ord and Dargh looked anxiously at Rhu, although they said no word to indicate how they felt regarding this proposed split. Yet, there was no mistaking their determination to abide by Rhu's decision whatever it was.

Rhu drew a long breath, and his eyes hardened. "Wardu, Hut and I started this plan because it met with the approval of the Elders. Hut made a little mistake in his manner of altering the Council before consulting them. We all make mistakes, and it was not Hut's desire to assume undue authority. He is now advising those with whom he talked that the Council is to remain as the Elders would have it.

"It was his desire and intention that he and I were to be at the head of the Council and work together as we always have. Therefore, you are mistaken in thinking there is any disagreement between us. But even so, I would not desert him or the people who have come here to help in forming this community. I have no desire to rule. I merely want to help the Elders in the forwarding of their Great Plan."

"But Hut told Wardu this Hut's plan," Wardu stated positively.

Ord's great chest heaved with pent emotion, his jaw tightening grimly, while Dargh half arose to his feet, then sank back, his face grim and unrelenting.

Rhu fully realized that this was no time for hesitation. "Wardu must have misunderstood Hut," he said. "Hut speaks fluently and sometimes a bit too rapidly for many to grasp his meaning." Rhu got to his feet. "I will not listen to idle gossip or form any opinions upon mere guesswork. I do not question

your sincerity, but it must be understood that Hut and I will
continue to work together as we always have. Never again
refer to this very distressing subject.

"If you do not like what we are doing, Wardu, I shall gladly
permit you to return to your tribe, but if you want to remain
with us and become a part of this work, then you must accept

Dargh, Rhu, and Ord

things as they are. You may leave now. Ord, I want you and
Dargh to remain."

As Wardu left, Ord looked at Dargh, who nodded his shaggy
head in vigorous agreement with Rhu's decision, and Ord's
face relaxed into a broad smile.

Although his heart warmed to the loyalty of these two fast
friends, Rhu's face was very grim as he faced them. "Ord, I
want both you and Dargh to know how much I appreciate
your loyalty to me, but the welfare of our people means far
more than either Hut or myself. Neither of us can expect to

live forever. Sooner or later, the Council will have to take our places, and then the Council will be directed by the Elders. We must all learn to think of the group's welfare first at all times, even though it might mean seeming to desert our dearest friends. Always must the welfare of the group come first in all our considerations.

"We three know that Hut made a mistake, but who among us has not made many mistakes? He realizes what he has done and is doing everything in his power to correct it. Who can do more? I am depending upon you two to correct any misunderstandings among those with whom you talk. It is not necessary to admit that Hut erred. Simply say there was a slight misunderstanding and that everything is now all right."

"What Rhu say, Ord do. Ord have own personal opinion. Hut mistake worse than Rhu say. Rhu too good. Ord work for group, but Ord never desert Rhu." The air of finality he gave to his words was very ample proof of the big fellow's unalterable determination, and Rhu would have been less than human not to appreciate this undying loyalty.

Slowly, Dargh got to his feet and stood before Rhu who had now seated himself. "Dargh agree with Ord. What Rhu say, Dargh do also. Hut did say what Wardu repeat. Speak to Wardu where Dargh overhear. He say often, 'I—my plan.' Too much Hut and too little Rhu. Few 'we,' many 'I.' Dargh glad Hut undo mistake, but Dargh kill any Muson who do not do as Rhu say. Dargh understand group most important, but Dargh follow Rhu always. Rhu always do what right."

Rhu felt the sting of unshed tears in his eyes as he looked into the faces of these two undyingly loyal friends. What could he have ever done to merit such fealty? His voice was rather husky as he answered. "I can only say that I hope I shall always merit the good opinion you two friends hold for me. I hope you both realize that I, too, would die gladly for either of you, and I truly hope it can never be said of me that I have been any less loyal to my friends than you two are to me. I am sorry Hut created such an impression, for I do not believe he meant to."

Ord's face twitched as he sought for the words that seemingly would not come.

Dargh cleared his whiskery throat, his own eyes very bright. He swallowed several times, then spoke. "Dargh say watch Marda. Marda lead Hut if Hut not careful. Dargh hear much Dargh not say. Marda want Hut rule." And before Rhu could think of anything to say, the two big men strode away.

RHU became so immersed in his own thoughts that he did not heed the passing of time or the unusual and steadily mounting heat of the day. Of all that had been said since Hut's departure, nothing had so impressed him as Dargh's last words and his admonition regarding Marda. This, coupled with last night's events and Hut's remarks concerning Marda and their disagreement was food for serious consideration. How much, he wondered, did Haitee know?

Understanding the taciturn Dargh so well, he realized that he had actually said far less than he knew. Ugly suspicions for which he bitterly reproached himself crept into Rhu's mind. Although he could not dismiss them entirely, the knowledge that Dargh was alerted to the situation brought him a sense of peace. Nothing of serious moment could eventuate without Dargh's advising him.

Meanwhile, Hut was about his mission which proved as disagreeable as he had expected. Yaug, his favorite brother, had flared up, and emulating Mai, told Hut flatly that from now on, his loyalty was pledged to the more competent Rhu. Nor was his position improved when Hun Yak, although far less vitriolic in his comments than Yaug, mentioned there was already developing among the tribesmen the idea of a split in their group. Something of a realization of the significance of Lord Lithargos' statements about the responsibilities inseparable from the assumption of power began to dawn upon Hut.

The climax came, however, when Mar Yak, after listening to his explanation of the change in the Council organization without comment, lifted his bushy head and looking Hut straight in the eyes, echoed the words of Mai. "Too much Hut and too little Rhu," he grunted. Then, to make bad matters still worse, he added, "Hut talk, talk. Rhu DO. Mar *like* Hut, *admire* Rhu. Ku Kut same," he finished. Deliberately turning his back upon Hut, he walked away.

Never in his experience had Hut been the recipient of such disdainful treatment as his father and now his friends had accorded him. But Hut was intelligent, and though his feelings had suffered, he forgot that part in the awakening realization that he had taken what might easily prove to be a very serious and ruinous step in seeking to gain control of the Council.

As he walked back to the meeting place, apprehensions regarding the probable outcome of his action assailed him. Already he could see an incipient schism taking place in the ranks of their group which, if not immediately arrested, would grow until the good which had been accomplished would crumple and finally disappear.

Then the words of Lord Lithargos came to mind: "The forming of this civilization no single man may defeat," and his uncertainty increased. Could it be possible that Lord Lithargos had meant that anything or anybody that threatened the success of this great venture would be swept aside? Might his ill-advised action cause him to lose his place in the growing civilization?

Vainly, he strove to reassure himself that he had nothing but the best of intentions when he sought to put his plan into effect. Somehow, however, he could not quite convince himself of the rightness of what he had done. His heart grew heavy, and his head ached with the oppressiveness of the heat. Dargh's pool was a welcome sight, and kneeling beside it, he bathed his throbbing forehead and flushed face in its cooling overflow, then drank deeply.

Revived physically, his mind began to function afresh, and he became almost cheerful. He would talk everything over with Rhu who, he was sure, would not only understand but would help him. Together, they would restore a united front and quickly end all speculation as to any possible rift in their group.

Getting to his feet, he observed Wardu approaching. For some obscure reason he could not fathom, he had never been able to warm up to this outspoken Cari Yan, but something in Wardu's purposeful approach caused him to wait.

"Wardu would speak with Hut," the Cari Yan announced after the customary greeting.

Hut led the way to a boulder beneath a nearby oak where they sat down. "What is on your mind?" he asked.

"Wardu have long talk with Rhu this morning," Wardu began, and Hut repressed a start. "Wardu spoke of trouble between Rhu and Hut. Wardu take no sides. Wardu would hear what Hut say."

A cold chill shot up Hut's spine. "What did Rhu say?" he asked.

"Rhu say no trouble. Say Rhu and Hut agree on all things, but Wardu know different. Perhaps Rhu not know what Hut and Wardu and others know."

Hut did not hear Wardu's last rather sarcastic comment so grateful was he to Rhu for covering for him. A comforting sense of well-being welled up in his heart. "How like Rhu," he thought to himself. "He is always to be depended upon." Aloud, he said, "There is no disagreement, Wardu. I can't understand why you should feel there is."

"Wardu no fool. Wardu know Hut form Council without Rhu. Wardu know Hut have many powerful friends. Friends gladly follow Hut. Hut head Council, Hut rule Plains. Split between leaders not good. Split between friends bad. Wardu know two cannot rule. Why Hut put friends on Council if Hut not want rule?" he asked abruptly.

Hut frowned heavily. "W-e-l-l," he drawled as he strove to assemble his thoughts into some semblance of order before answering this determined man's questions. "W-e-l-l," he repeated, "there are many reasons why I did as I did. In the first place, Rhu, as you well know, is a very busy man attending to many complex things. I had the time, and it was my thought to take this part of the load upon my shoulders to spare him. It was only natural that after the heads of the families, I should first approach those most friendly."

"Friendly to Hut or to Rhu?" Wardu asked bluntly.

Hut's frown deepened. "I did not think of it in that light." And then as though prompted by Wardu's question, the idea came. "I knew they were all friendly to Rhu. Ask even my brother Yaug, or Hun Yak. Ask my father," he added with growing confidence. "No, Wardu, this is where appearances are deceiving. Besides, I have just told Tun and Sol Kut, Mar and Hun Yak as well as my brother, Yaug, that the Council is not to be changed."

"Why? Because Rhu want it so?" Wardu persisted.

This was a trying spot, Hut realized, for he could not know what Rhu might have said. "What did Rhu say?" he countered.

"Rhu not say," Wardu answered truthfully, "except that it was now as Elders would have it."

"See?" Hut said with relief. "We are both governed by the wishes of the Elders. Rhu had not complained."

"But Hut tell Wardu Council Hut's plan. Hut not mention Rhu then."

"I took it for granted that you would know Rhu was included," Hut answered uneasily. Wardu was a difficult man with whom to talk, and Hut felt his dislike growing.

"Wardu not blame Hut." Wardu's tone became almost ingratiating. "Wardu merely think Hut smarter than Rhu and seek rule. Wardu like strong man."

These were pleasant words, and in spite of himself, Hut's feeling regarding the man began to reverse itself. Perhaps he should cultivate this forthright person. "Rhu is a strong man, so is Ord, and so is Dargh," he said.

"Ord big. Dargh crush ordinary man . . . . so." Wardu closed his fist slowly as if squeezing something in it. "Rhu not so mighty, yet Rhu strong thinker. Hut strong thinker. Hut smart. Think ahead. Wardu like that."

Hut tried to keep a rising sense of pride from showing in his face, but his chest swelled. It was good, especially after his morning's depressing experiences, thus to be praised from this unexpected source. "One has to think ahead, Wardu. It is due to this that our group has prospered. Rhu, however, is quick and fine at handling situations as they arise. That is why we work so well together."

"Wardu know." The Cari Yan smiled innocently into Hut's face, and for some reason, Hut found himself wondering how much of that innocence was real. "Wardu like Hut. Wardu like man think ahead. Hut like Wardu bring in Cari Yan friends? Good men," he added.

"Yes indeed," Hut hastened to assure him. "We can always use good men who are loyal." Here he stopped abruptly, remembering the plan of the Elders for training new people for the group. He frowned and wondered if he should tell Wardu of this, then decided against it. "The time is not right just yet," he said. "I will tell you when to go and interest them."

Thus they parted, each feeling he had made the start of a mutually profitable deal.

Hut started toward his and Rhu's meeting place just as there was a sullen rumble of distant thunder. Seeing the dense, swirling thunderheads begin creeping over the mountains, he decided to return to Marda and see Rhu later in the day, or in the morning if the storm developed into what his experience indicated was coming. The thought of Marda and the occurrence of the evening before had troubled him all during the day despite Rhu's advice that he forget the incident.

Well knowing Haitee's fear of storms, Rhu left for his own home with the first thunder growls still echoing in the still and oppressive air. A glance backward toward the mountains showed that their crests had already disappeared in the dense clouds which seemed to be settling into the Plains with tremendous speed. As he passed the pool, the moaning of the wind among the towering crags became quite distinct, and he broke into a run.

He reached his home just as, with a blinding blaze and a deafening crash of thunder, the very heavens seemed to burst asunder. The ensuing deluge completely blotted out everything more than a few feet from the entrance, across which he immediately began to tie the heavy cow hide which served as a door during such times as this. As he struggled with the heavy skin, Haitee joined him and between them, they soon had it secured. Already alarmed, Haitee had made tight the smaller skins which closed the windows.

Although both were accustomed to the devastating storms which sometimes scourged the country, neither remembered ever having witnessed anything to compare with this. At times, it seemed that not even their stone house would be able to withstand the pressure of the raging gale or the crashing reverberations of the thunder. With the windows and door closed, it became so stuffy inside they could hardly breathe. Then, with a roar that somehow reminded Rhu of a sorely wounded but gigantic hoogwar, the rain changed to hail, and where but a moment before the air had been suffocating, it now became so cold as to seem to eat into the very marrow of their bones.

In the brief intervals between the roar of the hail, the wind howled like a thousand ravening wolves as it swirled about the stout chimney and caused the heavy cow hide over their doorway to snap and strain against the rawhide thongs which bound it in place. There were times when Rhu was certain that neither the skin nor the thongs could possibly hold, but Grut had chosen well when he had first selected them. To make matters even more uncomfortable, the wind pressure caused their fireplace to smoke, and so heavy was the downpour that at times it almost extinguished the fire.

"I don't know which is worse, the smoke or the cold," Rhu grumbled through his chattering teeth as he tried to coax the blaze along after a particularly bad spell.

"If the sky fire god or the war god would only stop their battle, I could stand either one," cried Haitee, cowering close beside Rhu.

As if her words had broken the spell, both lightning and thunder stopped with such suddenness as to make their ears ache.

"They usually stop when the water rocks start to fall," Rhu explained out of his experience. Considering it fairly safe, he cautiously loosed a lower thong at the door and scooped up a double handful of hail easily as large as robins' eggs which he deposited in a bowl of water. "This will make the water very cold and fine to drink," he explained to the wondering Haitee. Then, as the wind showed definite signs of abating, he loosed another thong and peered outside. "C-come and look!" he exclaimed excitedly, and Haitee hastened to his side.

The great oak tree which stood before their house was stripped as bare of foliage as in midwinter, and many of its limbs had been torn from the tree by the storm. All about, the ground was hidden under a coating of ice a good eight inches deep, while the air was so bitterly cold that Rhu hastened to refasten the skin, and Haitee hurried back to the comfort of the now roaring fire.

Suddenly, an awful thought startled Rhu. The cattle! They

could not long have endured the pelting hailstorm! And their precious crops! Had any of their people been killed? Assuredly, anyone caught outside would not have survived. And where was Hut? He had not seen him return.

"I saw Hut arrive before you came," Haitee answered his unspoken thought. "I had already told Marda that Grut had prophesied a terrible storm and to close her windows against it. I am sure they are all right, as well as everybody inside the other houses. But the poor cattle! There must be thousands of them dead! What a calamity!" She paused as a sudden thought occurred to her. "Oh," she wailed, "I hope Grut got home in time. He left here but a short time before Hut arrived."

"Trust Grut," Rhu chuckled with an assurance born of long experience, but his heart was troubled. "If only this does not discourage everybody. Never before have I seen anything even approximating this storm. I hope it lets up enough so that I can get out before dark! I haven't seen Nohr today. He was not at the stone house."

"He arrived at Hut's house a short time before Hut. I saw him as I was closing the bedroom window facing Hut's house," Haitee explained.

Outside, hurried steps crunched on the icy ground, and Rhu hastened to open the flap over the doorway.

Water dripping from his heavy beard and hair, Grut stopped just inside the doorway and peered toward Rhu and Haitee, his heavy face breaking into a warm smile. "Grut come soon as can come. Haitee tell Grut afraid storms. Glad Rhu here. Grut go see family now. Bad storm."

"Where were you?" Rhu asked.

"Grut hide under rock pile. Grut caught in water rocks."

"Why were you not at home?"

"Grut come to Haitee when see storm bad," the big fellow explained, grinning sheepishly.

Rhu patted his hairy shoulder. "Thank you, Grut," he said, "I more than appreciate your care for her."

"Haitee good girl. Good to Grut," he stated simply and sincerely.

"You are good to Haitee," she declared, coming over to smile into his face. "Won't you stay to eat with us? We have had nothing to eat since morning and would like to have you."

Grut peered uneasily at the clean table and stools, then looked diffidently at Rhu.

"If you'll stay, I'll have Haitee serve us Mu Yan fashion," Rhu assured him, "and I'll bet I get the best pieces."

Grut's grin, or so Haitee thought, grew positively fiendish, then his chest began to rumble. "Huh!" he snorted. "Grut have no chance. Haitee give Rhu best pieces. Rhu take, Grut take away for Haitee!"

His eyes dared Rhu to disagree, much to that worthy's delight as he started to edge toward his mighty brother. But Grut's eyes were trained to alertness by long experience with this small brother of his, and he promptly slid around behind Haitee, from which refuge, he made a grimace at Rhu over her head.

With a laugh, Rhu sat down upon his favorite stool, while the astute Grut took one on the opposite side of the table. Haitee went to the great kettle of stew always kept in readiness, dipping from it the choicest bits she could find and filling a great bowl to its brim. With a happy smile, she placed this before Grut, to his infinite delight. For once, he had beat Rhu to it, and he dived in with gusto as Haitee brought Rhu his own.

Between bits of the savory stew, Rhu reached for a hunk of maize bread from the pile on the table, but once again, Grut got the best of him as, with an air of assumed nonchalance, he took the very piece for which Rhu was reaching. Haitee noticed, however, that his eyes never shifted from the grinning Rhu. Many, many times she had heard of the antics of these two, and she wondered just what devilment was hatching behind Rhu's twinkling eyes. For her part, she was prepared to vacate her seat upon a fraction of a second's notice, for she well knew the swiftness with which either of these two could move.

And then, Rhu's expression abruptly changed to one of intent attention. A second later, Grut slid effortlessly from his seat and mechanically reached for his heavy war axe, while Rhu hastened to unfasten the door skin. It was not until then that Haitee heard the soft pad of racing feet and the heavy breathing of some approaching person.

Chapter Twenty-five

YAUG SPEAKS HIS MIND

WELL ACQUAINTED with the severe storms which occasionally swept down from the mountains, Nohr realized that the approaching one bade fair to be one of the worst. He had started for Hut's home just as the first of the black clouds crept over the mountains, arriving there before the storm actually broke and a short time ahead of Hut.

Already warned by Haitee, Marda was fastening a heavy skin over the window in their bedroom when she saw him approaching and went to greet him.

Although Nohr's sharp eyes did not fail to observe the condition of her face, he did not betray it by either word or action. "You sent for me," he explained as he seated himself beside the table. "Just what can I do for you?"

"I want two more rooms added to our house," Marda stated directly. "I feel this is going to be too small."

Nohr's face betrayed some surprise which, apparently, he made no special effort to conceal. "They would be nice," he said simply, "but adding them is going to present some problems. Just where do you want them added?"

"You and Dargh can solve the problems," she stated definitely. "As to where to put them, I am not particular. You can make one like Haitee's extra one, only I want mine larger, and the other can be next to it. The important thing is to have four rooms."

Nohr's eyes bored into hers with disturbing intentness. "One more than Haitee and Rhu," he murmured, half to himself. Then to Marda, "As to making them larger, I am not so sure.

Two holes would have to be cut in the north wall of this room to get into the new rooms. The way Dargh builds, that will not be easy. It is one thing to build them all at one time and quite another to add to what is already built. Some way must be found to bind them to the wall of this house or they will leak and the wind will blow through the cracks. I shall have to talk to Dargh. He is busy now with the building of the place in which to keep prisoners. Hut should have mentioned this when the house was built."

"I am the one who wants the extra rooms," Marda declared flatly.

Again Nohr studied her intently, but anything further he might have said was interrupted by Hut who arrived on the run.

If he were surprised to find Nohr there, he gave no indication of it. "Hello, Nohr," he greeted the Tama Yan. "Will you help me close the door? This is going to be a terrible storm and it is almost upon us." He picked up the bundle of heavy skins which had been sewed together for this purpose—skins stiff, bulky, and hard to handle, quite unlike the curtain Grut had provided for Rhu and Haitee which was soft, although tough and heavy.

Nohr quickly stepped to Hut's side and together they worked feverishly to get the stiff and badly creased hides lashed into place. The storm burst, and the wind increased the difficulty of the task. It was not until the hail started that they finally managed to get the unyielding thing lashed in place, its hard wrinkles preventing its closing the opening well enough to keep out all the hail and rain. In addition, the rawhide thongs were so stiff that tying them was extremely difficult, and by the time they had fastened the last one, one or two of the first had come loose.

Panting and sweating from their exertions, they did not fully realize the sudden change in temperature, so that they were exceptionally sensitive to the rapidly increasing cold as they sat down.

"Better get a fire started," Hut ordered Marda through his now chattering teeth.

This proved to be far from easy due to the downdraft from

the high wind. They were all choking, and tears were flowing freely from their smarting eyes before Marda and Nohr, who had gone to her assistance, managed to get a blaze going. There was an insufficient supply of small wood, moss, bark, and twigs, and hardly was the fire finally burning well when the driven rain came down the wide flue and twice almost extinguished it, much to Hut's discomfiture and loudly expressed displeasure. His struggle with the lashings at the door, which had a most disconcerting way of coming undone exasperated him and brought on a fit of irritability.

At last, they managed to get a fire of sufficient proportions to withstand the rain, and gradually the chilly and drafty room grew warm, the light from the leaping flames making it almost cheery.

Marda placed a heavy earthen vessel of water almost in the blaze, then began taking from the table the dishes left from her breakfast. It was not until she was washing them that she thought to place the pot of stew in place to warm. The maize bread left beside the fire from the morning meal she now discovered to be well soaked and blackened from the rain and soot which had come down the flue before the hot fire had stopped it.

"Marda says she wants two more rooms added to your house," Nohr said to Hut as the warmth from the fire began to make it possible to talk without their teeth chattering. "She asked me to come to see her about it, but I was explaining how hard it would be to make such an addition after a place is built. Cutting through the wall for two doors will be hard enough, but I confess I do not know how Dargh can possibly manage to tie the new rooms to the old so they will be wind and water proof."

Hut frowned. "You did not mention this to me," he said sternly, turning to Marda whose face had grown quite red. "Why extra rooms? We have plenty now."

"I think we are entitled to as many rooms as Rhu and Haitee," she replied shortly. "Besides, I want them."

"But, Marda," Hut exclaimed somewhat petulantly, "don't you realize the Musons are working on the building for possible future prisoners? Besides, this is no time to be adding to their work unnecessarily. There may be a lot of repairing to be done after this awful storm, and it is going to take everybody here to clean up the mess after this heavy fall of water rocks."

"I imagine there will be many dead cattle, too," Nohr added thoughtfully. "These water rocks are large enough to kill anything exposed to them. And your crops are probably ruined."

"Hut is our leader," Marda announced stubbornly, "and what *he* wants is more important than anything else."

Nohr looked from her to Hut in surprise.

Hut's face flushed and his jaw set. "Our people come first," he said firmly. "After we get our work in hand again, I shall speak to Dargh about the extra rooms, but I don't see why we need them."

"Doesn't the fact that *I* want them mean anything to you?" Marda demanded angrily.

"Of course. But there are other important things to think about. Besides, I think Rhu should have something to say about it."

"Rhu?" snapped Marda. "Can't you, our leader, do *anything* without consulting Rhu? I'll bet *he* wouldn't hesitate if it were Haitee who wanted something done." Her flush deepened and tears of rage filled her eyes.

Hut's eyes hardened, but he did not reply. Instead, he spoke to Nohr. "I had not thought of the crops or the cattle," he said. "If the water rocks fell as hard and plentifully all over this part of the Plains as they did right here, we are going to have a very real problem on our hands. I must see Rhu before I do anything." He hesitated, then continued, "There has been some misunderstanding regarding Rhu and me, Nohr. I wonder whether it has come to your ears?"

"You mean about forming the Council?"

"Yes. What did you hear?"

"Only that you had selected members without consulting Rhu. From remarks Marda has made today, it would seem that you personally intend to take over the leadership of this group. I believe in strong leadership, but I have always thought you and Rhu worked together so well. I confess I have been somewhat disturbed. I would like to know something of your plans." Nohr's tone was noncommittal.

Hut frowned. "W-e-l-l," he drawled, thinking swiftly, all the time very conscious of Marda's keen attention, "my purpose was not to omit Rhu. Rather, I was simply trying to take some of the heavy load from his shoulders. Rhu is so impulsive and adventuresome that one never quite knows just what he will do next. In selecting members for the Council therefore, I was trying to keep in mind every eventuality so that if anything should happen to Rhu, I would be sure to have a proper control.

"However, the Elders suggested some changes, so I acceded to their plan to keep the Council as it was before I had this idea. However, I also have in mind the establishment of certain basic laws with which I am sure Rhu will readily agree because I feel sure of the backing of the Elders."

Hut's self-assurance had been rapidly returning ever since his conversation with Wardu, and he could not resist this opportunity to impress Nohr whose impersonal manner of speaking had rather nettled him. Furthermore, this confidence in himself should certainly satisfy Marda and keep her quiet. That his statement was not entirely true seemed not to trouble him.

"Then the Elders are in favor of your taking the position of leader?" Nohr inquired.

"W-e-l-l, I would not put it just that way. I do know they are interested in the establishment of certain laws of general conduct. Lord Lithargos was talking it over with me just yesterday and gave me some very fine suggestions. One of the Elders will be here to discuss them more fully before I submit them to the Council."

"How does Rhu feel about them, or have you talked them over with him?" asked Nohr.

"I have not yet had a chance to talk them over with Rhu, but what the Elders agree to, Rhu will do. That I know from long experience. There is no one else quite like Rhu, Nohr, for he is the best friend anybody ever had, but he does not figure far ahead. Nobody can equal him when it comes to the handling of emergencies or things immediately at hand. He is exceedingly practical, but I feel we need long range viewpoints so that we may plan well into the future."

"I see," Nohr commented. "You feel that because you have this long range vision, you are probably better suited to laying out extensive plans for the future. Perhaps you are right at that, although I have never found Rhu lacking in vision. Of course, you have known him all your life while my acquaintance is very short, but he is certainly competent to handle all types of men. They follow him naturally."

"They would follow Hut just as readily if Rhu gave him a chance to lead them," Marda interjected.

"That may be very true," Nohr half agreed. "I admire Hut very much, but so do I admire Rhu. If what you say be true, Hut, then it would seem you should be the real leader with final authority when it comes to planning, but I still think Rhu would be the best one to see that such plans were followed. However, that is only a personal opinion and is based upon too short an acquaintance to mean much as compared with your own."

"Oh, I would not consider any move in which I would not have Rhu's full support along the lines of his greatest ability. On the other hand, I find that Wardu is interested in bringing in several Cari Yan families whom he knows to be loyal and dependable. Now if you were to enlist some Tama Yan families of the same dependable character who would accept and follow your advice as Wardu says his people will do, we can soon control a sufficiently large group so that the success of my plans will be assured. What would you think of that?"

"It sounds plausible and like a far-sighted plan which I shall be glad to consider carefully," Nohr agreed. "I am sure there are plenty of my tribe who can be relied upon and whom I think I can interest. About how soon would you want them?"

"I could use them right away and if they arrive promptly, I will get them on the Plains with no delay," Hut assured him.

Rising and moving toward the door, Nohr remarked, "The storm seems to have stopped. Such violent ones seldom last long. I think I shall return to join Dargh."

"You did well," Marda complimented Hut as their visitor passed out of earshot. "Nohr will be a fine man for you."

"That is as it may be," Hut accepted her praise, "but in the future, I want to hear no more of this leadership talk when

others are present. If you are to be of help to me, you must
learn to keep quiet unless I ask you to say something when
others are with us. As for the extra rooms, why did you have to
drag in Haitee and Rhu? Don't you see that Nohr knows your
only purpose is to have a bigger and more imposing place than
they have? All such things will come about in due time."

AS RHU pulled aside the hide covering the doorway to see
who was approaching, Yaug Dan ran up to him carrying something in a skin bag. Already, the storm had dropped to a
dreary drizzle and the sky was growing brighter.

"Grut here?" Yaug asked when he saw Rhu. "Mother send
Yaug with sheep feed Grut want. Grut hurry back so Haitee
not be alone in storm. Yaug bring," indicating the bag he
carried.

"Grut is here," Rhu assured him. "Come on in and have
something to eat. How much damage did the storm do to
you?"

"Blow down Dan's open hut. Mai mad. Water rocks not fall
there. Water rocks fall near Rhu and Hut. Stop at Dargh pool."
With a wide grin, he followed Rhu inside where Haitee was
already placing a big bowl of stew for him.

"Give Haitee weeds," Grut grunted.

"Why Haitee want sheep food?" Yaug asked as he complied
with Grut's instructions.

"Marda wanted them for Hut," she explained. "Grut went to
get them for me as it was so hot."

"Haitee get for Marda. Grut get for Haitee. Yaug bring for
Grut. Why Marda not get for Hut?"

Haitee laughed at the puzzled Yaug. "Marda hurt her face
and did not feel like walking over," she explained.

Yaug's eyes flew wide, and he actually stopped gulping down
the savory stew, ample proof of his amazement. Then he
grinned, his eyes sparkling.

"Huh!" he grunted. "Hut have clawed face. Marda face hurt.
Hut better than Yaug think. Eye black?" he asked. But the
avidity with which he returned to the consumption of his bowl
of food showed very plainly that he neither expected or needed
an answer.

Nor did he speak again until his bowl was empty and his fingers licked clean. "Haitee fine cook," he complimented her. "Rhu fine leader. Hut fool." Splitting off a large sliver from a stack of firewood with his hairy thumb, Yaug proceeded to dig out from between his tusklike teeth the hunks of meat lodged there. "When Rhu need, call Yaug," he stated, and getting up, stalked away.

Grut grinned. "Yaug get sense," he growled.

"Yaug is just mad because Hut changed the Council," Rhu corrected.

"Huh!" snorted Grut. "When Hut small boy, think Yaug follow. Yaug not follow. Yaug chase. Catch Hut. Spank Hut. Same now." Getting to his feet, he patted Haitee's shoulder, and also strode away.

"Which, translated," Rhu commented with a smile, "is Grut's way of saying that while Hut thought Yaug would follow him and do as he said, Yaug never had any such intention. Poor Hut! Well, Haitee, maybe it *was* Marda, as you said. Dargh seems to have the same idea," and he recounted the morning's events.

"Well, I'll take these things over to her," Haitee announced as he finished, and picking up the bag, departed, meeting Hut on the way.

"Did Rhu get home for the storm, Haitee?" Hut asked.

"Just before it started," she answered. "He is sitting at the table now." She hurried on her way.

"Come on inside," Rhu called, his keen ears detecting his friend's approaching footsteps.

"I thought we'd better go see about the damage done by the storm," Hut explained as he entered the door, stopping to feel the still wet but pliable hide. "What makes this so soft?" he asked. "Mine is stiff and hard."

"It was tanned and softened for a roof covering. Mother always fixes them this way as they are so much easier to handle. I thought sure it would tear loose in that wind, though. I never saw such big water rocks! However, Yaug was just here and says none of it fell beyond Dargh's pool, so the only damage about which he knew was to the open hut we built for Mai. That won't be so hard to fix. Haitee says Nohr was over at your house when the storm came. Did he want something?"

"No, only to talk about enlarging our house. Marda wants two more rooms. I told her she'd have to wait until all storm damage is repaired and the prison house finished before we could discuss it. What do you think about it?" Hut finished.

"If you want it, of course Dargh will do it, Hut. I imagine it will take some planning to make the walls solid."

"That's what Nohr said," Hut agreed. "I am satisfied with it as it is, but Marda really wants the extra rooms."

"Then they will be built," Rhu agreed definitely. "Say, Hut, Wardu was in to see me this morning. I think he means well, but I'm not so sure I am in favor of his remaining here too long. In any event, before we take him in, he should be trained by the Elders." He made no mention of Wardu's proposition, although he could not have explained why.

Hut eyed his friend speculatively. What had passed between Rhu and the Cari Yan? Rhu's attitude indicated it had not been altogether pleasant. Wardu certainly had been friendly enough with *him* this morning. Hut could hardly repress a smile. Now he would have something to talk over with Marda. In fact, he was rather anxious to do so as soon as possible. His talks with Wardu and Nohr were real food for thought. Not that he would be disloyal to Rhu, he assured himself, but it was good to know where one's friends stood and upon whom he might depend.

"I had thought about our talking over those laws suggested by Lord Lithargos," Hut began, "but the more I think about them the more I believe we would do better to wait until the Elder comes and explains them more fully."

"Perhaps you are right, Hut. They represent something very important to our permanent growth and success, and if we talk them over we may form some erroneous ideas which it would be difficult to reconcile with those that are better and sounder. Suppose we wait as you suggest. It's agreeable to me."

"Then I think I'll go back home and take a rest. This was rather a trying morning, but I did as Lord Lithargos wanted. That was surely one bitter lesson for me. Phew! Never again do I want to go through another such ordeal. Oh well, it's over now, so we can proceed to the next step." He departed just as Haitee returned.

"What was Nohr over at Hut's for?" she asked as soon as Hut was out of earshot.

"Marda wants two more rooms on their house. Evidently she sent for Nohr to talk it over, though why she did not approach Dargh first, I don't understand."

"I can," Haitee stated so positively that Rhu was almost startled. "She thought she could order Nohr around, but she knew Dargh would not hesitate to say no if he felt that way, and once Dargh makes up his mind . . . . well, you know Dargh."

"Perhaps you are right. But what possible use can they have for two more rooms? We have never used even our *one* extra one."

"But don't you see, Rhu? We have that one more room than Marda has," Haitee explained. "From the very first day when she said she liked the larger rooms rather than three smaller ones, I knew this was coming. Marda can be very dear and sweet, in fact, she is that way normally, but she simply cannot stand it to see anyone have more than she does. It isn't that she is exactly selfish, for she would do anything on earth for those she loves, but even the Elders used to caution her about being proud. I was sorry we had that extra room because I knew she would never be satisfied with only two. Now, you can see for yourself that she is determined to have one more than we have. But that is all right. Like you, I would see her happy. But I am afraid she will not be content to stop at that."

The quizzical glance Rhu had cast toward her became serious. "What do you mean?" he demanded.

"She is very ambitious, Rhu, and you have already seen how she has urged Hut to aspire to leadership. She is very determined, and I cannot believe that once she has established that idea in her mind, she will ever let go of it."

"Huh!" Rhu almost snorted. "She doesn't know Hut! I don't believe he will allow her to influence him that far."

"Then you don't know Marda!" Haitee tossed her head and her stubborn little jaw set firmly. "He was not above *trying* it, and if I know her, she will give him no peace until he tries

again. After all, Rhu, a woman can do much to influence a
man, even against his better judgment and desires. Watch her."

Rhu recalled that Dargh had given him much the same
warning and for some time, he sat immersed in deep thought.
Could he be wrong and both Haitee and Dargh right?

Haitee busied herself clearing away and washing the bowls
from which they had eaten, for having said her say about
Marda and Hut, she was wise enough to let the subject drop.
There was, as she had already learned, too much of old Sol Ku
in Rhu's disposition to make it safe or wise to try to push him
too far. She well knew the depth of Rhu's feeling for Hut, but
she also knew he was far too shrewd not to give careful
thought to what she had pointed out and which recent events
certainly seemed to confirm.

Besides, Nohr had been at Hut's home for a long time after
Hut had arrived, and had remained even after the storm had
subsided. It could never have taken all that time merely to talk
about those rooms! Four rooms! Huh! She had always liked
Nohr, having found him invariably pleasant, but their acquaintance had been short, and despite her training by the
Elders, she could not entirely rid herself of that deeply inherent tendency to distrust those whom she did not know well.

Had Rhu and Haitee been able to know the thoughts of the
other, they might have been surprised to see how closely their
musings paralleled. Rhu, too, was concerned about Nohr's
visit, but determined to wait to learn just what Hut and Nohr,
especially Nohr, might have to say about it. Somehow, he had
great faith in Nohr who always seemed very fair and understanding.

Presently, the sun broke through the clouds and before long,
the hail disappeared. But for the damage to trees and foliage,
nothing except mud and swollen streams remained to show
there had been any storm at all. Birds reappeared, and the evening was filled with the music of their songs. The air was sweet
and balmy, and Haitee and Rhu sat side by side in their doorway drinking it all in.

"It is very peaceful and very beautiful," Haitee breathed, as
if afraid speaking aloud might break the spell.

"It is usually this way on the Plains," Rhu assured her. "How glad I am that the water rocks did not reach the herds. Surely, N'Kul made this a wonderful place in which to live. Did you ever see a more peaceful scene? And just to think, we have nothing to fear. No lurking Forest Dwellers seeking to raid us, and certainly far more comfortable homes than any of us ever dreamed possible. Life is good and full of happiness for us."

Haitee sighed as she nestled closer to Rhu, and her eyes grew dreamy as she drank in the full beauty of the scene. Fortunately, neither knew nor suspected the conversation at that minute being carried on in Hut's home.

Chapter Twenty-six

THE ELDER EXPOUNDS
THE LAWS

AFTER HELPING Hut remove the heavy skin from the door, Marda launched into a discussion of the day's events. "Tell me about your talk with Wardu," she said finally, "I have an idea he is going to be a big help in our plans."

"Listen, Marda, I want you to stop talking as if we have some very definite plans of our own. You managed to get me into enough trouble before, and this scheme of my being the leader is not to my liking."

For a brief second, Marda's eyes hardened, but having found there was a very definite limit beyond which Hut would not stir when his will was opposed, she wisely made no direct reply. Instead, she went back to her original question. "Well, there can be no harm in telling me about your talk with Wardu, can there?" she asked.

From his retentive memory, Hut repeated almost verbatim his talk with the Cari Yan. As he talked, his mind unconsciously reverted to the nebulous plans he and Marda had talked over before Lord Lithargos had upset the start he had made in carrying them out. Hardly realizing that he was doing so, he began thinking of some of the intriguing possibilities Wardu's talk had opened up for him.

This, Marda was quick to suspect, and when Hut had completed his tale, she expressed her satisfaction. "You certainly did a wonderful job with him," she announced, cunningly appealing to Hut's pride, and the brightening of his eyes and mounting color told her far more than words how well she had done in choosing this approach.

"Yes," he agreed, unwittingly responding to Marda's clever bait, "and I am sure that we could easily persuade him to see things from our viewpoint. It was rather a delicate situation, for everybody thinks highly of Rhu. So do I! But Rhu is so impulsive and quick to jump to conclusions that I seriously question the advisability of his being given too much power. He might easily throw the whole group into a turmoil. Fortunately, he does not seem ambitious to take advantage of his popularity. He has told me he has no desire to become the leader."

"Humph!" Marda almost snorted. "Did it never occur to you that this may all be a cunning pose on Rhu's part to disarm you while he takes over behind your back?"

"Rhu would never do that," Hut stated flatly, although Marda sensed a certain lack of conviction in his voice and manner. "Why, he just told me that he was going to talk to Dargh about the two new rooms for you and would see that they were added just as quickly as possible."

"Whatever that means," Marda persisted skeptically. "He is far more likely using this as a means of throwing dust in your eyes so you won't suspect him of planning to take over when he considers the time is right. You can't fool me, Hut. Rhu is just as ambitious as you, and you have often bragged to me about his astuteness in outguessing his enemies.

"How do you know but what he plans to add two more rooms to *his* house? If *he* isn't, Haitee is not going to let us have anything more than they do. She is ambitious too, so don't you be fooled by her quiet acceptance of our having four rooms while she has only three!" Marda's voice took on a deriding tone as she warmed to the subject. "Thus far, Haitee has been content because they have more rooms, but just wait until she sees us with four and see how quickly she will start working for more than we have!

"I'm telling you, Hut, if you don't look out for yourself, the first thing you know, Rhu will be ahead of you in everything. He is far too smart not to realize that sooner or later one of you will have to assume the real leadership here, and you know you are much better qualified than he is for that position!"

"We have always worked together," Hut demurred. "Rhu has

never at any time tried to take any advantage, always insisting upon my sharing in the credit for everything he has done."

"But that was before you ever asserted your ability to lead!" Marda shrewdly assailed the one weak spot in Hut's reasoning, and Hut's deep frown told her that her words had struck home. "With your having been smart enough to get Wardu to as good as pledge you his support and to bring in a large group of Cari Yans, why would it not be an excellent plan for you to persuade his friend Harco to do the same with an equally large group of Hata Yans? By being circumspect and quiet about it, you can soon have a preponderance of backers and thus have sufficient people to make you the real leader. Let us get them to come here where we can talk with them."

"W-e-l-l," Hut mused thoughtfully, "there is really no harm in finding out just where Wardu and Harco stand. We do not necessarily have to give any inkling of our plans. We will just do our best to weld them to our cause by talking about what I can do for them after they are here and see how they react. Rhu does not trust Wardu any too much, though what reason he may have for feeling as he does, I do not know."

"I'll bet he has already tried to work out just the same plan we have in mind, but failed. Otherwise, why should Wardu have come to you and talked as he did?"

Marda's idea had already occurred to Hut, only to be dismissed. However, the fact that she expressed almost the same thoughts as he had entertained now lent weight to his suspicions. Well, if Rhu could plan, why not he? Besides, there was no need for any definite commitments. Since Harco had formed a great attachment for Wardu and followed his example in most of what he did, Hut was sure the Hata Yan could be easily persuaded to accede to the main plan if Wardu did.

Weary from the unusual mental disturbance of the day, Hut promised Marda that he would see Harco and Wardu and ask them to come to their home some evening soon, and with this Marda had to be content.

AS HAD been arranged, before dawn the following morning, Hut and Rhu arrived at the big stone building and prepared to go to the grove.

From the hammocklike shelf which hung just below the ceiling of the room, Rhu took down two bundles of soft doeskin. Silently, the lads unfolded these, disclosing two robes of snowy down feathers which they placed carefully about their shoulders, fastening them at the neck. The flowing robes reached almost to the ground, with openings for the arms, and had been made by sewing the feathers of white swans upon a rather coarsely woven fabric. Beneath them in the bundles were two shorter capelike robes, also of white swan feathers, but edged with a two-inch border of bluebird feathers. These capes were lined with the fine red feathers of a bird closely resembling our modern cardinal grosbeak, or redbird, with a border of bluebird feathers. Rhu and Hut threw these over the longer robes, and they covered their arms and reached to the knees.

These beautiful garments were greatly treasured for they were gifts from the Elders, each piece having required more than a year in its fashioning.

Because the sun gave heat and light and was a necessary attendant to the growth of all plant and animal life, their people believed it was the creator of all things and had worshiped it from time immemorial. Since they could not conceive of anything greater than a human being, they personalized the sun and called him N'Kul. In periods of drought and cold, they appealed to him for mercy, and during times of prosperity and comfort they voiced their gratefulness.

Such prayers were offered in the early morning as N'Kul made his appearance upon the horizon, and it was not at all unusual to see a man or his family standing before a hut with outstretched arms welcoming what they believed to be the arrival of N'Kul in their midst.

In addition, each family or sept, particularly among the Plains Dwellers, maintained one grove on their holdings to which, as a group, they repaired to pay homage, especially in the Spring when the grazing was at its best and in the Fall when they gathered nuts and certain herbs for Winter consumption. Also, on the Short Day which marked the beginning and end of the year, they gathered here to give thanks for the past year and to ask for good luck in the coming one.

Now that they were on the Plains, there was a communal grove, and even the Forest Dwellers among them would join in the ceremonies conducted there. In the shade of the great trees, too, a lone figure might often be seen, walking to and fro seeking the solace the peaceful surroundings could give, or imploring help of the great god N'Kul in the solution of some problem with which he was confronted.

It was toward this grove that Rhu and Hut directed their steps, and so intent were they upon reaching there in time for the rising of the sun that they failed completely to observe the shadowy figure following them. For all his size, the man made no more sound than a shadow, his eyes alight as they followed Rhu.

"Rhu worried or Grut not escape Rhu's eye," he half growled under his breath, slipping behind a tree from which he could watch the familiar ceremony he knew was about to be enacted.

At the top of a knoll surrounded by twelve towering redwood trees, the two knelt facing the rising sun. "O, Mighty N'Kul," they began in unison, "upon whose beneficence we depend for all that is good, we come to thee in all humility to ask thy blessing upon our every undertaking and that we may be granted the wisdom to solve the many problems before us."

At this point, the glowing edge of the rising sun appeared through a notch in the distant hills, and both arose as one, extending their arms so that the feathered capes fell back, forming scarlet triangles with apexes at each shoulder. Standing thus, their elongated shadows made two crosses across the ground behind them. Peering at them from his hiding place, Grut observed not only this, but that with their arms extended, Rhu and Hut themselves formed crosses.

"Welcome, O N'Kul!" they repeated, again in unison as the sun rose with what seemed to Grut unusual rapidity. "N'Kul is pleased," he murmured to himself, as, piercing the dense foliage, a golden shaft fell upon the head and shoulders of Rhu, creating the appearance of an aura, a second later embracing Hut also in the same warm glow.

"We salute thee!" Rhu and Hut continued the time-honored formula, remaining in the same position until the sun had cleared the hills, after which, they dropped their arms, drew their capes about them, and bowing, retreated to the trees before they ceased to face the glowing orb.

Not until they had departed and were well beyond earshot did Grut get slowly to his feet and head for home. His face was thoughtful as an idea slowly took shape in his mind. Arrived at the Ku home, he searched out a piece of soft white pine, then headed for the Hatamukulian Gorge and his favorite retreat where he kept many of his most treasured possessions. From a cunningly contrived hiding place, he took two small and beautifully made obsidian knives which Dargh had given him, and seating himself so that he overlooked the river, he began hacking away upon his pine stick.

With infinite patience and a skill that was surprising, day after day during his spare time, Grut labored until there emerged a small but surprisingly lifelike image of a man with arms extended, the folds of his feathered robe plainly discernible.

Here was being fashioned the first of all crosses, symbolizing man in supplication to, or adoration of, the god he worshiped.

WHEN Rhu and Hut returned to their old quarters, they found an Elder awaiting them. After the customary greetings and the careful replacement of the robes, the Elder announced that he had come to discuss with them the ten laws previously given them by Lord Lithargos.

"In our discussion of these laws," he began, "I shall depend upon you to ask any and all questions which may aid in your gaining the utmost understanding. As we proceed," the Elder continued, "you will discover that these laws are interdependent. By that I mean that one often involves the use of another. Therefore, an explanation of any one or more of them is necessarily going to involve one or more of the others.

"These laws are based upon the Laws of Nature established by God for the harmonious functioning of everything in the Universe. You have previously learned that Natural Laws are self-operative and exacting, applying to all equally and so are absolutely just. If properly adhered to, your people will be happy and secure, and your civilization will endure.

"Law number one is that *no man shall profit at the expense of another.*

"To be cosmically sound, both parties to any transaction

must profit equally. For one to profit more than the other means that the one so profiting incurs a cosmic debt for which, sooner or later, nature will exact compensation or repayment.

"This means the eventual establishment of certain standards of value in your community. Since these values must ever be fair and just for all, they will be established by the Council which represents the people as a whole and has jurisdiction over the commonwealth, or government, as you may prefer to designate it.

"As an example, let us say that cattle as such will be given a common valuation, each animal of a particular breed being worth a certain number of sheep. Broadly speaking, this is comparatively simple and you already have such general standards. Yet, cattle may have varying values. Perhaps one man has a cow that gives an unusual amount of milk, or milk that is better than that of the average cow. Obviously, this cow is worth more than one of the cattle raised merely for food. The Council will eventually establish standards by which such exceptional values can be definitely determined.

"For the present, however, we shall consider such animals as merely cattle and of standard value, according to size and condition. Let us call them beef for the purpose of making our meaning clear. According to your present custom, you consider a beef as worth four sheep. Therefore, if a cattle raiser attempts to get *five* sheep for one beef, he is trying to get more than he gives.

"If a man suffer misfortune and be compelled to dispose of his belongings, one who takes advantage of the circumstances and pays him less than the true worth of that which he secures violates this law. He has profited at the expense of another. Therefore, he will have incurred a cosmic debt for which he is responsible and for which, sooner or later, he must compensate. If the repayment is made voluntarily, all is well and good. But if Nature must enforce it, the repayment will bring grief and pain. The Laws of God operate for the happiness and welfare of man. Abide by them, and life's greatest blessings will be yours. Violate them, and misfortune and affliction will ultimately follow. This applies not only to individuals, but to communities as well, for communities are but groups of individuals.

"To sum up this law as it relates to the success of your commonwealth, no individual citizen or member of any society or community may hope to prosper permanently except as the society or community prospers. Conversely, no society or community may hope to prosper permanently except as each individual member thereof prospers. Since the prosperity of the whole is dependent upon the prosperity of each individual composing it, it becomes a governmental duty to see that this first law be obeyed implicitly."

Hut frowned. "What should be done to the man who refuses to obey this law?" he asked.

"He shall be required to compensate for the unfair advantage he has thus taken. It is only by this procedure that the commonwealth may insure justice to all. It is only thus that it may hope to prosper permanently. *Proper cooperation is essential to permanent prosperity.* The man who seeks to take an unfair advantage over his brother man violates this first law. *Keep this ever in mind.*"

Somehow, the Elder's voice reminded Rhu of Lord Lithargos. He shot a swift glance at Hut whose face had grown quite pale as the full purport of this last admonition of the Elder impressed itself upon him.

"The second law states that *no man singly, nor the commonwealth collectively, may take anything away from another by force.*

"This law, too, requires some explanation. It is a Natural and Universal Law that anything taken from another by force shall, in turn, be taken away from the aggressor by force. Thus, if either a person or a government takes anything away from another by force, he or the government so guilty shall have such things taken from them by force. Violation of this law means the ultimate downfall of the guilty perpetrator.

"To take away by force does not mean by force of arms alone, my sons. The use of trickery; taking unfair advantage of another's ignorance of law or custom; taking advantage of another's misfortune; deceit; misrepresentation; cunningly contrived inferences of a misleading nature designed to work to the advantage of the contriver; threats designed to create fear in the heart of another in order to make him act as the one who threatens desires. All these and many more come under this heading."

"What about imprisoning a person?" asked Rhu. "Isn't that taking away his liberty by force?"

"Whom would you imprison?" the Elder inquired.

"Those who attack us or who violate our laws," Hut suggested.

"Yet, my sons, what about the *cause* which brought about such a reaction? Those who violate laws make themselves liable to such reactions as imprisonment. On the other hand, to imprison unjustly brings dire repercussions. Therefore, always take heed before making any accusation which might possibly lead to such an unfortunate condition.

"You will observe that, to an important degree, a violation of this law is also a violation of the first one because the violator is attempting to profit at the expense of another.

"The third law is that *all natural resources shall remain the property of the state or commonwealth and may not be claimed as a personal possession by any individual or any group of individuals not constituting the entire citizenry.*

"There are many reasons for this, not the least of which is the fact that God provided natural resources for the use of *all* people . . . ."

Here, Hut interrupted. "Several times, you have mentioned *God* and that all Natural or Universal laws originated with Him. Now you tell us that God provided all natural resources. It has been my understanding that N'Kul is the one to whom we owe all such things."

"My sons, until the coming of Lords Hiroto and Lithargos, we, too, have always believed as you have been taught, but, like you, we also are learning many new and important truths. God is the Creator of the earth, the heavens, and even of the sun. Furthermore, They teach us that the name N'Kul is incorrect because it means simply the sun which we see and which provides us with our light and heat.

"It is not the sun that we must worship, but the Great Being Melchizedek whose home it is. It has been to Melchizedek that we have unconsciously prayed when we addressed ourselves to N'Kul. Melchizedek is to God as the Lords Hiroto and Lithargos are to Melchizedek, as the Elders are to Lords Hiroto and Lithargos, and as you are to the Elders."

There was a pause as the Elder gave them time to assimilate what he had said.

Rhu broke the silence. "Then should we no longer pray to N'Kul?" he asked.

"In the light of our greater understanding, it will be better that you address Melchizedek directly. However, long habit may make it difficult for you to change at first. The fact that you knew no better before this made your supplications no less effective; it makes little difference what *name* we use when we pray, provided we are sincere. There would be little justice if one's sincere and earnest supplications were ignored merely because, in his ignorance, he used the wrong title. After all, it is the thought behind our prayer that counts."

"Why not pray direct to *God?*" Hut asked. "It seems to me that would bring the surest and quickest results."

"You can. But let us look at this from a viewpoint you can most easily understand. You and Rhu are at present the head of your group. You have established a Council composed of the oldest men, or patriarchs, of each family. Each family is directed by its patriarch. Let us assume that one of the cattle belonging to a family is to be killed for food. Would the son in charge of that portion of the herd come direct to you and Rhu for advice as to which to kill, or to the Council, or to the patriarch of his family?"

"To the patriarch, of course!"

"Why?" the Elder asked.

"That is simple," Hut replied promptly. "He would go to his patriarch because he is in closer touch with the herd than either the Council or Rhu and me. He could give an immediate decision. I know I would refer him to his patriarch rather than take the time from my many other and more important activities to investigate and say which to use."

The Elder smiled. "Might it not be much the same with God?" he asked kindly. "In a manner of speaking, you and Rhu have created this new society, and because of your many responsibilities, you have little or no time to attend to the *trivial* problems of your people, especially those they can solve for themselves.

"As the Creator of *all things,* God has responsibilities far be-

yond our understanding. Is it fair, then, to call upon Him for
help with problems which you can either solve for yourself or
with which *we* can help you? If we can help you, even the
Lords Hiroto or Lithargos need not take time and thought
from Their greater duties. As in your case, there is no unwill-
ingness upon the part of God or of Melchizedek, but others
with lesser obligations can usually do fully as much, thereby
relieving God or Melchizedek of matters of small importance.

"Rhu, when you were on the way to the Cave Dwellers to
get your first helpers, upon whom did you call for help when
your discovery seemed certain?"

"Lord Lithargos!" Rhu answered unhesitatingly.

"Why did you not ask N'Kul?"

"Because I knew Lord Lithargos would understand, and
somehow, he seemed more real and more accessible, although
to tell the truth, I never reasoned it out. It just seemed the
natural thing to do."

"So it is. Then, why should we call upon God, or even upon
Melchizedek when there are others nearer at hand who are
fully capable of giving us the help we need?"

"I get the idea," Hut agreed. "If we are unable to handle a
problem, it is better to come first to you who are our Elders. If
the problem is too great, then you can call upon the Great
Ones who, in turn, can call upon Melchizedek, or upon God if
necessary."

"Quite right, my sons. In His infinite wisdom, God has arranged limitless help for us so that He need be called upon
only for truly important occasions. His powers are infinite and
He is the ultimate of all that is good, true, and beautiful, but
we can and should ever avail ourselves of the help He has provided for us before we seek to trouble Him with our trivial
problems, most of which we can solve ourselves when we set
ourselves to it.

"Now let us return to our discussion of the third law. As I
stated, as with His Laws, God also provided us with natural
resources which, like the air, are intended for the use of all
people. If it were possible for an individual, or any group of
individuals not composing the entire citizenry, to own such a
natural resource, its use could be denied others. Eventually,

the best of the resources would become the personal property of a very few, thus depriving the citizenry of rights provided by God for their use and pleasure.

"Furthermore, such personal possessions could be passed down from parents to children, and thus, it would be possible for a few great land owners, for example, to force others less fortunate into a state bordering upon abject servility.

"Such personal ownership is a violation of Natural Law as you will see when we discuss the sixth law. Therefore, in the final analysis, such possession will react to the detriment of the possessor.

"The fourth law states that *every citizen and every child thereof shall be entitled to and receive equal education, equal opportunity for the expression of his ability, and equal standing before the laws of the land.*

"At this time, you may feel this has little significance, my sons, but the time is not far distant when its importance will be fully understood and appreciated. Just as each new person brought to the Plains will have been trained by the Elders in all that it is necessary for a citizen to know, including these basic laws, so will all children now growing up be trained before they can become citizens and thus have a voice in the Council, and later, the government.

"Each citizen shall have what will become known as a vote. Before any new laws beyond these ten can become operative, they shall be submitted to the citizens, and each will, by his vote of yes or no signify his desire in the matter. This will be discussed further under the tenth law.

"The fifth law states that *all advancement in position shall be based upon merit and the performance of service alone.*

"This is a law which you have always followed without knowing it to be a law. Have you not always advanced only those who have shown outstanding ability and a willingness to use it for the common good? Did you not give each Forest Dweller every possible opportunity to prove his ability as a bowman? Have you ever advanced any man to a more important position or work until he proved he was fitted for it by having actually performed such work? You advance your soldiers according to what they have earned by performance.

"So should it ever be. By providing each child with an equal education, and every citizen with equal opportunity for the expression of his ability in any field of his choice, each is given full and equal opportunity to exercise his power of self-determination and self-expression just as long as he does not interfere with the same rights of all other citizens.

"Under this same law, no man may be deprived of his position so that one less apt or qualified may replace him. Furthermore, before any may be removed from his merited position, even to be replaced by another better qualified, the one to be displaced must be provided with another position equally as good."

"But suppose a man, otherwise fully capable, should try to take some undue advantage of his position?" Hut asked.

"Unfortunately, there will be those guilty of such attempts, but by that time, there will be additional laws and rules to be applied. However, and you should ever bear this fact in mind, such a procedure will be a violation of one or more of these fundamental laws, the seventh particularly, as you will see. It would also be a violation of the second law.

"The sixth law states that *no individual shall be entitled to retain as a personal possession anything for which he has not personally compensated in equal value.*

"This, my sons, is another Universal and Natural Law established by God for greater harmony among men and throughout the Universe. In fact, it is only those things we have earned through services we have rendered to others that we may hope to retain permanently.

"With the passing of time, there will be many who will seek to gain and retain personal possessions they have not earned, but they will discover in due course that this law cannot be evaded. Many will be stripped of such possessions by misfortune. Some will lose all pleasure of possession through ill-health and other personal troubles. Fear and worry will be the lot of all who violate this law, and many there will be who will declare they would gladly exchange all their possessions for peace of mind, yet cannot because the action of these laws is inescapable.

"The seventh law states that *no individual shall have the*

right to operate in the environment or personal affairs of another unless asked to do so by that person. The commonwealth or government may do so only where criminal or treasonable intent can be proved, or the civil rights of another have been violated.

"Alas! This law will be one of those most commonly violated, either consciously or unconsciously, by countless thousands. Many there are who, through their lust for power, will seek to dominate others and to bend them to their will, and countless will be the devices and schemes used for this purpose. Observe carefully the working of this law. That no one has the *right* to operate in the environment of another does not say that one cannot do so, but woe unto one who does! The repercussions can be little less than devastating!

"There are other important phases of this God Law that deal especially with those who unconsciously or unknowingly violate it, often with only the best intentioned motives, but this we shall discuss at some other time. For the present we are most directly concerned with those who may deliberately violate it in their lust for power and control over others. Let me caution you both to heed well this law and to use great care in making sure you do not violate it, thus inviting the bitter and often heartbreaking repercussions which invariably follow the violation of Natural Law."

"Well, for one, *I* do not intend to do it," Hut asserted.

"May it ever be so, my son, yet heed well my words."

For a moment there was a silence, and glancing up, Rhu was deeply stirred by the Elder's gentle smile and the sorrow in the eyes which rested tenderly upon him. A sense of premonition for which he could not account crept over him.

Then the Elder continued. "The eighth law is also a Natural or God Law. In the millennia to come, it will often be misquoted, and many who do not understand the inexorable action of Natural Law will violate it to their sorrow. It is as follows: *No one may intentionally kill or injure another person, except in the defense of life or State.*

"Under this, one may not so irritate, harass, plague, annoy, or torment another by either word or action that he will attack, thus rendering defense necessary on the part of the one so contriving to force the attack. The intent is just as real and just as potent in such a case as if the tormentor were to make an unprovoked attack, and Natural Law will react on this basis.

"This law applies equally to individuals, groups of individuals, tribes, and even to nations, for, as you will come to understand in time, you are now in the process of forming a nation which is an amalgamation of tribes dedicated to a common mode of life.

"This and the second law are closely affiliated.

"The ninth law is so broad in its scope and meaning that we might well spend a day discussing it and its many far-reaching implications. However, we shall mention only a few of the more important points, the others all being subject to later explanations. Lord Lithargos insists that it be kept simple in order that it may be understood at this time, the other details being reserved until your citizenry has grown large enough to make such matters important.

"The sanctity of the home shall be kept inviolate, and no woman may be taken in marriage without her consent.

"The latter part of this law you have already established, which is well and proper, but that portion dealing with the sanctity of the home requires some explanation. First and foremost, no man shall seek to destroy the chastity of another's wife. To every married man is given the right to know that he has sired his own children. For this reason, both the wife and her seducer shall be deemed equally guilty unless the man has seduced the woman by force.

"The home of every man shall be immune to search or seizure of its contents, except only by due process of law wherein just cause affecting the welfare of the commonwealth, or the rights of another individual, has been shown beyond all reasonable doubt. No one has the right to enter the home of another except upon invitation from the occupying family or a member thereof, except for the foregoing.

"The tenth law is that *in all matters affecting the common good and when no violation of Natural Law is implied or involved, the opinion of the majority shall rule, subject only to the consent of the Elders whose decision shall be final.*

"The determination of the opinion or desires of the majority is to be established through the vote which I mentioned in discussing the fourth law. Neither the Council nor the later government shall have the right to enact and enforce any laws affecting the citizenry as a whole without first submitting them to the citizenry who will be affected by them. Anything less is a violation of both this and the seventh law which states that the commonwealth or government has no right to operate in the environment of an individual except under the conditions set forth in that law.

"With reference to these ten basic laws I have been expounding, those which are definitely Natural Laws, no one can change. They are established by God and are inviolable, immutable, and self-executing, and all must abide by them from the lowliest citizen to the Great Ones, or suffer the consequences. These ten laws are first to be discussed with the Council who will then explain them to the present inhabitants of the Plains. When the people understand them, they will all be called together to vote upon their acceptance. After this formality, the Council will officially sanction their adoption as permanently established.

"The Elders have long abided by Natural Law and are therefore able to judge the relative merits of any proposed laws without personal bias. Also, we are ever in direct communication with the Lords of Venus and Mercury. For these reasons, Lord Lithargos has made it a part of this tenth law that the Elders shall ever have the final authority in all cases of disagreement and in the enactment and enforcement of all manmade laws.

"Furthermore, the life of no man may be placed in jeopardy because of an infraction of man-made laws until the Elders shall first have passed upon the case, and their judgment shall be final.

"All the laws you have been given are either Natural Laws or they bear some relationship to one or more of them. None may be evaded or tricked. God is never mocked with impunity, and in the end His Laws will exact the last jot and tittle of retribution. In the millennia ahead, man will make many changes in these basic principles, completely ignoring their origin, and for many millennia, they will experience much misery as a result. But the day will come when they will awaken to the fact that only as they understand and adhere to these basic rules can they enjoy permanent security and peace of mind. I mention this only that you may appreciate the importance of these laws which Lord Lithargos has set forth.

"This will be sufficient for today. Tomorrow I shall again meet you here in case you have further questions to ask before we call the first meeting of the Council to explain these and others matters. Into the keeping of Melchizedek do I commend you both, and may He, in His gentle mercy, guide you through your troubled hours." With these words the Elder left them.

For some time, Rhu and Hut sat immersed in deep thought, each correlating his own ideas. Hut, Rhu observed, seemed ill at ease. Several times he drew a deep breath as if about to speak, but each time, appeared to think better of it. Rhu's questioning glances increased his restlessness, so that after rising and stretching, he excused himself.

"I think I'll go over to see how the building for the prisoners is coming along," he explained, and before Rhu could volunteer to go with him, he hastily departed.

Seated on the outer edge of the room, Rhu stared moodily into the distance, his eyes casually following Hut's progress. Suddenly, he roused to attention for within easy eyesight of Hut, yet utilizing every available bush, tree, rock, or other bit of cover to keep Hut from seeing him, Grut was trailing him. Rhu was unable to repress a warm smile. Grut had some idea in his shaggy head, and Rhu knew only too well that nothing short of death or some vast cataclysm would either dislodge the idea or deter Grut from carrying out whatever plan he had in mind.

"Good old Grut," he murmured, sighing heavily as the sense of foreboding again settled upon him. "Why does everybody seem to distrust Hut, or else seem to feel he should be watched all the time?" he mused. "Grut is so stubborn in his ideas that there is no use in asking him. He'd likely say, 'No good,' and nobody could get beyond that. Still, I just can't believe that Ord and Dargh are right in their suspicions. Hut isn't like himself lately, I must admit, but he had a hard time over that Council stuff. Oh, well!" With a grunt he rose heavily to his feet and started for home, but changing his mind, went to see what Dargh was doing instead.

Chapter Twenty-seven

DISCOVERY OF THE WHEEL PRINCIPLE

DARGH'S WORKSHOP was located out under a grove of trees where he could supervise the building activities while engaged in making and repairing the sleds they used for hauling stones. The workshop proper consisted principally of two large flat stones supported by rocks which served as a workbench. Here it was that Rhu found Dargh after the Elder and Hut had left him to his own devices.

"I have been doing a lot of thinking about our way of carrying stones for building," Rhu began. "I have an idea, but I must admit that I have never been able to make it work. Maybe you can help."

Dargh was all attention for he had long since discovered that Rhu's ideas were well worth looking into.

"Once Hut and I took a heavy fall by stepping upon a log that rolled from beneath us. I have long thought that if there were some way in which a roller could be substituted for our sliders which stick to the ground, they would not only be stronger, but much easier to pull. We have tried to make such a thing, but have never had any success."

Dargh's heavy frown betrayed his lack of comprehension even while his stubborn jaw was set in determination to understand.

Picking up a piece of charcoal, Rhu made a crude drawing of a log or "roller." "Now," he said, making another crude drawing of a platform above the log, "if we could make something like this above the roller to carry the stones, but so attached to it that the roller could turn without throwing off this—this table thing," pointing to the platform, "I believe we would have something easier to pull, especially in dry weather. What I cannot figure is how to hold it on the log while it rolls."

Dargh, who had been hanging over Rhu's shoulder watching each move he made, now nodded gravely, and going to the pile of short logs from which he was accustomed to splitting sections for sled runners, he selected a piece about a foot in diameter and some four feet long for the roller itself. This he laid upon his workbench. Next, he took two six-foot poles between which he lashed twigs and smaller pieces, making a crude platform about four feet wide, much as they had made their bridge.

He then concentrated his attention upon the log, thoughtfully rolling it back and forth on the workbench. Finally, his face brightened and he placed a hairy finger at the center of each end of the log where it was least affected by the rolling motion. Taking up his ax, he hacked into the center, creating a rough depression at each end. With the log standing on end, he then built a ridge of wet clay around the depression, and taking some dry bark and small twigs, he proceeded to build a tiny fire. Patiently, he refueled it time and time again until a deeper hole was burned into the log. Then turning it over, he did the same with the other end.

Rhu was the puzzled one now, but he waited patiently to see what Dargh had in mind. Evening approached, and the light grew dim. Seeing he could do nothing further, Dargh finally explained his idea. "Make round pegs. Drive in holes. Tomorrow morning Dargh do, then Rhu come help work out next step."

MANY times since its original construction, Dargh's Pool, as it was called, had been enlarged until it was now a good fifteen feet deep, some fifty feet across, and at least a hundred yards long. Beyond its lower end, there was another pool, roughly circular in shape, some four or five feet deep, and perhaps a hundred feet in diameter. Dargh had paved the bottom of this one with slabs of stone and then covered it with about a foot of clean, white sand so that, although used for bathing, the water remained as clear and inviting as that in the main pool which furnished the water for drinking and household use for the entire community.

Beneath the wide-spreading oak trees along the northern side of both pools were rudely fashioned seats made of logs with the top side smoothed by the crude stone axes, and polished by constant use. It was not unusual to find a hundred or more people there almost any evening, for, since the lower reservoir had been completed, bathing had become quite popular. All during the day, children could be found in numbers disporting themselves in the shallower parts provided for this purpose.

Hut could not resist the peaceful scene and sat, seemingly fascinated, gazing into the clear depths. Listening to the Elder, he had been greatly impressed, but now he was glad to be alone to think over what had been said. He reasoned that if he had stayed to discuss the laws with Rhu, his own ideas would have become confused with those of his friend, and just now he did not want to be influenced by anyone.

While the Elder had expounded some of the laws, he had felt not a little trepidation, but now as he mulled over the matter, he began to wonder why he had had such fears. After all, these laws were designed for the people he was destined to lead so they might have the understanding necessary to insure permanent harmony between them. As a leader, he was superior to the people and certainly had no need for laws applicable to them!

Having tasted briefly the sense of power, Hut had little difficulty in convincing himself that these rules were not meant for him, however fine they were for the population as a whole. All thought concerning the origin of the laws and their scope of activity he dismissed as of little consequence, leaving his mind free to revert to the intriguing possibilities of the suggestion Marda had made the evening before. For some time he became lost to anything else until he suddenly remembered that he had promised to speak to Harco and Wardu about coming to the house to discuss this very matter.

Reluctantly, he rose from his log seat, only to find Harco approaching him. Harco had always felt an attachment to Hut, and he smiled broadly as he came up to him. On the other hand, although he had never repulsed the man, Hut had done little to cultivate his friendship. Now he greeted him warmly, much to Harco's gratification. For a few moments, they commented on matters of common interest before Hut broached the subject uppermost in his mind.

"Harco, do you believe you can interest a number of Hata Yans to come to the Plains and join our group?"

There was a pause as Harco strove to comprehend Hut's rather unexpected question. His answer, however, indicated he had previously given some thought to such an eventuality. "Harco do. Harco know nine families come. About two hundred men and women. Many children. Good men. Do as Harco say."

"That will be fine," Hut agreed enthusiastically, and but for the mutual interest of the two in each other's conversation, they must surely have heard the soft grunt of the hairy Grut who was hiding not ten feet from where they sat. "I am anxious to get as many dependable men as possible, and as soon as it can be done. How soon do you think you can bring them?"

"One, two moons," Harco answered, frowning as his slower working mind calculated. "Harco get men Hut can trust. Mind Harco. Harco Hut's friend. Harco like Hut." The big fellow's face reddened under his heavy, black whiskers.

From behind the trunk of the huge tree where he stood, Grut was hard pressed to restrain a snort.

"I like you, too, Harco," Hut acknowledged the declaration. "I think you and I can always work together," he added, smiling into Harco's face. "It will be best not to bring too many at one time. Do you suppose you could bring one or two families soon?"

"Take Harco one moon. Harco know two families come quick when Harco ask."

"I would like to talk more about this a little later, Harco. Would you like to come to my house tomorrow just after dark?" asked Hut.

The Hata Yan's heavy face brightened with surprise and pleasure. "Harco glad come," he said. "Harco never at Hut's home," he added, for this unaccustomed favor meant much to him, and he wanted Hut to know it.

"I have been going to ask you to come see us," Hut said, rather wishing he had not been quite so aloof before.

"Harco come. Come quiet," the other assured him with much nodding of the head.

Hut patted Harco's hairy shoulder—quite an unusual departure for him—and getting to his feet, started in the direction of the new building which was being erected and where he was almost sure he would find Wardu.

Growling under his breath, but moving as silently as a shadow, Grut followed him, and while it was impossible to get close enough to overhear all the conversation between Wardu and Hut, he did manage to learn that Wardu also agreed to come to Hut's home the following night. Having all the information he wanted, he slipped away unobserved and hastened to Ord to whom he related his findings . . . . and his suspicions.

Ord's comment was characteristic. "Ord get Dargh. Grut, Dargh, and Ord listen. Grut not tell Rhu!" he admonished.

If the vigor with which he shook his shaggy head meant anything at all, it indicated Grut's full agreement with Ord.

THE NEXT morning, the first rays of light saw Rhu leave Haitee at their door and make his way toward Dargh's workshop, where not many minutes later, Dargh joined him. After examining the work of the evening before, they immediately set about making some fairly round pegs with the axe, driving them into the burned-out holes of the log. Dargh then found two long, fairly heavy pieces of timber of equal length which he flattened on one end. Into these flat ends, he proceeded to burn holes in the same way he had burned them into the log the previous day.

Rhu followed each move with intense interest, but neither he nor Dargh attempted to carry on a conversation. The latter fitted the holes in the poles over the pegs in the ends of the logs, and Rhu saw that they could be used to pull the log along. His eyes flew wide, however, when Dargh set the thing upon the ground to demonstrate how the "roller" rotated as the pegs turned in the slightly larger holes in the poles.

Rhu grunted his approval. "That's fine, Dargh! Shorter poles with holes in them can be used to hold the platform. We can mount them on the pegs just as you did these two long ones." As he spoke, he added to his drawing, then looked at it thoughtfully. "This will necessitate our making the pegs in the roller much heavier and longer."

They finally managed to pull out the pegs, and Dargh enlarged and deepened the holes so that the pegs ultimately used were a good four inches in diameter, and were driven at least a foot into each end of the log. Upon installing the two short pieces, however, they found that only one end of the platform was supported. This they remedied by adding two more short poles, making the entire affair stronger and steadier. Dargh was full of ideas, and he now set to work lashing two lighter and shorter poles across what we would call the shafts. These crossbars extended about eighteen inches beyond the shafts on each side.

Dargh and Rhu viewed their handiwork with not a little satisfaction shared by Pflugh and Nohr who had been interested, but silent, onlookers during most of the procedure. Seeing them for perhaps the first time, Dargh sent Pflugh for Ord and a few of the other Forest Dwellers. When these arrived, man's first cart was lifted from the bench and several laughing men piled upon it. Four of the stoutest Forest Dwellers grasped the poles extending over the shafts and started gayly across the land, the protesting squeaks of the rough axles adding to the joy of the occasion as the pullers strove with all their combined might to upset their riding companions.

Rhu and Dargh watched the performance with eyes that studied the action of their latest invention. "If roller bigger around weigh more but pull easier, Dargh think," the Muson commented.

"I think so too," agreed Rhu. "Let's get one about so thick," he suggested, indicating a log about three feet in diameter. "This one is long enough. It it were any longer, it would be too heavy to pull."

"Ord know where get one," boomed that interested Forest Dweller. "Ord and men take roller and bring back." Suiting the action to his words, he ordered his cavorting friends to come with him.

HAITEE delighted in the occasions when she could surprise Rhu with a baking of the sweetened bread he liked so much. A few days before the storm, Grut had discovered a large and hollow tree in which, for many years apparently, a great swarm of bees had settled, and from it, he had secured a number of skins of honey. Each skin held about the equivalent of our modern five gallons, and he had brought four of them to Haitee. She and Rhu soon found that it was especially good with the maize bread, and after that, it was not long before she conceived the idea of adding some to the dough before baking. The result was so delicious that Haitee always made the sweetened bread when she wanted to particularly please Rhu.

Since he had not been his usual cheerful self the evening before, she decided this was a good time to make the delicacy. She was more than happy when he arrived with Nohr, whom he had invited to come home with him and partake of Haitee's cooking. Never having tasted anything like the sweet bread, Nohr was loud in his praises and this, of course, was a great pleasure to the little cook.

The serving of the dainty prolonged the meal as well as filling them all to repletion so that little was said until Haitee had cleaned up their bowls and attended to such other simple duties as were customary after meals. Not until she joined them was there much conversation, and this rather surprised Nohr. When he had been at Hut's home, it was true that Marda had intruded into the conversation, but it was the custom for a wife to stay in the background, especially when her husband was conversing with another man. Since coming to the Plains, however, Nohr had come to look for the unusual, so he gave no indication of his surprise that a wife should be expected to take part in a conversation between men.

"Hut was telling me of your visit with him and Marda the night of the storm," Rhu opened the conversation.

"Yes," Nohr agreed easily, "and we had quite an interesting talk, especially about those laws the Elders instructed him to prepare."

Haitee's eyes opened wide. "The Elders instructed *him* to prepare!" she exclaimed impulsively, and before Rhu could stop her, she continued, "It was *Lord Lithargos* who gave Rhu and him the ten laws. Hut had no more to do with their preparation than did Rhu, and that was nothing. Rhu told me about them, and an Elder was here just yesterday to discuss them with both Rhu and Hut!"

Nohr's face betrayed some astonishment. "Hut told me specifically that he had been instructed to prepare them," he said positively. "I thought little of it as he has often mentioned something of this sort." For a moment, he hesitated, and then asked, "Rhu, are you not anxious to bring new families from other tribes into the group here?"

Although he wondered at the sudden change of subject, Rhu answered promptly. "Indeed I am," he said, "but from this time forward, all who desire to come must be trained first by the Elders. All too many newcomers find it hard to become accustomed to our new ways, so the Elders are preparing to train each aspirant for what they call citizenship. Then, when they come, they will be prepared to fit into our way of life and be ready to take an active and productive part in the organized and unified group. Just the same, I certainly would like to have more Tama Yans like you. We need hundreds of families."

"Hut gave me to understand that if I would bring in several families, he would see that they are admitted right away. In fact, he said Wardu was going to bring in some Cari Yan families."

Rhu stared at Nohr in incredulous amazement. "I am sure you must have misunderstood him," he stated calmly. "Hut was present when the Elder talked about this and knows we are to admit no more of any tribe until they are specially trained."

"Is it possible that there might be some exceptions?" asked Nohr. "Not that I would seek to be an exception, but Hut was so definite that I could hardly have been mistaken. I think the idea of training all who want to participate in what you are doing here is very fine. In fact, it is the only practical way I can see to prevent misunderstandings and confusion."

"No, there are to be no exceptions. Hut knows this, and I am sure he would not seek to go contrary to the expressed wishes of the Elders. Yet, if he has left *you* confused, I wonder about Wardu. Will you mind if I get Hut to come in and talk this thing over? It just doesn't seem possible that he could have misunderstood, for the Elder was very specific."

"I shall be glad to have Hut come in," Nohr agreed readily. "He certainly does not talk as you do, and I would like to be sure about this. It is not that I question what you say, Rhu. Not by any means, but there is certainly some difference of opinion between you, and I think it should be settled before any damage can possibly be done.

"Somehow, Rhu, I had the feeling that Hut expected me to bring in people who would be loyal to me, and in turn, that I was supposed to be loyal to Hut. In fact, although he may not have said so in so many words, I gathered that he expects to become the leader here and is anxious to get people upon whom he can depend. It may have been Marda who stressed this angle most, but Hut did not object."

As Nohr talked, Rhu's eyes narrowed. Were Dargh and Ord right after all? Could it possibly be that Hut really did seek to rule? Well, there was but one way to settle the matter. He would get Hut and bring the affair out into the open.

IT WAS dark when Harco and Wardu arrived at Hut's, almost at the same moment. To the sharp-eyed and sharper-eared Ord, Dargh, and Grut, it was all too obvious that they were taking care not to be observed and that neither knew of the other's coming. Silently, they approached the lighted doorway from opposite directions, keeping well to each side of the light so that one became aware of the other only as they met when they started to enter. Dargh peered through the gloom toward Grut who promptly held his nose and grimaced so convincingly that Ord was hard put to it to keep his laughter from booming through the silent night.

Lighting facilities other than the family fires and an occasional pine knot were as yet unheard of. Therefore, it was fortunate for the four in Hut's home that the night was sufficiently cool to make a fire comfortable, for so much had to be conveyed by signs and facial expressions. The three watchers outside also benefited, for creeping close to the door, they could hear and see clearly all that took place without being seen.

Hut and Marda welcomed their visitors in subdued tones,

inviting them to sit around the table. "I hope you two managed to come tonight without attracting too much attention," Hut opened the conversation. Upon being assured that not a soul had witnessed their arrival, and that neither of them had known of the other's approach until they met at the door, he complimented them upon their care.

The three eavesdroppers grinned at one another.

"It is not that secrecy is so important," Hut said, "but in view of what I want to talk about with you, it is probably better that none knows of it, especially for the time being. Later, we shall, of course, take Rhu and the Council into our confidence, especially if things work out as I hope. For the present, however, I think it best that no one else know about it.

"I know what good friends you two are, so I asked you to come tonight so that I can talk to you both at the same time. It has to do with the matter of bringing to the Plains a number of thoroughly reliable and especially loyal families upon whom we can depend.

"One of the principal laws to be adopted by our Council is that all new laws and actions which affect the people as a whole must first be agreed to by the majority of the people on the Plains. Therefore, it will always be important to know in advance all who are sufficiently loyal to follow our advice and vote for what we think is best for the group."

(As customary, for the sake of simplicity and better understanding, the following conversation is quite liberally translated into far more modern words and terms than were actually used.)

"Just whom do you mean by 'we'?" Wardu asked.

Hut hesitated, well realizing the care he must use in giving these men a logical understanding while, at the same time, concealing any purpose he had in mind to accomplish for himself. "Well," he began, "to make this perfectly clear, I shall have to explain what the Elders have taught us. In a community such as ours, all must work for the common good. First, each individual must be considered, then each family, then each tribe, then the entire group as a whole. Clearly, no group can be any stronger than the individuals composing it. Do you understand that?"

They nodded, and Hut drew a long breath. "In time, even the Council must have a leader," he stated. "By that I mean some one who is sufficiently farseeing to be able to guide them properly. Rhu and I cannot live forever, you know, so we must have this group so organized and operating that it can go right on ahead without either of us. This is one of the things I mean when I speak of having the ability to see ahead and to plan for such things."

Unable to stand quietly by and listen any longer to Hut's indirect statements, the outspoken Marda interrupted. "Hut has that vision," she declared, coming right to the point. "To be a real leader, one must not be impetuous, acting without careful forethought and careful consideration for the future. It is one thing to be able to meet emergencies of the moment, but quite another to be able to foresee such things and prepare for them long before they happen.

"Has Rhu ever talked to either of you as Hut is now doing? Has he ever talked about plans necessary for the future? Has he not always talked only about what is to be done now? And when anything goes wrong, doesn't Rhu drop everything else and hurry to take care of it?"

Marda's voice was so convincing that both men nodded as though confirming all she said. "A real leader would have been prepared for such an event," she continued. "He would have appointed the proper ones to handle the situation without allowing it to interfere with his more important work. *Hut is always doing that.* It was he who first recognized the necessity for the very laws which the Elders have had him prepare for us. Rhu has always been opposed to such rules and regulations, and that probably explains why Hut was selected for this important work."

Harco's eyes, as he gazed at Hut, were bright with the admiration he made no effort to conceal. Wardu's brow was furrowed as he digested her words. For a time there was complete silence.

Finally Wardu spoke. "What Marda says is very true," he said. "Rhu is a fine director of men. We all like him and admire his ability to handle emergencies, but if Hut is able to foresee them and prepare for them in advance, as Marda says, then he should make a fine leader. That the Elders have asked him to prepare the laws would seem to indicate they feel much the same. Yet, if his vision is so good, why did Hut have to change the Council he originally selected? I have never known of Rhu having to change anything he started to do."

"W-e-l-l," Hut drawled, his nimble brain seeking a proper answer to this poser, "the Elders want us to work together for the present. I suggested the Council membership without consulting him as I did not want him to be bothered. The laws have been discussed with him as I do not intend to go contrary to the wishes of the Elders. With the Council, I was merely trying to take some of the load from his shoulders—not to ignore him. The Elders recognized this, I am sure.

"I do not want you two to feel that I am suggesting anything that will hurt Rhu. He is as a brother to me and is always present in my thoughts, and is taken into consideration in all my plans. As Marda says, Rhu has no equal when it comes to handing emergencies or to getting things done, but he does not plan ahead very far, and I have that as my share of our work together."

All the satisfaction Hut had felt as Marda talked had vanished, and he scowled at her. Why should she open up a subject involving Rhu! Why must she always be so thoughtless!

"My plan is merely in its formative stage and is, at best, but an idea," he continued. "Rhu will be brought into it as soon as the time is right. What I want to know now is whether you and Harco think you can bring in several families from your tribes, families upon whom each of you can depend to do exactly as you suggest. To know this will help me immeasurably in planning for the future. The people who are here all know Rhu so well that they are apt to be influenced by their love for him. If it is ever necessary to override an idea of his, we might easily make some serious mistakes because of this."

"Harco can and will do," the Hata Yan announced, speaking for the first time. "Harco bring people who do as Harco says, and Harco do as Hut says."

Wardu nodded his head thoughtfully. "Wardu can do this thing also, but I do not want it to appear that I am taking sides for or against either Hut or Rhu. Still, what Marda says is true, so I shall return to my tribe and see about gathering a few strong and dependable families. They will do as I say. That I can assure you, and when Hut is right, I will back Hut. However, I do not want to feel that in so doing, I am taking sides against Rhu. I will let you know as soon as I have these people ready. How many families do you want at this time?"

Like Rhu, Hut was beginning to wonder about Wardu. Was some of what he said "double-talk"? Of course, he, Hut, would never do anything against Rhu either. He never had, and the words of his father were deeply burned into his mind. "Well, nothing is ever gained without taking some chance," he thought, unconsciously repeating in his own mind words Rhu had often used, and Wardu was a chance he must take.

"That is all anybody could ask," he commented. "This is not a matter of taking sides with anyone, Wardu, but of doing what is best for all concerned and taking the future into consideration. We must have deeply loyal people who, while they may not always understand everything, will be willing to take their leader's word for it until they can grasp the idea fully. Does this answer your question, Wardu?"

"All but how many such Cari Yan families you want now?"

"Well, I think we should not try to bring in too many at first. It might cause some comment or suspicion, and we must always work as a unit, the Elders tell us. Do you suppose you could bring in two or three such families, consisting all together of not more than a hundred grown men and women?"

"Easily," Wardu agreed promptly. "How about you, Harco?"

"Harco can do in one moon." He smiled at Hut. "Can bring more any time."

"Fine! That will be enough for a start, and I shall see that the Council is enlarged so that their patriarchs can become members. Now let us say nothing of this to anyone, but you two can leave as soon as convenient and start gathering your people. It might be better if you depart separately so that when you return, you can arrive separately. Make it appear perfectly natural."

Outside, three listeners hastily melted into the night and soon were busily engaged in discussing all they had overheard. Ord was for stopping both Harco and Wardu, but Dargh wisely counseled allowing them to go as if no one suspected anything. Grut wanted to tell Rhu, but again Dargh was opposed. "Why bother Rhu with what we can handle?" he asked, and the agreement was unanimous.

"Neither lies nor truth was told tonight," Ord growled. "Some day, Ord choke truth from somebody!" Angry reactions still rumbling in his mighty chest, he strode away.

WARDU and Harco were barely out of sight when Rhu appeared in Hut and Marda's doorway. At sight of him, Marda's heart quickened in alarm. Had Rhu overheard the interview just consummated, or any part of it? What would they say if he had? How could they explain it away? He had arrived so promptly after their visitors' departure that he could even have been outside listening to the entire conversation! A sense of depressing fear gripped her.

Then Rhu spoke. "Hut, I wish you could come over to my place. Nohr is there and we would like to talk over some matters together tonight. It won't take long," he assured Marda.

Watching them depart, Marda resolved to find out for herself what it was they were going to discuss. If it had anything to do with Wardu and Harco, she would be ready to spring to Hut's assistance if he found himself at a loss to explain what had been taking place in their home.

As soon as they were out of earshot, she followed. With a smile of satisfaction she crouched in the deep shadow outside Rhu's door. She heard Rhu open the conversation by asking Hut to explain to Nohr just how the new laws had been formulated. Settling herself more comfortably, she sighed softly.

Slight as was the sound, it reached the sharp ears of Grut who had but that minute returned from the nearby spot where he had left Dargh. With a wolfish grin, he clamped a great and hairy hand over Marda's mouth, and with his other arm, effortlessly swung her to her feet. Striding to Hut's house, he unceremoniously tossed her inside, and was away into the night before she could gather her befuddled thoughts and dash outside to see who was guilty of this outrage!

Failing to see anyone in the gloom, she caught her breath

and started to rub her aching sides which Grut had so rudely grasped, also amazed to see the trickle of blood from her lips over which he had placed a none-too-gentle hand. She decided she was far safer inside, and in a flurry of futile tears, collapsed upon a stool. Much later, when Hut returned, she had quite recovered and had decided to make no mention of her misadventure, which was probably just as well for Grut was outside listening. Grut was without scruples.

"HUT," Rhu began as they seated themselves at the table with Nohr and Haitee. "Nohr seems to be somewhat confused as to how the ten basic laws were formulated. He brought up the subject himself as I have not mentioned them to anyone. I thought it best for you to explain to him how and by whom they were prepared."

So quietly did he speak and so gentle was his tone that Nohr listened in wonder. In speaking of the conversation later to Dargh, he said, "I marveled at the manner in which Rhu approached the situation and the way in which he phrased his question. He knew very well that Hut was in a bad spot, yet he did not get excited, nor did his voice seem anything but kindly. I know that under the circumstances, *I* would have been abrupt and harsh."

For a brief moment after Rhu ceased speaking, Hut was rather stunned. What business had Nohr talking of the matter with Rhu after he, Hut, had told him about it? Quickly recovering his aplomb, however, he stated, "Why, there was nothing unusual about it, so I don't see how Nohr could be confused. Besides, I told him all about it, but that was only after you and I had talked of them."

Then because Rhu and Nohr seemed to be waiting, "Just what do you want to know about them?" he asked, turning to Nohr with a little less assurance.

For several seconds Nohr gazed at him thoughtfully. "Did you not tell me that the Elders had instructed you to prepare them?" he asked at length.

A drop of icy sweat trickled down Hut's spine. "Why, I hope I did not give you any wrong impression, Nohr," he replied. "I had no such intention. I think I said that we had talked them over with an Elder prior to submitting them to the Council."

"But did you not say that *you* were told to prepare them, and that you had done so?" Nohr persisted.

Rhu's natural disposition to uphold Hut at all times caused him to intercede. "Nohr says you told him that *you* had been told to prepare the laws, when we both know that Lord Lithargos gave them to us," he stated. "I merely want you to set him right. He seems to feel there is some sort of rift between us, and I want him to have the straight of things."

"Why certainly, Lord Lithargos outlined them to us, but did He not ask that we think them over before the Elder came to discuss them with us?"

"He asked that we discuss them in order that we might better understand them as well as to have ready any questions we might like to ask about them. Isn't that right?" Rhu asked.

"Surely," Hut agreed promptly, seeking to dispose of the matter quickly and depending upon his promptness to offset what might be construed as his admission of an incorrect statement.

"Another thing," Rhu continued, satisfied to have made his point and unwilling to embarrass Hut unnecessarily, "Nohr says you asked him to bring in several Tama Yan families right away, and that you would see they were admitted to the Plains. I told him I am sure he misunderstood you, for our instructions concerning new people are specific. I would more than welcome Nohr's friends, but I do not see how we can ignore our instructions and admit them without their first having been trained. Why, we cannot admit any more of *our own tribe* without this!"

This was a point for which Hut was ready, for, in having Harco and Wardu bring in new families, he well realized that sooner or later, he would be expected to explain his action. "The Elders are not yet ready to train them," he asserted, "so I saw no good reason why we should not make an exception in Nohr's case—at least until the Elders are ready. Of course, if they get ready before Nohr returns with some Tama Yans, we would naturally expect them to go first to the Elders."

"But what about Wardu?" asked Nohr. "I am sure he feels as I did—that he can bring in his people without delay. Hut, if people are brought here without knowing of this training period and the terms to which they must agree, there will be trouble. It will discount those of us who influence them to come and result in even worse suspicions than now exist, and they are bad enough. Frankly, I do not think this is a very good example of the far-visioned leadership which you and Marda mentioned during the storm." Nohr's voice had become quite emphatic.

"I am afraid you misunderstood," Hut replied, his mind working at top speed for some logical way out of the dilemma in which he was finding himself. "This leadership is two-phased. One of us plans, while the other works the plans."

Suddenly, he thought of how this might sound to Rhu who was alert to all double meanings, as Hut had long since learned. He must say something that would counteract the impression his words might give. "Actually, that is not exactly as I mean it," he said hastily. "Rhu and I always plan together and work together. We always have, and I see no reason why we should not always do so. Rhu is like a brother to me. I love him more than any other man in the world, and I certainly would never dream of doing anything that could possibly work to his disadvantage or hurt him in any way.

"If one of us had to be leader here, Rhu is the man I would choose above all others. All that I ever say or do is for him and for his advancement. I would die for him." Carried away by his own eloquence, Hut was for the moment really sincere in his expression of loyalty. "I owe him my very life," he added with increased ardor.

Rhu flushed and began to regret having ever doubted Hut.

"Not only that," his old friend continued, "but I shall prove it at the first meeting of the Council by asking that he be made the leader of our group!"

"You will not!" Rhu snapped. "We began this thing together, Hut, and so far as I am concerned, we shall finish our work together as long as we are both alive. I have no desire for leadership. I have no ambitions in that direction. As Marda has often said, I am impulsive and apt to be too deeply concerned with the immediate present, while you are disposed to look more into the future."

Turning to Nohr, he said, "I was certain that it was all merely a misunderstanding. I hope this has cleared up the confusion for you, Nohr."

"Yes," echoed Hut, "it was all just a misunderstanding, but it just goes to prove how easily one can give a wrong impression." Rising, he bade them good night and left for his home.

As he watched from his self-appointed post, Grut saw Hut wipe the sweat from his forehead as he hastened away—and his grunt spoke for itself. Trailing along to complete his vigil, he grumbled, "Some day Hut try make *Grut* understand and Grut twist neck!"

THE FOLLOWING morning, Rhu's spirits were high as again he made his way to Dargh's workshop. Rhu was not one to permit himself to be long depressed, and all the unfavorable reactions he may have experienced the evening before were now forgotten as his mind focused on the cart which he and Dargh were constructing.

For two more days, they labored. Encouragement was plentiful, for Ord and his men were vitally interested, and at last, the new vehicle was ready for testing. The shaft poles were much longer than those of the earlier cart, and cross-pieces, at four-foot intervals for pulling, accommodated twenty men. They found that four could pull it with four of their cohorts riding upon it, but with six pullers, the fourteen others managed to crowd upon the platform, and they hurried away to see how many stones they could haul.

Rhu and Dargh could hear the loudly protesting axles screeching away long before the excited chatter of the returning, sweating pullers could be distinguished. And when they saw that the cart carried twice as many stones as twenty men

The First Wheeled Vehicle

could pull on the sleds in dry weather, Rhu and Dargh knew they had turned another milestone in their progress.

Immediately, Dargh and his men set to work on the construction of another cart and the lumbering devices screeched over the countryside delivering the necessary stones where most needed. Then, one day, one of the Musons accidentally slipped and spilled his pot of the clay and water which was used as cement, and the mixture dropped on one of the axles. It was afterwards noticed that this particular wheel no longer screeched. The other axle was promptly doused with the mixture, and the cart moved ahead silently and much more easily than before. However, the clay did not last long, so relays of men were established along the trail to douse the axles as soon as they began to squeak.

When Rhu heard of this, he recalled a hard fall he had taken when he accidentally had stepped upon a piece of suet, so he melted a quantity of fat and carefully poured it upon the axles. In a very short time, and as the axles became saturated with the grease and were kept so, the screeching finally ceased almost altogether. Thus, to an extent, the matter of lubrication was solved.

The principal difficulty in the construction of these first crude vehicles lay in securing logs which were uniformly round. Quite by accident, Dargh made another discovery which ultimately enabled him to suit any log to his purpose, thus revolutionizing the production of carts. Long since, he had devised a method for cutting rawhide thongs. By affixing a sharp bit of flint in a log and holding taut a piece of skin between both hands, he could run it over the flint, dividing, or cutting it into pieces of the desired size. One day, as he was rolling a log past this, he happened to brush it against this bit of cutting stone, making a sharp gash in it. Always alert to take advantage of everything new, he sent for Rhu and together they studied this event with the result that the first approach to a lathe was devised.

By suspending their "roller" from its axles between two forked logs, they could turn it with comparative ease. This contrivance was placed lengthwise alongside one of the workbenches. With their stone axes, they peeled the bark from two willow logs, then chopped the knots off one side, making a reasonably smooth surface which they thoroughly greased. Fastening these side by side on the workbench, smooth side up, they laid another log on top and between them so that the willow logs formed a groove to hold it. A very sharp flint was firmly fixed in this log on the side adjacent to the roller suspended on the forked sticks so that when the roller was slowly turned, the flint cut into it in much the same manner as the modern lathe operates. By revolving the roller and slowly sliding the log holding the flint backward or forward along its greased platform, they were able to cut the roller to a fairly uniform roundness.

In time, this operation was so perfected that they turned out logs that were almost perfectly round. The newer and better vehicles thus made possible enabled the people of the Rhu Hut Plains to practically double the speed of construction, for getting ample supplies of stone no longer presented such a great problem.

The First Lathe

Chapter Twenty-eight

THE FIRST DISAGREEMENT

THE FIRST meeting of the Council was an epochal event, marking as it did the beginning of an organized and representative government for those who lived on the Plains. It is doubtful whether any of its members, except possibly Rhu and Hut, realized just what was to take place at these meetings and since the people of this day were creatures of fixed habits and customs, and this Council affair was an entirely new experience, it was not surprising that restless shuffling feet and countless throat clearings should betray their agitation.

As promised, the Elder who had explained the ten basic laws to Rhu and Hut was present. The first thing he did was to assign places to Rhu, Hut, Sol, and Mai, a seating arrangement which was held to meticulously for the remainder of their lives. A dozen stools had been made for these assemblages and sitting upon one of them, the Elder had Rhu and Hut sit on either side of him while Mai Dan and Sol Ku, the best known and most respected men among the new citizenry, sat directly facing them. The other members were free to make their own choice as to where they wished to sit. As a consequence, they formed a semi-circle facing Rhu, Hut, and the Elder with Ord and Dargh seating themselves beside Sol Ku and in front of Rhu.

(What follows may seem rather erudite for the comprehension of these people, adhering as they did to the old manner of speaking. It must be remembered, however, that their understanding of new words and phrases had been steadily expanding and like many learning a new language, they often understood much more than they were capable of expressing. Also, if it seems strange that they should have been able to remember much of what was told them on this day, bear in mind that at that time there was no such thing as the written word so that these people had to depend upon memory for all such things. As a consequence, their minds were more retentive than is true today.)

After all were seated, the Elder rose to speak, thus establishing the custom for each one addressing the assembly. "My friends," he began, speaking slowly and with great deliberation in order that all might understand and grasp his meaning, "this marks one of the greatest events in the lives of all of us. We, here, form the first ruling body of men upon this earth. It will be our work to guide our people in the formation of an orderly way of life by the establishment and maintenance of law and order.

"First, however, the Council itself must have some definite rules for conducting these meetings so that all may ever be regular and in order. These I shall explain to you, but if you do not understand, you must speak up and I shall explain further.

"There must always be someone who is the head of the Council. When, as at this meeting, an Elder is present, he will act in this capacity. When, as will often be the case, no Elder is present, Rhu and Hut will act as the head. Later, aside from the Elders, the Council will elect the one to be its head, and because he will preside at the meetings, he shall be known as the Chief."

"What does Elder mean by 'elect'?" Sol Ku asked.

"That I shall explain," the Elder replied, "but to make it clear, I must first mention certain other rules. When a member of the Council desires to speak on any subject or ask a question, he should say, 'Chief, may I speak?'

"If someone else is speaking, the Chief may or may not grant such permission, depending upon whether he thinks it advisable to interrupt the one speaking. In this case, Sol, you would have said, 'Chief, may I ask a question?' I would have agreed and you would then ask your question.

"If Sol had wanted to make a suggestion which would call for the agreement of the entire Council, he would state his idea, then say, 'I move this suggestion be adopted.' If he doesn't say this, any other member of the Council who agrees with him may move that it be adopted. In either event, before it can be acted upon by the Council someone else must say, 'I second the motion.' No member may second his own motion.

"When it has been moved and seconded that the idea be carried out, the Chief will say, 'You have heard the motion moved and seconded. All in favor say 'Yes.' Or he may ask all in favor to raise their hands. Then he will ask those not in favor to say 'no,' or to raise their hands. If more say 'yes' than say 'no,' the Council has then agreed to the suggestion and it becomes an official act of the Council.

"On the other hand, if no one seconds the motion, it means the others do not think well of it, and the Chief speaks of it as 'being lost.'

"If a member of the Council suggests that a certain other member be made Chief, a motion to that effect must be made and seconded, then voted upon. If the majority votes for him, he is said to have been elected. Do you now understand, Sol?"

"Yes, but Sol think much talk for little done."

The Elder smiled pleasantly, his eyes twinkling at Sol's blunt opinion. "You are quite right, Sol, but since everything to be acted upon by the Council affects all the people, directly or indirectly, there must be an established and definite way of doing things. This makes the acts official, Sol, and no one may later claim that it was not done regularly or properly."

"Still think many words," Sol insisted, but his rugged old face was wreathed in a warm smile. "If Elder say, Sol do. Sol want do right. Elder way right. Sol's way same." He nodded vigorously and beside him, Mai's head nodded in unison.

His face rather red, old Ku Kut got to his feet. "Chief, may Ku Kut speak?" he asked.

"Ku Kut may speak," the Elder agreed.

"Suppose vote even. What do?" Mopping his brow with relief, he sat down.

"When the vote is even, then, and only then, may the Chief vote."

Ku Kut was back on his feet, his keen eyes bright. "What if Rhu and Hut not agree? They are Chief when no Elder."

"Then the matter must wait until an Elder is present and be brought up again. That would be called 'unfinished business.'"

Ku Kut hesitated a moment as if about to say something more, then sat down abruptly, evidently thinking better of it, but he nodded his understanding.

"The Chief always opens the meetings," the Elder continued, "but any Council member may move that the meeting close. If this is not seconded, the Chief speaks of the motion as being lost, and further business will be taken up. If the motion is seconded, the Chief can either take a vote or declare the meeting closed. Is that clear?"

All heads nodded, and the Elder than took up the discussion of the laws previously explained to Hut and Rhu. Three hours later when he finished, Sol Ku moved their adoption. This was seconded almost instantly by Mai, and the vote was unanimous. About to suggest a motion for the meeting to close, the Elder was interrupted by Rhu's request to be heard.

"Chief, it seems to me that only one man should be Chief when an Elder is not here. I move that Hut be elected to that office now."

Overturning his stool in his haste, Ord jumped up, his great bellow drowning the murmur among the other Council members. "NO!" he shouted.

"No!" echoed Mai and Ku Kut.

Somewhat startled, the Elder asked, "Does anyone second Rhu's motion?"

A deep silence followed.

"Apparently, your motion is lost," the Elder said, smiling at Rhu. "I am glad it is so. It is best that you act together as you have always done."

Then he turned to Hut, saying, "The Elders are not unaware of what has been taking place here, Hut, and of Marda's desire that you become the leader. Also, that you have said you would ask that Rhu be made leader. But this is not good. Leadership is vested in the Council, my son, and no one should seek to take it from them lest he lose the right to live here. Any who feel themselves capable of planning or who have plans for the future of the forming civilization should suggest such plans to the Council for acceptance or rejection."

At this point, Dargh rose to his feet, and immediately each Council member sensed that something of importance was pending. Rhu and Hut stirred restlessly, both uneasy as to what the direct-thinking and outspoken Muson might say.

Having received permission to speak, Dargh stated, "There has been talk of bringing in other families before the Elders have trained them. Are there to be any exceptions? Dargh understand Elder say not."

Rhu looked questioningly at Hut, whose heart was pounding sharply, but Hut's eyes evaded those of his old friend.

"You are quite right," the Elder replied, "but we are willing to listen to the feeling of the Council in this matter. Mai, what is your idea?" he asked, turning to Hut's father.

Mai got to his feet. "Ku Kut very wise. Ku Kut shrewd. Mai and Sol prefer Ku Kut speak first," he said, then sat down.

Ku Kut rose, his grizzled beard standing well out from his chest due to his outthrust chin. "Ku Kut would know who try do this thing."

"Dargh, do you wish to say who suggested this?" the Elder asked.

Hut winced and his face grew pale.

Dargh's eyes were now on Rhu who shook his head so slightly that perhaps only the Muson caught it. "Dargh prefer not say . . . . but it was not Rhu."

"Ku Kut know that," the shrewd old Plains Dweller stated flatly, his own keen eyes upon Hut. "Ku Kut think plan of Elders best. Ku Kut move no more families be brought to Plains until Elders say so."

"Mai second motion," that individual spoke up quickly.

"All in favor of Ku Kut's motion hold up their hands," and the hands of all but Rhu and Hut were raised.

"Rhu and Hut not in favor?" Ku Kut asked.

"We do not vote except when the Council cannot agree," Rhu explained.

"Rhu is right," the Elder agreed. "The Council has voted unanimously that no more families be brought to the Plains until first endorsed or agreed to by the Elders who will soon be ready to start the training. Now that you have established good laws, ever abide by them. If there is no further business, a motion to close the meeting is in order."

MARDA and Haitee were sitting at the table in Haitee's home while the Council was holding its first meeting, Marda having come over to learn what had taken place while Hut was there the night before. Hut, she had explained, had been very depressed and refused to tell her, although she felt she had the right to know. By an effort, she managed to conceal her true feelings, or so she believed. Haitee, understanding more than Marda could know, maintained her usual friendly attitude and steered a middle course.

"Oh, it was nothing very much. Nohr thought Hut had said the Elders had authorized him to prepare the laws which we all know were given him and Rhu by Lord Lithargos. Also, Nohr said Hut wanted him to bring in some Tama Yan families before they were trained by the Elders."

Well knowing that Hut had actually said and done these things, Marda was quick to assume that Rhu had taken full advantage of this opportunity to put Hut in a bad light. And having *assumed* it, she accepted it as fact and reacted accordingly. "Rhu must have felt very big and smart to drag Hut over here and deny what he had said," she snapped.

Haitee's cheeks grew hot. "Rhu did nothing of the sort!" she denied. "He told Nohr he must be mistaken, and brought Hut over to confirm it."

"Humph!" Marda snorted skeptically. "I don't believe it. Rhu has been mad at Hut ever since that Council matter when he thought Hut was about to take over the leadership."

"He has not!" Haitee retorted promptly. "Rhu does not want to be leader. He even told me this morning that he was going to propose making Hut the leader—since he wants it so much," she added a bit waspishly. "You know, Marda, you and Hut have been planning upon Hut's becoming the leader, even though I can't see where he has ever done anything to warrant it."

"Why, Haitee! This coming to the Plains was Hut's idea in

the first place, and Rhu could have done nothing without him!" Marda exclaimed tartly. "In fact, Hut brought in most of the people here anyhow, and what did Rhu do? Got a few Cave and Forest Dwellers! Anybody could have done *that* well," she concluded sarcastically.

"That is a deliberate lie," cried Haitee, flouncing to her feet, her eyes ablaze. "Hut could no more have got any Cave or Forest Dwellers to join with us than he could fly, and you know it! And how did he get those Plains Dwellers you brag so much about? By telling them that *Rhu* had found this place and was back of the whole idea! I've heard Ku Kut tell about it many times, and so has Dorg Mauk and others of the first ones. And just tell me where we would be if it hadn't been for Dargh and Ord! Leader! Why, even Hut's own father and brother refuse to follow him!"

With a scream of rage, Marda sprang to her feet and started for the smaller Haitee, just at Grut's great, hairy hand seized her and jerked her to one side.

"Marda touch Haitee, Grut spank like little child. Go home. Stay home. First, tell Haitee Marda sorry she lie." Grut's grip on her arm tightened until Marda almost screamed in pain. "Tell Haitee Marda sorry," he snarled.

"Don't, Grut." Haitee came to Marda's aid, and Grut obeyed so promptly that Marda almost fell as he dropped her arm. "She just got mad at what I said."

"Grut hear. What Haitee say true. What Marda say, all lies. Marda tell Haitee sorry."

"I am sorry, Haitee. I should not have said what I did in the first place," and she began to cry as she rubbed her bruised arm where Grut had grasped it.

"Oh, that's all right, Marda. I said a lot of mean things too, but you made me mad. You don't have to go home. Stay to lunch with me. Grut, everything is all right. Thank you just the same. You are good to me."

Grut flushed and began to shuffle his big feet uneasily. "Grut thing Haitee too good to Marda, but if Haitee say Marda stay, Grut say stay too." Turning on his heel, he strode away, but once out of sight, he slipped back to within easy earshot. Grut did not trust Marda. Also, he knew things of which neither Rhu nor Haitee was aware, and he was determined that no hurt should come to Haitee while he was able to prevent it.

ALTHOUGH none of the Elders was present, the following three weeks saw three more Council meetings called by Rhu and Hut in order that the laws might be rehearsed and more fully explained. Before the Council members could begin to familiarize the people with these laws and put them into force, it was essential that each one become thoroughly versed in them and their many ramifications. This was a slow process, for although they remembered them, merely being able to repeat the laws verbatim was far from sufficient. These men had to understand them and what they meant to everyone on the Plains.

With infinite patience, Hut and Rhu explained and re-explained in minute detail all they themselves understood about them, and at the end of the three week period, the Council members felt equal to doing the same in their families and to all who were affected by them.

It was following this third meeting that Harco returned with two Hata Yan families consisting of more than a hundred adults, only to be refused admittance by Ord. Harco was enraged, but bitter experience had taught him the futility of trying to force their way past Ord and the defenders of this pass. He demanded that Hut be advised, and Ord agreed, but first sought out Rhu to whom he explained the situation.

Rhu sent for Hut, but Hut, getting the story of the new arrivals from the messenger, went directly to Ord. "Why do you not admit Harco and his people?" he demanded. "Did he not tell you that I authorized this?"

"Council say admit no one not trained by Elders, so Ord not let enter."

"I will assume the responsibility, so I order you to admit them!" Hut declared with some heat.

"No," Ord refused stubbornly. "If Rhu say yes, Ord agree, Council or no Council. But Rhu say no. Better Hut see Rhu."

Knowing Ord, Hut realized there was nothing else to do except follow the big fellow's advice, so he then went to Rhu.

"Why do you refuse to let Harco and his people enter?" he demanded as soon as he saw Rhu.

"When the Elder was here, Hut, it was unanimously agreed by the Council that only those endorsed by the Elders be admitted. You know this. You have always insisted upon the establishment of laws and rules, and now that we have them, you are the first one to want them ignored. Why, Hut?"

"Ord says that if YOU say so, he will admit them, Council or no Council."

"Then Ord is wrong," Rhu stated flatly, "and I shall tell him so. I would not think of doing any such thing, Hut, and I am surprised at your attitude. Did you promise Harco that you would admit him and these Hata Yans this way?"

"That was before the Council had acted," Hut hedged, "and when I give my word, I expect to see it carried out. You well know that I would not let *you* down!" he cried vehemently.

"I'm sorry that you feel this way, Hut. What Ord may say or feel is something with which I have nothing to do. He is a man and has a right to express his own ideas, but I would never dream of seeking to go contrary to the wishes of the Elders. If you told Harco you would make an exception in his case, you will have to explain to him. Nohr felt you had promised him the same consideration, but you denied it, and I accepted your word without question. He also mentioned Wardu, but you indicated you had made no such promise.

"If you did promise him and Harco that they would be admitted, why did you not say so at that time? Had you done so, perhaps the necessary arrangements could have been made at that first Council meeting when the Elder was here. Hut . . . . just why are you so anxious to have these people come on to the Plains?"

"Because I pledged my word," Hut answered promptly.

"Yet, you denied to Nohr and me that you had made any such promises. Hut, if you really want to be the leader, I shall not stand in your way. But I do not think it is a mark of good leadership to start out by making exceptions to the laws established by the Council and the Elders. I truly wish you could show me some good and sufficient reason for admitting Harco and his people, but you have not done so. We might call the

Council together for a special meeting, but that would necessitate your explaining away what you told Nohr and me that night because there are others besides ourselves who know of that conversation."

"Aren't we the accepted leaders of these people?" Hut demanded impatiently. "Did not the Elder say so? If we are the leaders, then it is our right and power to make any exceptions we see fit. Otherwise, of what use is a leader? If he has to abide by what all the others want, then he is only their servant, not their leader."

"I don't look at it that way, Hut, and I don't believe you do either. A true leader is one who sets an example for his people to follow. Do you think it is setting a good example to enact a law, then break it on the first occasion when it does not suit your convenience?

"I have never deceived you, Hut. I have never tried to do anything that would not work to your advantage and credit. Even now, if only the two of us were involved, I'd gladly support you, but when you ask me to go contrary to the will of both the Elders and the Council, you are asking that I violate every fine principle back of what we are trying to accomplish, to say nothing of its effect upon everyone here. No, Hut, you are wrong."

"Do you mean that you refuse to stand by me as you have always done before simply because the people we have brought here and trained are trying to tell us what we can or cannot do?" Shrewdly, Hut sidestepped the matter of the Elders' desires.

"Have they not the same rights as you and I have?" asked Rhu.

"Do you think they have merited them?" Hut retorted, secretly pleased that Rhu's attention had apparently been diverted.

"I most certainly do," Rhu stated flatly and firmly. "It has never been any part of my idea that I was better than Mai or Yaug, for example, and I would never dream of asking them to do something I would not do. Neither do I intend to begin it now."

Seeing that he was getting nowhere, Hut suddenly changed

his tactics. "Listen, Rhu," he began in his most engaging manner, "you have never yet failed to find some way out of any dilemma in which we have ever been placed. I have every confidence you can do it now. It will ruin my prestige if I have to admit that I am wrong now and disappoint Harco after I have given my word."

With uncanny skill, Hut was assailing Rhu in his weakest spot, and he continued to press his advantage. "Everybody knows your resourcefulness and all respect your judgment. They know you have a good and sound reason for anything you do, even to admitting Harco and his people. They will never question what you do, any more than Ord does. As a brother who loves you, I am asking that you help me out of this situation and order Ord to admit them."

This ardent plea from one who had always been dear to him touched Rhu just as Hut had known it would. Rhu's heart ached that he must refuse Hut any request . . . . ached that Hut should ask this thing of him. Slowly, he shook his head. "To do this for you would be contrary to the wishes of the Elders, Hut, and I cannot do it," he said.

"But did not the Elder say he was willing to leave this to the Council?" pursued Hut persuasively. "The Elders could not have been so determined that there be no exception if he could say that. Why not call that Council meeting? If *you* will ask them to make this exception, I know they will do it."

"I am willing that we call a Council meeting and put it up to them to decide. But you will have to present your own case to them as well as explain how and why you made this arrangement when we both knew how the Elders feel about it. And if they ask my opinion, I shall have to say that I consider it a direct violation of the rule they established and contrary to what the Elders have suggested. I am willing to try to explain the situation to Harco, but I will not order Ord to admit him and his people unless the Council requests it."

"Rhu, this is the first time you have ever failed me. It is the first time I have ever found you unwilling to stand behind me. I feel like a drowning man who places his dependence upon a bush only to have it come out by the roots and he drifts to his death. You have failed me in my need."

This was an appeal to all the love and generosity of Rhu's nature and should bring the result Hut wanted. Beads of icy sweat stood out upon Rhu's forehead. His mouth was suddenly dry, and he felt rather sick. But he was adamant in his loyalty to the Elders and in his adherence to the principles in which he believed. Drawing a deep breath, he spoke firmly and decisively.

"Hut, right is right. We have made a law and we are going to abide by it just as we shall expect others to do. If you and I do not abide by our own laws, by what right may we ask or expect others to do so?

"You force me to say things I do not want to say. You have lied to me. You have lied to others. With Marda's connivance, you have tried to establish yourself as leader of our people, when you could have had the honor freely and with my cooperation had you come to me and expressed that desire. Now, you are trying to bring in people pledged to back you against the best friend you ever had, according to your own words. Your and Marda's plans were overheard by others. Until now, I have refused to believe them. Now, I can plainly see what the Elder meant when he said, 'Now that you have established good laws, ever abide by them.' "

This was all so different from anything Rhu had ever expected to be forced to say, and his spirits were low. "Do you want me to go with you to Harco," he asked wearily, "or do you prefer to tell him yourself? I shall not ask Ord or the Council to admit them—not because of your plan—but because I do not believe it is right."

Chapter Twenty-nine

THE SHRINE

"I WILL TALK to Harco alone," Hut answered rather stiffly. "You have said many unkind things, Rhu, which I am sure you are going to regret when you think them over. Never by word, deed, or thought have I failed to stand by you in everything, and I have always depended upon you to do the same for me. Now I know this can no longer be.

"I shall try to show Harco that it is better for him to take his people to the Elders for training, but I do feel that by making ourselves subservient to this rule, you and I are making a big mistake. I do not believe the Elders will like our disappointing Harco and his people this way. However, without your support, there is little use in my trying to do anything about it."

"I cannot help wondering just how much the Elders already know, Hut," Rhu replied. "They seem to have full knowledge of so many things which no one could have *told* them. If you would heed more carefully the remarks they make, Hut, you would know that you have no cause to feel that I have failed you. In this situation, there is nothing for me to do but refuse to support you, but I proved that I am entirely willing for you to become the leader when I proposed it in the Council meeting. It was not my doing that the Council refused my request."

"You did not insist very hard," Hut commented rather bitterly.

His eyes boring into Hut's, Rhu said nothing. Hut's eyes dropped and he shifted uncomfortably.

"I'm sorry, Rhu," he mumbled. "Perhaps you are right. At least, I know you *think* you are, but this is the first time, right or wrong, that we have failed to stick together, and it hurts. Still, you well know I would be the last one to want you to go against what you think to be right. Just the same, were the situations reversed, I would have been sure you had some good and sound reason for your insistence. However, I am not blaming you. You are as my brother, so I shall try to forget your failing me this once."

Hut seemed to be deliberately dodging the situation, and Rhu's patience was wearing thin. Besides, he had no liking for being blamed, especially when the shoe was on the other foot.

"Are you sure that it is not a case of YOUR failure, Hut?" he asked quietly. "I have never sought to deceive *you;* neither have I ever tried to do anything behind your back. So far as I am concerned, what you have done makes little difference, but you don't seem to realize you have probably done our work great damage. Harco will be upset and angry. It is going to be hard for you to explain away what you promised him. Wardu will present the same problem, sooner or later.

"And what is Nohr going to think? You denied to him and to me that you had made any definite commitment to Wardu, and Nohr was rather insistent upon his belief that you made the same promise to him. You convinced him at the time that he misunderstood, but now he is going to be even more certain that he was right and that you and I are working at cross purposes.

"I can forget this and all that led up to it, Hut, but with Wardu, Harco, and Nohr, you are risking our failure to enlist three of the most powerful tribes in our work here. Why on earth did you do it?"

Hut's face flamed and his gaze did not meet Rhu's. "It was Marda's doing, Rhu," he mumbled. "She is the one who made the promises, and I am sorry to have to admit that she was both definite and insistent with all three." His tone had become more positive, and now he looked Rhu full in the eyes.

"Then why did you not correct her before this could happen?"

"You don't know Marda as I do," Hut hedged. "She is very ambitious."

"Are you, or are you not, the head of your family?" demanded Rhu. "I would do much for Haitee, but I certainly would not allow her to do anything like this."

"You just don't know how determined Marda can be," Hut insisted. "She is very proud."

Puzzled amazement not unmixed with disappointment lay in Rhu's eyes as he looked at his friend. "Are you sure, Hut, that her plans for you do not strike a responsive chord in your own heart?" he asked gently. "If you really want to be the leader, I will not stand in your way but will do my best to bring it about. But not if you are going to adopt such tricky methods to accomplish your purposes," he added, his voice hardening. "By attempting to bring in people pledged to follow you, you have failed the Council as well as the Elders. However, as I said, I am entirely willing to help you explain to Harco."

Hut's mouth was a thin line now, and he looked everywhere but at Rhu. "No," he said quite firmly, "since I got us into this mess, I should be the one to straighten it out with Harco. Nevertheless, I want you to know that I had not even the remotest intention of going against the wishes of the Elders."

Rhu shook his head slowly, wondering how Hut could so deceive himself. Surely he must realize that the Elders knew of his actions . . . . or were his senses so dulled with the thought of the power he might wield that he did not care? Feeling it useless to speak further of these things, Rhu only said, "All right, Hut, Harco thinks much of you, so you can probably handle him better than anyone else."

Neither was aware that Nohr, having come to talk with Rhu and finding him occupied, had paused to listen to the conversation. Finding it most interesting, he had remained, for there was no stigma in eavesdropping in those days when one's life often depended upon his knowing everything going on. As Hut left, Nohr shook his head heavily. Rhu and Hut's great idea had seemed so wonderful. Too bad they seemed unable to work things out between them!

EMERGING from the stone door leading to the trail, Hut stepped into a scene of tumultuous confusion not the least mitigated by the bawling of hundreds of cattle and the bleating of many sheep. The big Hata Yans were clustered in a knot around the fuming Harco, while between them and the door, Ord and a group of Forest Dwellers stood nonchalantly watching.

Hut was in no sense deceived by the attitude of the Forest Dwellers, for each was fully armed, and a swift glance upward disclosed the heads and shoulders of many others on the roof. For all their seeming unconcern, the eyes of every fighting man were alert, and the men themselves were so placed that, at a moment's notice, they could spring into deadly action, either individually or as a unit. It was clearly obvious to Hut's discerning eye that Ord was prepared for any eventuality, and to judge from the grins upon their faces, all his men were secretly hoping for some excuse to go into action. Yet, so thorough was Ord's· discipline that there was not a single act or motion among them that could give offense to anyone.

As he neared the gesticulating Hata Yans surrounding Harco, Hut began to question his wisdom in thus coming alone for he knew all too well that the slightest hesitancy on his part might easily precipitate violent action. He was greatly relieved when upon glancing behind him, he discovered the giant Ord and two of his men keeping pace with him. True, there were several among the Hata Yans almost as tall as Ord, but the calm self-assurance expressed in Ord's bearing made them seem of little consequence. Ord's every motion indicated the confident efficiency that all too clearly stamped him for what he was—a leader of fighting men.

As Hut neared Harco, the Hata Yans parted, leaving a clear path to the gloomy man whose heavy face broke into a smile as he saw him. He came eagerly forward to greet his friend, apparently believing that all their troubles were now over. "Shall Harco order men to move?" he asked.

Hut shook his head, even as he smiled his greeting. "No, Harco, not until we can have a little talk."

Harco waved his hand to his followers and they withdrew. Then Hut saw that Harco was glowering over his head at something beyond him. Turning, Hut saw the reason. Neither Ord nor his men had withdrawn, but were standing close behind him.

"You may go back to the door now," Hut told Ord.

"Ord stay!" the big fellow grunted with an air of such finality that Hut, long since accustomed to his ways, knew that to order him back would be futile.

He frowned. This was not as he wanted it. He had expected to talk to Harco alone. Since there was nothing else to do, he decided to ignore Ord's presence, and turned to Harco. "Let us sit down." He indicated a stone close beside them. "I have much to tell you," he added, smiling into Harco's heavy face with much more assurance than he actually felt.

"Harco's people go on Plain now?"

Hut shook his head. "Not yet, Harco," he repeated. "I have much to tell you before we can discuss this."

"Hut promise Harco. Harco promise people. Harco not like delay."

"Neither do I," Hut agreed readily. Harco's face lightened perceptibly. "You see, Harco, after you had left, our Council was organized. At the suggestion of the Elders, one of the first laws was that no more people were to be admitted to the Plains until after they had been trained so they will understand everything. At the time we were talking, there was no such law." Here he lowered his voice, "But if it had not been that Rhu refused to permit it because of that law, I would have made an exception in your case, Harco, and admitted your people. As it is, the only thing I can suggest is that we take them to the Elders and get them trained as rapidly as possible."

This was quite a bit for Harco to understand and it actually required much more time to explain than this would indicate before the Hata Yan fully grasped the idea. His reaction was characteristic.

"Harco not blame Hut. Harco blame Rhu and Ord. Ord not let Hata Yans enter Plains. Rhu not let Hata Yans enter. Hut not leader. Rhu chief. Harco like Hut. Harco's people do as Hut say on Plains. Make Hut chief. Harco get Hata Yan Forest Dwellers take Ord's place." His voice was so low Hut was sure Ord could not overhear.

"You have a fine idea, Harco, and we can work along these lines in time," he said smiling into Harco's face. "But we must first get them admitted, and that means we must take them to the Elders for training."

When this was explained to the Hata Yans, it took all Hut and Harco's persuasive powers to prevent them from returning to their valley at once. However, Harco was well liked and he had chosen them well. When, at last, they agreed to go to the Elders, provided Hut and Harco accompany them, Hut returned to his home to make the necessary arrangements.

Little need be said of the difficulties which confronted the Elders in persuading the Hata Yans to part with half their possessions in return for their training and in getting them settled. The important thing is that it was accomplished, and a triumphant Hut finally returned to report his success to Rhu.

FIVE years elapsed and the Elders had established their School on the land formerly used by the Ku and Dan families. Dargh had secured more than fifty families of Cave Dwellers who, in addition to undergoing their training, were busily engaged in erecting school buildings for the Elders under Dargh's competent direction. These buildings comprised both homes and classrooms, for more than two hundred families were now training for citizenship, with more and more applying.

The plan requiring applicants to give the School one-half their possessions, and initiated by the Elders when Harco's people began the training, had been perfected. Forest and Cave Dwellers who had practically no possessions, compensated for their training by services rendered as herdsmen, builders, guards, farmers, and other activities in which man power was the important element.

The Plains Dwellers, regardless of the tribes from which they came, were required to give half their herds to the School. Upon the aspirant's arrival, the Elders immediately divided his herd so that the half remaining to the family was the best of the herd and composed almost entirely of female breeding stock. The Elders specialized in the breeding of choice bulls and rams, supplying each family with these superior animals. Thus, the herds which remained to the aspirants for citizenship increased rapidly as well as becoming steadily of much finer grade. By the time the training was completed, not only were the herds as large, if not larger, than those they had brought with them, but their quality had been greatly improved.

The Elders utilized the inferior stock of the half they took for feeding the students since there were soon many times as many people being trained as lived on the Plains, and their numbers increased from day to day.

Helpers from Venus and Mercury were brought in by Lord Hiroto to teach these people many things new even to the Elders. Women were trained to spin and weave so that skins for dress were used less and less as cloth began to take their place. Cotton and flax now being raised, both at the School and on the Plains, these Great Beings instructed the most skilled in the weaving of fabrics such as cotton and linen goods, as well as wool.

The philosophy of the Elders ran through everything these aspirants for citizenship were taught to make them more efficient and their living pleasanter. Thus they were never allowed to lose sight of the fact that although such improved material conditions were very fine, they meant little unless, as a group, they lived harmoniously together. And while the people on the Plains were learning to govern themselves by complying with the laws given them by Lord Lithargos, those at the School were also taught to abide by them so that when they, too, should be admitted to the Plains, they would harmonize perfectly with the established routine.

MUCH else had occurred during these five years. Marda had the two extra rooms for her house completed, one of which she used for their first child, a girl. To Marda's surprise, Haitee had not asked for any more rooms, something Marda could not understand. After his experience with Harco, Hut had done nothing more toward assuming leadership. Indeed, he seemed to have lost all interest in it, a frame of mind probably brought about by the many and diverse problems inseparable from such a rapidly expanding program. Marda had become so interested in the raising of her child that she, too, appeared to have forgotten her ambitions for Hut. Rhu and Haitee had no children, but if either were disappointed, they were careful not to betray it by either word or action.

Nohr had departed for the Tama Yan Valley after having expressed to Rhu his belief that the dissension between him and

Hut endangered their entire plan. "I think the basic idea is ideal, but when leaders cannot agree, there is little likelihood of success. If and when you get this straightened out and your success is assured, I shall return with many Tama Yan families. In fact, I believe you will eventually solve your problem, so I am going to begin trying to interest other Tama Yans and will keep in touch with your progress so we can come at the right time," he assured Rhu just before his departure.

Wardu did not return to the Plains. Eventually, it was found that in his efforts not to "take sides," as he termed it, he had dropped the matter. "It is a good idea," he commented to Harco, "but I am not one to be a party to any disagreements, so I am not going to do anything about it. Hut is too impractical and visionary, while Rhu is just the opposite. If he would combine his manner of getting things done with Hut's vision of the future, all would be fine. I shall wait until either Rhu or Hut, or the two of them, get this thing upon a sound basis."

(Of course, the above is a very liberal summation of Wardu and Harco's conversation which was such a long and labored process, the retelling would be wearisome to the reader.)

Que, on the other hand, had gone with the Elders and was growing steadily more and more enthusiastic. Shortly after his arrival in their valley, Que listened with a heavy heart when they discussed with him the matter of the differences existing between Rhu and Hut.

"Hut is the victim of a desire for power, which can easily bring him disaster," one of the Elders had explained. "It is not that he is inherently bad or deceitful; he is simply blinded by his desire to rule. If, as we hope, he will learn to employ his ability to plan for the common good instead of for personal authority and control, he will go far.

"Rhu with his ability to make the best use of anything available, his courage to try new things, his ingenuity and ability to reason things through, can go equally far, and his unswerving loyalty plus his willingness to serve without desire for personal power entitle him to every consideration.

"However, for us to interfere between them would result in the complete defeat of their great opportunity to work together. Lord Lithargos recommends that for the time being, we allow each to work out his own problems in his own way just as long as they do not interfere with the progress of the Great Work of establishing the civilization."

"It was my intention to stay and help Rhu for I much prefer his way, but I am entirely willing to follow your advice," Que had said. "I do not like the idea of Hut's allowing his thirst for power to make him deceitful and cause him to work slyly. And then, there is Marda who is apt to become domineering. Already she has had too much influence with Hut."

"But only because Hut is willing thus to be led," the Elder commented. "It is possible that after his experience with Harco, he will relinquish his desire for personal glory. He should have found that the responsibilities which are inseparable from the exercise of temporal power are apt to be far more dangerous to his well-being than the pleasure gained. He is to be given every opportunity for his advancement, but should he not awaken to the truth, and if Rhu is sufficiently strong to rise above the trials resulting from Hut's failure, he will be rewarded according to what he has thus earned."

"It seems hard to allow him to work alone when a few words from you might encourage him," Que commented softly. "Rhu is utterly sincere, no matter what his other faults, of which I must confess, I do not see many. Rhu can plan, and he can also work his plans. Hut can plan, but I do not like his methods of trying to make them operative. Yet, I can readily see that Rhu will be infinitely stronger for having met and overcome these trials, and that Hut also can profit immeasurably from his self-instituted lessons. Were I to return to the Plains, I know I would be unable to resist the temptation to help Rhu," he finished frankly.

"That is why we recommend your remaining here for the present. You are to be commended for your loyalty, but you can see for yourself that it is usually better to let each work out his own problems until such time as he reaches his limit. Then, and not until then, can our active cooperation be of real and lasting benefit to him. Thus far, the two have done this in most instances. Better that they should continue to do so until one or the other deprives himself of his opportunity to advance.

"But like you, I sometimes fear for Hut. The thirst for power is the hardest of all ambitions to overcome. On the other hand, humility will bring its inevitable rewards. And Rhu is sincere in his lack of desire to rule. He has, when he chooses to exercise it, the very power for which Hut thirsts. Thus far, his use of it has all been good. May it ever be so."

SOME four months after the birth of Marda and Hut's daughter, Grut sat in his favorite retreat on the river bluffs and near the big hollow tree. The little figure he had started carving almost a year before had been completed and its lifelike quality bespoke the many long and patient hours he had expended upon it. Few would have believed the big and hairy hands capable of the really fine and delicate carving, especially with such crude tools. He had painstakingly tinted the little wooden image with coloring made from various plant juices, and one knew instantly that it was a rear view of Rhu in his ceremonial robe as he stood, arms outstretched, in an attitude of prayer.

From his cache in the tree, Grut had taken a boxlike creation which was an equally startling depiction of the sacred grove. With a smile of satisfaction, he was placing the finished image inside this setting when his alert ears caught the sound of sobbing. Carefully replacing his shrine in the cache, he rose and with the greatest caution tiptoed over to the spot from which it seemed to come.

Seated on a fallen log, her head resting upon arms folded across her knees, was Haitee.

For several minutes, Grut studied the sobbing girl, his whiskered face a study. Repeatedly and unconsciously he balled his big and hairy hands into formidable fists. Then silently he stole away, only to return, deliberately making plenty of noise and humming his idea of a tune he had often heard Nohr sing.

The startled Haitee leapt to her feet, knife ready to defend herself, but seeing Grut, she relaxed and vainly tried to remove the traces of her tears.

"Huh!" Grut exclaimed, striving his best to feign great surprise. "Haitee!" Striding to her side, he laid his great hand upon her trembling shoulder. "Why Haitee cry?" he asked gruffly.

"Oh, I guess I'm just tired," she tried to reassure him. But the gentle touch of this big fellow who had always been so good to her broke down her restraint, and burying her face against his hairy chest, Haitee burst into a fresh spasm of weeping while Grut, his eyes bleak, held her close.

"Marda?" he asked, and Haitee could hear the thudding of his mighty heart.

"No, Grut," she finally managed. "It's nothing. It's just—just— oh, why can't we have a child?" she wailed.

Starting deep in his barrel chest, what Grut would have termed a chuckle gradually worked its way past his heavy lips. "Haitee got Rhu. Rhu enough baby for so small mother!" he mumbled. "Marda have no baby, Marda have nothing!"

Despite herself, a smile broke out on Haitee's face, seeing which, Grut announced abruptly, "Grut make Haitee present," with uncanny luck, selecting the one thing best suited to rouse her from her depression.

"For me? A present?" she demanded. "What is it? Where is it? Can I see it now?" Her face was now alight with curiosity, and her eyes twinkled as she stared into Grut's puzzled countenance as he tried to force his slow moving wits to follow her rapid questions.

"Come!" he growled, taking her hand and leading her toward his cache.

"What is it?" she asked, but Grut only strode the faster until she needed all her breath to keep pace.

"Sit here," he invited, leading her to the log where piles of chips and shavings littered the ground. "Grut get," he said, turning to the big tree.

To Haitee's surprise, he carefully removed a section so cunningly fitted that not even her sharp eyes had detected it. Setting this to one side, he reached into the opening, bringing forth his creation which, in modern times, we would call a shrine, the first ever made by anyone except the Elders, of which, of course, Grut knew nothing.

"For you," he announced, setting it upon the log beside her.

"It—it's Rhu!" Haitee exclaimed, hardly able to believe her own eyes as she marveled at the fine workmanship and lifelike pose of the figure. "Oh, Grut! It's beautiful! Will you bring it home for me?"

Judging from the warmth of his smile, his flushed face, and the light in his eyes, Grut's pleasure over his gift's reception was fully equal to Haitee's joy over being its recipient.

Arrived at her house, Haitee had Grut place the shrine upon one end of the mantel. "I'll get Dargh to fix a place for it beside my bedroom window where I can see it every morning," she told the happily perspiring Grut. "And I want everyone to see it. Oh, Grut! It is so beautiful! Every time I look at it, I'll always remember your sweet kindness to me." Whereupon she kissed the flustered Grut who promptly fled, so suffused with pleasant embarrassment that he was close to choking.

A NEW method of trading had also come into being during this five-year period. The old system of direct barter had become altogether too cumbersome to be practical, so Lord Hiroto and His Co-workers began preparing the people for the introduction of money. In order that they might not attach too great a value to the medium of exchange, the Lords of Venus first used shells for this purpose. Since the use of a medium of exchange involved the establishment of flexible values for various types of service and an ever increasingly wide variety of products, the inauguration of the new system was a slow and laborious process.

The new manner of bargaining was so completely different from what they had been accustomed to that the people, who always found it difficult to entertain and accept new ideas, unconsciously obstructed its establishment. However, they were accustomed to abiding by the wishes of these Great Beings, as well as the Elders, so that slowly but surely the great change took place. Not only did they use the system among themselves, but a not inconsiderable trade between them and aspirants for citizenship at the School was established.

Many of the shells the Lords of Venus suggested using had to be brought from distant places, and as their use increased, the supply of certain types began to be a serious problem.

Pursuant to Their usual custom of allowing the people to evolve as much as possible for themselves, They made no suggestions beyond the original ones. With the passing of time, therefore, Rhu and Hut were compelled to give serious consideration to some variation which would not only enable them to use more of the common variety of shell, but which would distinguish them so that one could not simply go out and gather shells for his personal use.

In talking this matter over, Dargh spoke of Pflugh as having rare skill in fashioning small things. "Suppose Pflugh made an intricate design such as only he can make," he suggested. "This could be scratched upon each shell worth a cow or more. I do not believe any other man could duplicate it. I know I would not like to try," he said frankly.

"Many of the shells we use are rather large and tough," Hut remarked. "Why would it not be possible for Pflugh to cut these into different shapes and on those having the greatest values, scratch these designs? They would be more easily handled, and we would save much time and trouble in trying to find sufficient shells for our growing needs. It would also prevent anyone who found a supply from using them to trade with."

After some discussion, it was agreed that Hut's idea was a good one. Pflugh was immensely pleased to be given this important assignment, and for quite some time after, this medium of exchange was used.

IT WAS nearing the close of this five-year period when Pflugh, who had been absent for nearly a month, returned and hastened to Rhu. "Look!" he exclaimed in pleased excitement as he handed Rhu a chunk of reddish substance liberally streaked with blue and greenish spots. "Look what Pflugh find! Red stuff that can be hammered flat," digging from his pouch a lump of copperish hue hammered into the shape of a spear head. "See! It bends," and he bent the spear head with his hairy hands.

With great interest, Rhu examined both pieces carefully. "It's very heavy," he said, weighing them in his hand. "It is strange substance to me. Let me take it to the Elders," he suggested. "Perhaps they can tell us more about it. Is there much more where this came from?"

"Pflugh find in canyon. Lots more show in wall. Pflugh have hard time break off these pieces. Stuff bend. Pflugh make stone cutter. Drive through. *Cut* off. Break three cutters." (The cutters Pflugh had made were wedge-shaped stones which he used as chisels. By pounding these with his stone-headed club, he had chiseled off the hunks of raw copper he brought with him.) "Rhu see Elders," he agreed. "Rhu tell Pflugh what Elders say?"

"Indeed I will," Rhu concurred heartily. "Hello! Here comes Grut," as his sharp ears caught the padding of his brother's flying feet, and a moment later, covering four steps at a time, Grut sped up the stairs and bounded into the big room.

"Hut's little girl! Snake bite!" he panted. "Haitee say come quick!"

Chapter Thirty

THE PASSING OF MARDA

THE UNFORTUNATE and tragic death of their first born had a marked effect upon Marda. At first, she seemed to be only moody and to have lost interest in everything except her sorrow. All efforts of Hut, Rhu, and Haitee to help her met only with tearful rebuffs which slowly changed into hinted, then direct, accusations that Rhu and Haitee were, in some obscure way, responsible for her loss. It was Rhu who carried the little body and placed it upon the funeral pyre, afterwards putting its ashes in the beautifully designed urn supplied by Pflugh and placing it in the stone crypt constructed by Dargh. Marda seemed unable to disassociate this loving consideration for her and Hut from the death of her child, and it was as if she somehow blamed Rhu for the child's passing.

Day after day, she would creep to the little crypt upon which Haitee and Grut daily placed fresh flowers, and there she would sit staring at the place which held the ashes of her child. Then in sudden anger, she would tear away the flowers and hurl them to one side, seemingly beside herself.

"It is for Hut's sake," Haitee explained when Rhu admonished her to stop placing the flowers there. "I think the gods have smitten her brain. Marda knows there is no need for any such sorrow. The Elders have explained all these things to us."

Nothing anyone could do seemed to help, and Hut grew thinner and thinner as she neglected their meals and grew steadily more detached. But for Haitee and Rhu's insistence that he eat at their home, Hut would have fared far worse, but finally even he began to show evidences of the mental strain under which he labored, often forgetting important things he had planned to do.

After a time, Marda developed a habit of getting up from the crypt and wandering away, seemingly in a daze, and Grut took up the self-appointed task of following and bringing her home.

Rhu then decided to go to the Elders and they, feeling he needed greater help than they could give him, took him to Lord Hiroto.

"My son," Lord Hiroto said gently, "this is a situation in which none may interfere. There is not one among us who would not gladly do all in his power for Marda, but here you are witnessing the operation of the Great Law. By planning and working for the destruction of another, Marda has created a situation which she alone must face, and by abetting her in her wrong ideas, Hut has brought certain repercussions upon himself. For us to interfere would result only in creating a situation that would exact its toll in future lifetimes. It is better that she make her atonement now than to be obliged to carry it forward through our interference. What you and Haitee have done is entirely praiseworthy, but you can see for yourselves that your sincerest efforts to help have come to naught.

"The entire Work in which we are all engaged has been jeopardized by Marda's attempts to change things to her liking. That is a very serious offense and even as things are, she must carry some karma into future lifetimes. It is a far greater kindness to her and to Hut that this be allowed to work out in its own way than for us to interfere at this time. Come what may, and no matter what the appearances, just know that all will work out for her greatest good."

"But what of Hut?" asked Rhu. "While she may have influenced him, I do not believe that at heart he would do wrong intentionally."

"That, my son, time alone will tell. Within every person's mind is a secret place that none may penetrate and of which even he may not be aware. This is his inner Holy of Holies— his innermost secret place—to which only God has access. To try to change what we might suspect is contained therein is a violation of God's Laws and would defeat that person's right of self-determination.

"To every Ego is given the right to make its own decisions, after which, it becomes a matter of the action of the Law. If he chooses aright, then all will work out to his eventual advantage. If he chooses wrong, then must he accept the repercussions of his violation of the Law.

"Marda must reap according to her sowing, for if one sow the seeds of personal pride, he can expect to reap only the weeds of sorrow. Though one may think he can transcend the Law, yet shall he discover that it cannot be mocked. What he sows, that shall he reap, and not the smallest infraction of the Law shall fail to exact its just recompense."

"Then there is nothing I can do to help," Rhu said sadly.

"It will have been taken from your hands, my son, ere you return. It is best for all that it be so. Think well upon my words for in them lies the key to many things."

Despite the knowledge that Lord Hiroto had only repeated much of what the Elders had long since taught him and Hut, it was a saddened Rhu who returned to the Plains where he repeated to Haitee what he had been told.

"It does seem almost heartless," she commented as he completed his explanation. "It seems so coldly impersonal."

"The Elders have long since explained to the four of us that all God's Laws are impersonal and inexorable, but absolutely just. What may seem cold and heartless to you and me can well be the kindest thing of all. If I crush my hand so that it is no longer useful and cannot be cured, resulting only in continued suffering and trouble, is it not better that it be cut off? Yet, it might well seem cruel and heartless thus to cut it away at the time. I know Lord Hiroto is right, yet I would gladly do anything to help alleviate Marda's grief if I could."

"Yes," agreed Haitee sadly. "It is as the Elders taught Marda and me. We must learn to look beyond the personal and see the operation of the Great Laws which govern all things. We have done everything we can—to try to do more is to meddle with what is beyond our understanding."

Going to Rhu as he sat upon one of the stools, head bowed,

Dargh's Canal

she placed her arm comfortingly about his shoulders, and his encircled her waist. Thus they mused upon the troubles Marda had brought upon herself, and the workings of the immutable Laws of Nature.

The quiet was broken suddenly by a horrified shout amounting to almost a scream from Hut's home. "Rhu! RHU!" Hut cried frantically.

Rhu bounded to his feet and closely followed by Haitee, quickly covered the ground between the houses. There stood Hut staring at Grut in whose great arms lay the dripping and lifeless form of Marda.

"Marda jump in river. Grut could not stop her. Too far away," Grut explained as they came up. He shook his shaggy head slowly.

A swift vision of the Hatamukulian River passed through Rhu's mind—the steep and rocky embankment and the mighty raging torrent. Well he knew that no man before had ever been seen again once he was caught up in its turbulent waters "How did you get her body?" he gasped.

"Grut jump too. Grab Marda. Dead when crawl out." And that was all anyone was ever able to learn about it.

TWO MORE years passed, during which period Pflugh brought to Dargh many lumps of the virgin copper which they called "red stuff," as well as considerable gold in the form of nuggets and lumps. The nuggets he found in a rude basin formed in some distant past age by a waterfall, now long since dry, and he had laboriously haggled the lumps from a bank of rotting quartz.

They did not care much about the gold because it proved to be too soft for any use they could devise, although they liked the ease with which it could be worked with their crude stone tools.

From the copper, they managed to fashion excellent arrow heads, knives, and axes which they easily kept sharp by whetting with the fine sandstone Dargh had previously used on his obsidian knives and axes. Because the copper was of a pliant nature, they were able to hammer it into any shape they wished, and since it was not brittle as was the obsidian, it assumed a greater value in their eyes.

Their elation reached its height, however, when it was discovered that the knives could be made so sharp they would even shave off the coarse hair upon their arms and legs. It was but a step to trying them out on their bewhiskered faces. Neither Hut nor Rhu were very liberally endowed with beards, but it was they who made the initial venture. Had they been other than who they were, there doubtless would have been many adverse comments from their cohorts at this shaving business, and while the irrepressible Grut had the temerity to talk of "woman faces," his twinkling eyes robbed his remarks of all offense.

This method of shaving would today seem a laborious and rather painful process, and so it was, but their skins were well toughened by much exposure, and neither Hut nor Rhu was overly particular as to whether or not they had a smooth shave. Then they found the knives haggled off the hair which overhung their faces much better than the crude stone knives they had previously used so that, all in all, their appearance was so greatly improved that others who were so fortunate as to secure these coveted copper knives were not long in following their example.

The duplication of practically all their cutting tools in copper revolutionized many aspects of living for the dwellers on the Plains, and a law was passed that, aside from the Elders, no one outside the Plains was to be permitted to secure or to possess one of these valuable tools. Thus a new incentive for preparing one's self for citizenship was added. Until one has been deprived of the use of such things so common to us, he cannot fully appreciate the value these primitive people attached to their possession.

Some time later, Pflugh conceived the idea of using bits of gold as the medium of exchange in trading. The shell was proving difficult to handle and broke with too much use. The fact that gold was soft and easily worked and the pieces readily handled, made it seem ideal for this purpose. Because it was malleable, it was easy for him to hammer into different shapes and scratch them with various intricate designs for the higher denominations.

While engaged in fashioning these, Pflugh accidentally discovered that when two pieces of pure gold were placed together and hammered, they welded into one piece. Enthusiastically, he set about putting together all the scraps he had gathered, utilizing most of it for the new money. Much of the gold which might otherwise have been lost was saved in this way. Naturally, he and Dargh lost no time in trying the same process with copper scraps but without success, cold welding being one of gold's unique characteristics. Many years later, it was found that gold is practically unaffected by exposure to either water or air, by which time, they had discovered many other sources of supply.

During this period, Dargh created the invention which also enabled his people to utilize to better advantage the many fine and durable woods with which their forests abounded, thereby bringing about many more great changes in their mode of life.

He had been making a new type of ax with a blade about eight inches across its cutting edge. In trying to give it weight, he had evolved an axe shaped somewhat like our modern ones, with the end opposite the cutting edge blunt and heavy. He was hammering this into shape with his crude stone hammers and had not yet sharpened it when, in drawing it toward him across the workbench, the sharp but still irregular edge bit into the heavy but soft slab of stone. In so doing, it cut an appreciable groove in the stone which the ever alert Dargh was quick to observe.

Promptly picking up a piece of wood, he placed the edge of the blade upon it, then began drawing it back and forth across the grain. To his undisguised satisfaction, it cut a deep groove far more rapidly and neatly than he could have done by chopping. Only the thickness of the blade prevented his cutting the piece completely in two.

Dargh liked nothing better than to prove his ingenuity, and he had an idea. With great zeal, he hammered out a reasonably smooth sheet of copper, probably four or five inches wide and about two feet long, deliberately leaving all the irregularities along one side the length of his metal strip. These he laboriously sharpened with sandstone. This done, he again attacked the piece of wood, sawing it completely in two with no loss of wood in the form of chips, and most satisfying of all, leaving two smooth surfaces.

For some time Dargh sat staring at these two surfaces. They intrigued him, and slowly, another idea took shape in his mind. After again sharpening the irregularities, he stood one of the pieces of wood on end on his workbench. Holding this firmly upright with one hand, and grasping his new tool with the other, he slowly sawed down through the wood, cutting it in two *lengthwise*. Greatly elated with the area of smooth surface thus created, he hastened to Rhu, a chunk of wood under each arm.

Rhu suggested a handle for the blade, and they both decided that the irregularities be made uniform. They cut and haggled away at these until they had what we have come to call "teeth" which Dargh carefully ground. While Dargh was doing this, Rhu fashioned a handle and the two bound it in place as soon as Dargh pronounced his part finished.

Searching out a redwood log about fourteen inches in diameter and about four feet long, they started on another experiment. Taking turns, and with frequent sharpenings, they proceeded to saw the log lengthwise, later duplicating the process as nearly parallel to the first cut as possible. The result was the first board mankind ever produced.

Fired with enthusiasm, they proceeded to saw off another of approximately the same thickness—about three inches—and with them replaced one of the stone slabs Dargh had used as a workbench. They removed the heavy bark with their axes so the planks joined fairly close, and Dargh fastened them together with four narrow slats as long as the width of the two boards, lashing them in place by running rawhide thongs lengthwise with the slats and around the two boards. He then proceeded to enhance the smooth surface by rubbing it with stones, and for days afterward, the populace swarmed to Dargh's shop to see this new marvel.

In this manner, the saw, one of man's most useful tools, was devised.

NEARING the end of this two-year period, Harco and his people again arrived at the great stone door. This time they were welcomed by the Council and there was great rejoicing that they had completed their seven-year training and had met the requirements for citizenship on the Plains. With them were a number of Mu Yan families who also had completed the training, and the entire group was accompanied by one of the Elders.

Harco was greatly startled to find that Hut's hair had become white, and that Rhu's was liberally streaked with gray. The two had been called upon to solve many problems in the intervening years, and tragedy had also left its mark upon both of them. Soon after his arrival, Harco paid Hut a visit at his home where he learned of Hut's losses. As Hut told of what had happened, the eyes of the big Hata Yan filled with tears, and it was some time before he spoke.

"Harco is very sorry, Hut. Life is now lonely for you," he said at last, and Hut noted that his diction was greatly improved. "Harco would gladly do all he can to help you. What can Harco do for you now? Do you still want leadership?"

Hut hesitated. "Well, I have given that matter but little

thought these past few years, Harco," he said finally. "I have many important plans and ideas for our future, all of which will, in due time, be brought about."

But the lust for power which had lain dormant through the years was once more stirring within Hut. It was as if the pages of time had been turned back, for he and Harco were taking up where they had left off seven years before.

"For the present," he continued, "I think it most important that you get as many more Hata Yans to come with us as you possibly can, Harco. With the training the Elders have given you and those you have already brought, you now have a far better understanding of what I am trying to do. Do you believe you can get some more families? There is no need for limiting the number now, just so they are dependable and loyal to you."

"I have at least six more families totaling about three hundred grown men and women who are interested," Harco replied promptly. "They, in turn, will interest others, just as will those now here. At least three of the men here have friends back in the valley who are dependable. Shall I send them to get them?" he asked.

"Yes, Harco, as soon as you can, and if you want to return to see those others you have mentioned, it will be all right for you to go right away. In fact, the sooner the better for, as you know, it will be at least seven more years before they will be ready to enter the Plains. In the meanwhile, I would like to meet the heads of the families you have brought now and see about getting them on the Council. Your tribe should be recognized. In time, there will be but one patriarch from each tribe on the Council, but that is years ahead, and for my purpose, we must begin working with those we now have."

"It has been a long time," Harco said softly. "Seven more years will see many changes here. What about these new Mu Yans who came in with us?"

"I shall call upon their patriarchs right away. It will be well for them to get started right, Harco, and since some of them are already well known to me, I think I shall have no difficulty."

"Then you still would become leader?" Harco asked.

"I cannot say now," answered Hut. "Without Marda, I have

not the same incentive as before. Her ideas present some fine possibilities, and I have some of my own for the future. However, we shall have to win over the Council. Rhu will back me up, I am sure. He tried to get me appointed as head of the Council at its first meeting. It is entirely possible that the attitude of the Council may have changed. It seems to me that it is better to have one man as leader, although I must say that Rhu is an able helper for me. He is always amenable to my suggestions and ever helps me to advance my ideas. He, of course, will always be second only to me."

Apparently, nothing had changed in Hut's mind. Strangely enough, he did not feel that he was being unfaithful to his best friend in even the slightest degree. Had he not stated flatly that next to himself Rhu would outrank all others? He truly wanted Harco to have no illusions on this score. Such was Hut's idea of loyalty to his best friend.

"Does Hut expect to marry again?" Harco asked bluntly.

"I have given it no thought," Hut replied, smiling. "Have you some one in mind, or are *you* thinking of marriage?"

Harco's smile was both bland and knowing. "Harco have sister who is beautiful and smart. Harco sure Hut like. Tomorrow night Hut eat at Harco's pot?" he asked. "Ana cook and serve Hut. Hut see if like. Ana do what Harco say anyhow, but she like Hut now."

Hut grew thoughtful. This was going pretty fast, even for him. Still, if he were to marry a Hata Yan, might it not increase his prestige with those of that tribe now here as well as the later arrivals? The idea was worth serious consideration, he decided.

"Yes, I shall be glad to come," he agreed. "However, do not mention anything about marriage to her, Harco. This will come about in due course if we like each other. I know of none whom I would rather have for a brother than you," he flattered.

Harco's face flushed to the roots of his dark hair, and he grinned with satisfaction. "Ana good girl—and very beautiful," he insisted. "She make Hut fine wife. But Harco say only you are coming and she is to make meal. Harco know what Hut like, and Ana fine cook."

Hut looked up at Harco and a qualm of misgiving entered his mind. If Ana looked anything like her brother, he was not so sure whether even prestige could offset the rest. Well, he was not committing himself, and it would not hurt to see her, at least. He had been observing Maida, a daughter of Ku Kut, one who was, to Hut's way of thinking, far from unbeautiful, and her smiles of welcome when he had visited Ku Kut had not lacked encouragement.

Perhaps, however, it would be wiser to consider Ana than to marry into a family whose head was definitely pledged to the support of Rhu, as Ku Kut had pointedly remarked upon several occasions. On the other hand, the septs were very clannish in their allegiance to their own, and his marriage into the family might easily change Ku Kut's feeling. He had never given Maida an inkling of what had been passing in his thoughts regarding her, but now he decided to consider more thoughtfully the matter of taking her for his wife.

The following noon, Hut made it a point to be at Ku Kut's home at noontime. Of course, he was invited to eat with the Kut family, but Maida, who usually made it a point to wait upon him was nowhere in evidence. Old Ku invited him to eat at his pot, but the zest he had earlier felt for this meal deserted Hut. He accepted with the best grace possible, but his appetite was not at all increased when, in the course of the conversation, Ku Kut mentioned that Maida was going to marry Grut Ku. Grut, it seems, had asked just that morning, and Maida had only too cheerfully agreed.

"Grut good man," Ku Kut growled. "Maida lucky girl, but make good wife."

Chapter Thirty-one

GATHERING CLOUDS

TO HUT'S SURPRISE and very much to his satisfaction, Ana proved to be all and more than her brother had said. She was a blue-eyed, golden-haired blonde, slightly above the height of the average woman of that time. Although only eighteen, she was full-breasted and willowy, her carriage erect and stately from carrying things upon her head, a pronounced custom among Hata Yan women. Her form would have aroused the unqualified enthusiasm of the most exacting artist of today. Her high, broad forehead and well-placed eyes betokened a thinker of more than usual ability and unlike Harco, she was quick in both thought and speech, as Hut quickly discovered.

Seemingly, it did not occur to Harco to leave the two together as Hut found himself secretly wishing he would do. However, he did encourage Ana to talk with them, and Hut found that aside from the usual paucity of pronouns, her vocabulary was exceptional for that period. Her thirst for information seemed unlimited, and when he used a word or expressed an idea she did not understand, she immediately demanded a complete explanation, cataloguing and retaining everything unusual in her alert mind.

It was a much lighter hearted Hut who took his somewhat reluctant leave that night. Walking homeward, all his thoughts were of Ana.

Unlike the average woman of that day, she was not in the least subservient, and Hut was greatly impressed by her apparent independence. While in no sense disrespectful, she had not hesitated to disagree with Harco, and she had not been the least shy or backward when requesting further information or when asking questions, some of which had called for swift thinking on Hut's part. She was kindly and friendly although her mannerisms were different from those of Maida and other girls he had known. Ana displayed a natural camaraderie that was more like a boy's, and while Hut would have enjoyed seeing her display this freedom toward anyone else, he wished she had been a trifle more inclined to regard him with the degree of respect due a leader of men. He wished she had tried to merit his approval, but she did not seem even to have been impressed that he should call upon her and her brother.

After due consideration, however, Hut arrived at the conclusion that she was not only the most beautiful and desirable woman he had ever met, but that her natural attitude would inevitably reflect the position she would hold as his wife. Yes, she was well worth considering. That Ana might possibly have other ideas did not occur to him. Besides, who would dare to appear as his rival once he started calling upon her? Assuredly, there was none on the Plains who could offer this wonderful creature what *he* could, and there was no question but what she was smart enough to realize this.

AT THE time Hut was at Harco's, Grut was visiting with Dargh and Pflugh as he so often did. When Grut arrived, Pflugh was just putting the finishing touches upon a colored design he had painstakingly painted upon an elaborately designed vessel. He had mixed colored clays with a little white sand and with a sharply pointed stick, had drawn the designs.

As Grut well knew, the vessel itself had been finished several days before and aside from the designs upon it, was thoroughly dry. Whatever slight moisture was in the clays was quickly absorbed by the vessel itself, and Pflugh hurried the process by setting it close to the fire, turning it from time to time until they, too, were dry. As Grut watched, he saw that the fire surrounded a stone box or oven, and to his amazement, Pflugh set the now dry vessel inside the oven which certainly appeared to be very hot. Dargh added hard wood sticks to the blaze and Grut could see the vessel grow red from the heat. Then Pflugh placed another stone before the opening and brought the fire around to cover it.

"What Pflugh make?" Grut finally asked Dargh.

Dargh grinned into Grut's puzzled face, at the same time drawing a duplicate vessel from beneath his new work table. Grut observed that it was half-filled with a milklike substance which remained fixed in the vessel regardless of Dargh's handling. From the middle of it extended a bit of fibrous stuff which when touched with an ember from the fire burned with a bright light. Still smiling at the staring Grut, Dargh placed the vessel upon his workbench where it continued to burn long after such stuff would ordinarily have been consumed. There being no breeze, the tiny blaze was steady and in the growing dusk, gave off an unusual amount of light.

Grut stared, fascinated. Even *his* slow-moving mind comprehended some of the advantages this first lamp was to provide them. Pflugh explained that the grease in it was a mixture of bear fat and goose grease, and though a vile smell emanated from it, this meant nothing at all. Every new thing created was a source of pride and wonder and so far beyond what they had before they never saw its drawbacks.

"Why burn other vessel in stone box?" Grut asked.

"This one burned too," Pflugh explained. "Grease not soak through when burned in box. Make hard, like rock."

"Pflugh in love!" Dargh unexpectedly announced with a broad grin, and Pflugh's heavy face darkened as the blood rushed to it.

"Grut in love, too," that worthy announced. "Grut marry with Maida Kut." He studied the faces of his two friends thoughtfully, then motioned them to come close while his sharp eyes glanced about them to make sure no one was near enough to overhear what he was about to say. "Last night," he whispered, "Grut hear Harco tell Hut Hut marry sister Ana. Hut make love eyes at Maida, so Grut go see Ku Kut and make marry talk. Marry next new moon!"

Pflugh's face was a study as Grut talked, ranging from blank astonishment to stubborn determination. "Pflugh ask Ana for marry tomorrow," he declared. "Ana like Pflugh. Say so. Pflugh love Ana. Hut not get Ana! Ana Pflugh's."

Grut nodded his shaggy head and a look of positive cunning danced in his eyes. "Grut know Pflugh make love eyes at Ana.

That why Grut speak now. Burning bowls for Ana?" he asked naively.

Pflugh nodded, even as he studied Grut's now immobile face. "So Grut know Pflugh love Ana," he said softly, then smiled widely. "Grut tell anybody?"

Grut shook his head vigorously. "Grut not want Hut get Pflugh's woman. Grut keep Hut away tomorrow night. Pflugh better make marry talk quick. Where Pflugh learn burn bowls?"

"From Harco," Pflugh answered. "Harco make bowl for Ana who accidentally drop in fire. Bowl greasy, burn hot, then grow hard. Pflugh put sand in clay. Fire melt sand, make bowl shine. Pflugh break many in fire." Having completely disposed of this matter, he returned to the really important subject. "Make marry talk with Ana's father tomorrow night," he stated. "Grut keep Hut away if can?"

"Grut keep," his friend growled. There was no uncertainty in *his* mind, and both Pflugh and Dargh grinned. They knew Grut.

SEVERAL times the following day, Hut was tempted to go see Ana. He was finding it extremely difficult to keep from thinking of her. True, he had loved Marda, but he had to admit to himself that never before had he seen any woman who so stirred his pulses and who seemed to possess so many entrancing characteristics. Well, he would drop in that evening to see Harco concerning the proposed trip to secure more Hata Yan families, he decided, at the same time hoping Harco would not be there. He had not seen the Hata Yan all day, so his excuse for the visit was all the more logical and valid. Hut did not know that Harco had taken him at his word and was already on his way back to the valley on his mission.

He decided to prepare his own supper, for if he were to eat with Rhu and Haitee, he would not be able to get away as soon as he wanted, and he could not explain his reason without embarrassment. Haitee had left some sweetened maize bread beside his fire to keep warm for him, and that helped his somewhat sketchy meal. Haitee always prepared some dish for him when she knew he wasn't going to eat with them, but it was characteristic of Hut that he accepted such little attentions as a matter of course.

His simple meal finished, he stepped outside to glance at the sun, for it would hardly do to arrive so early that he would appear too eager. To his chagrin, he observed Grut and Dargh approaching.

Hour after hour, the two remained, discussing with him the intimate details of Dargh's plan to substitute two wheels for the logs in their conveyances. Never before had he been thus consulted and introduced to such intimate and detailed explanations. Under different circumstances, he would have been flattered beyond words. As it was, he found it difficult to keep his mind on what Dargh was saying, important though his idea was and even in his anxiety to get rid of them, he realized something of the great value of this innovation to their methods of transportation. As Dargh explained with elaborate detail, it would more than double the speed of moving stones for their building operations. Instead of twenty men to pull a load, Dargh was sure half the number could do it, and thus they should be able to move twice the number of stones with the same man power.

"I still have time," Hut half moaned to himself as Dargh concluded his dissertation.

But he reckoned without Grut who then took up a matter that required as much explanation as Dargh's. He had, he explained laboriously and *very* slowly, even for Grut, been training two young bulls to work together. With Dargh's help, he had devised what we now know as a yoke, but which he called a "wood puller." Of course, Hut thought he meant something with which to drag trees from the ground, and to his surprise, Grut took a flattering amount of time to clarify his idea.

The "wood puller" was a heavy pole fastened to the horns of two bulls, thus connecting the two animals. By tying heavy vines to this "puller," and fastening them to logs, he had been dragging them to the Ku home with his pair of bulls. It was not until later that Hut realized Grut was explaining something he had long since accomplished, not—as was the case with Dargh —a plan for something to be tried.

"If Grut make two bulls work, Grut make more do same

work. Grut make them pull rock haulers. Save men." And so he dragged the conversation along until it was far too late for Hut's contemplated visit.

Even in his anxiety and disappointment over the upset of his plans, Hut realized that these two staunch supporters of Rhu were establishing somewhat of a precedent in thus coming to him instead of going direct to Rhu. Evidently, they were beginning at last to recognize his importance! Long after their departure, he sat thinking over the many intriguing possibilities of this changed attitude. Never before had either Grut or Dargh shown him such marked consideration, and if *they* were changing, assuredly, those less biased so far as Rhu was concerned would be even more so.

It was a very happy Hut who retired to dream of Ana and of being the leader of his people.

The following morning he decided to visit the building being erected for Harco's family, ostensibly to inspect it, but in reality so that it might appear to be by chance rather than intent that he came to the temporary hut they were now occupying. Nearing the partly erected structure, he met Grut and would have talked further concerning the idea he had promulgated the night before, but Grut was much more like his normal self—blunt and very uncommunicative. In fact, to Hut's wonder, he deliberately turned away leaving one of Hut's questions unanswered. Hut frowned. What could have changed Grut?

As the noon hour approached, Hut strolled over to the big hut where, for the first time, he met Murdo, the head of the family. The old man's face wreathed in smiles as Hut came toward him. Harco had done his job well, and Hut's heart swelled within him. However, he did not see Ana.

"Hut stay and eat with Murdo?" the old Hata Yan invited, and Hut agreed readily.

"Hut be glad learn Ana make marry with Pflugh," the old man announced proudly.

"What!" Hut exclaimed sharply. "Ana is going to marry Pflugh! When did this happen?"

"Last night Pflugh and Ana tell Murdo. Murdo glad. Pflugh great man. Harco and Murdo like."

"But . . . ." Hut started to remonstrate. Thinking better of it, he merely said, "I did not know Pflugh had ever met Ana."

"Pflugh come often. Murdo like," the old patriarch assured him.

Hut's appetite suddenly left him, and he strove desperately for some excuse to leave before the shrewd-eyed old man might guess his disappointment.

Happily, Rhu approached and after greeting the two, re-marked. "If you are not busy, Hut, I'd like you to see a new idea Dargh has developed. If you can come with me, we'll go see what he has already done with it."

As Rhu and Hut approached Dargh's workshop, they found him ruefully examining a broken wheel. He had made a small duplicate of their usual hauling body, but with two circular slabs sawed from a redwood log replacing the usual log roller. He had loaded the cart, only to have one of the wheels split in two. This wheel was about two inches thick and a foot in diam-eter. Of course, it was too small to be of practical use, but if it had not split would have served as a model for a larger one. However, this splitting presented a new and difficult problem.

"If they are made too thick, we are not much better off than with our roller," Dargh explained.

After carefully examining the parts of the broken wheel, Rhu selected two flat pieces of wood which Dargh had split while making a cart body the day before and laid them on the work-bench. Finding a piece about eight inches in diameter which had been sawed crosswise from a log, he laid it first on one of these pieces and then on the other, using it as a pattern to out-line a crude circle on each. This done, he began to whittle them with his copper knife until he finally had two rough cir-cular pieces of the same size and about half an inch thick.

He now placed them together so that the grains crossed Then laboriously, he dug holes completely through the two. driving pegs into the holes so that the two pieces were held firmly together. "Now, let us see you split this," he said to Dargh who, with Hut, had stood by, quietly watching the pro-ceedings.

Dargh picked up the laminated wheel, grinning his delight as he turned it over and over. But his satisfaction was short-lived as the big wheels which would be needed for their carts came to mind. "This small roller fine. But how get big wood pieces for big rollers?" he asked, frowning heavily. "When we cut through tree, we get round pieces, but cannot use. Not strong like this," he said pointing to the small wheel Rhu had just made.

Rhu comprehended the problem immediately. For a time he was silent as he thought through a solution to it. Then his face brightened. "First get long flat pieces like these in your bench," he explained. "Make edges straight with saw. Lay three side by side like in bench, then three across on top, and peg together, like this," he said, holding up his crude wheel. "Take round piece of tree the size we want the wheel and mark out circle. Too big to shape with knife. *Saw* off little pieces until almost round, then put on turner," referring to the lathe Dargh had long since devised, "and make round same as we do with logs."

Dargh's smile had again returned. "Red wood split easy," he announced. "This," picking up an oak slab, "not split easy. Hard saw, but strong. Make narrow roller from it. Take long time but worth it."

Rhu frowned thoughtfully. "Making the holes will be hard," he commented.

Grinning broadly, Dargh picked up a copper bar he had previously fashioned and placed it in the fire. When it was so hot it turned the blaze a bright green, he withdrew it, and proceeded to burn a hole about an inch in diameter into a piece of wood. "This Dargh's hole maker!" he announced proudly.

AT THE end of several days of labor, Dargh and Rhu turned out two laminated wheels about four inches thick and three feet in diameter, and so securely pinned together as to make them practically solid. The big holes for the axles took much time and care, but the wheels were eventually ready for their great test. Installed on the frame Pflugh and another Muson had been fashioning while Dargh and Rhu worked with the wheels, they operated to the satisfaction of all concerned with one exception. They wobbled.

But Rhu was ready with a solution for this too. "The old rollers did not wobble because they were so wide," he ex·

plained. "Let us put blocks at the center and on both sides of each wheel, then extend the holes so that the axle can pass through these blocks. This should keep the wheels steadier."

This proved to be highly satisfactory and so the first crude hub was developed.

When the cart was finished and found to work, Grut hurried away for his pair of bulls. Instead of the shaftlike arrangement usually used, a single shaft, or tongue, extended from the cart, and the bulls were placed on each side of this. Then, with Dargh, Pflugh, and another Muson on the cart, Grut led his bulls along, and their march throughout the settlement resulted in a near riot of wild enthusiasm among the people. Their next job was hauling stones, and the two bulls pulled as much as half the load usually drawn by twenty Forest Dwellers with the log roller vehicles.

Thus, the wheel—that most important of all man's creations —came into being.

It must not be supposed that these wheels were in any sense perfect nor that there was not still some wobbling, for they could not be made perfectly with the crude tools of that time. It was really remarkable that they worked as well as they did.

Not many months passed before the old roller vehicles were all supplanted by the newer carts, and each one was an improvement over the one before it. Then it was discovered that they could get from place to place by means of the carts much more rapidly than by walking. Riding was also far more comfortable, though the carts were springless and there were no roads. Usually, the shortest route was taken with detours to escape especially steep hills and other natural obstacles. As more and more drove over these same trails, the idea of developing better roads took hold and soon it was possible to ride in comparative comfort. Before long came the genius who made a cover for his cart so that neither rain nor burning midsummer suns deterred him from traveling in this manner, an innovation soon copied by the others.

THE MONTHS wore on and Murdo, representing the Hata Yans, had become one of the Council members. Hut seemed to have lost interest in the matter of remarrying after his two rather unfortunate experiences; he had little time to consider it in the press of affairs, and besides, other ideas were holding his attention. Soon after the arrival of Harco and his family, Rhu observed a change taking place in Hut—a change which was strongly reminiscent of his attitude years before when he had been overcome by the thirst for power. Little and often seemingly unrelated actions and words betrayed the fact that the desire for leadership had been reawakened.

These might all have passed unnoticed by Rhu had there been no previous experience of this kind. Hut's words and actions at that time, however, although forgiven and almost forgotten, had left their mark on Rhu's consciousness, and he became steadily more concerned, though he did not reveal his growing uneasiness even to Haitee. As so often happens, it was over a rather small matter that Rhu's suspicions of Hut's motives finally resulted in their first serious disagreement.

About a year after Harco's arrival on the Plains, at a meeting of the Council, Hut summarily ordered Rhu to go to the Tama Valley to try to interest Nohr in returning with some of his people. Stung by the fact that Hut should feel it was within his rights to so command their beloved Rhu, and never having been able to overcome the doubts engendered by Hut's actions years before, Ord and Dargh objected promptly and violently.

Although also provoked by Hut's undiplomatic manner, Rhu smothered his own resentment. However, when Hut ordered Ord and Dargh off the Council as punishment for their insubordination, he quickly rose to his feet to oppose this uncalled-for expression of authority. An ominous silence fell upon the assembled members. Ord grasped his big copper war axe, and Dargh reached for his bow.

Mai Dan, now nearing his eightieth year, turned to Sol Ku, his eyes frosty. "Hut is my son, Sol, but if he again speaks thus to Rhu, I shall kill him."

"It will not be necessary, Mai. Ord will do it," old Sol grumbled. "His mind must be touched by the gods!"

Murdo's expression was one of amazement as Sol's whispered remark, intensified by the dead silence, was plain for all to hear.

Then Rhu spoke.

"It is with deep regret that I am compelled to exercise my right as one of our leaders to speak as I must do," he began. It was so still that a bull could be heard lowing in the distance. "Hut, in allowing your resentment against Ord and Dargh's disagreement with your suggestion to cause you to try removing them from the Council, you have overstepped your right and power. Neither you nor I have the right to remove from this body any member who has been sanctioned by the Elders.

"It has been no secret that you once aspired to become the sole leader of our people. Neither were your plans to bring this about unknown to those of the Council. Until recently, we have looked upon that as something in the past, believing it was more Marda's idea than your own. In the past months, however, there have been indications of a reviving interest on your part and today, by this unwarranted assumption of power which is not rightfully yours, you have gone too far. It is apparent that Marda's ambition for your supremacy found a responsive ambition in your own heart.

"Until today, I have been entirely willing that you should assume this position. But today, by your act, you have demonstrated that you are not the man to take upon himself the sole guidance of our people. To order Ord and Dargh to do your personal bidding for purely personal reasons is a violation of one of our ten basic laws, for it is an attempt to interfere in their lives and in their affairs. Also, the Elders have expressly stated that the rule of our people is vested in the Council, so that if you desire any of our members removed, you should state your case to the Council and let them decide. All this you well know.

"Personally, I am entirely willing to make the trip to the Tama Valley if it is the wish of the Council that I do so. Ord and Dargh merely expressed their disapproval of your method of asking this of me, particularly when there is so much here which demands careful thought and consideration.

"Murdo, you are our newest member and therefore less apt to be influenced by previously formed ideas than the rest of us. Do you care to make a motion that I go on this trip which, at best, will probably necessitate my absence for from three to six months?"

When Rhu began to speak, Hut paled. Rhu had always been so non-resistant that he fully expected him to carry out his order. That he should openly oppose anything he, Hut, suggested was totally unexpected. As Rhu continued, however, Hut's jaw set, for he was determined, once and for all, to have his own way. He fully intended to speak as soon as Rhu finished, but when Rhu called upon Murdo, he sighed with relief. Rhu had done exactly what he would have had him do. He could depend upon Murdo's loyalty, and Hut smiled confidently into Murdo's concerned face as the gray-haired Hata Yan patriarch slowly rose.

"Murdo think no man do job better than Rhu." Here the old man paused, evidently groping for words to make his meaning clear. "Since Murdo come to Plains, Murdo learn many things. Hut good man. Hut smart man. Hut see far ahead. Rhu better man for getting things done. Rhu smart as Hut. Rhu see both now and ahead. Without Rhu, nobody here able get things done. If Nohr worth getting, Murdo move *Hut* go."

Hut's confident smile vanished and he stared at Murdo in amazement. All the other members of the Council, except Ku Kut, vigorously nodded their agreement, but before any one could second Murdo's motion, Ku Kut stood to speak.

"What Rhu say very true. What Murdo say also good, but Ku Kut not like plan Murdo suggest," he declared. "Hut dreamer. Hut plot to rule long time. Hut smart. Rhu smarter. Rhu rule, but say not want rule. Rule anyhow!" He paused and there was a concerted nodding of shaggy heads. "If Hut go, Hut plot bring only Tama Yans who promise to make him ruler. Not good. Nohr been here. If Nohr want come back, Nohr come. Ku Kut think better let Tama Yans make own choice."

His face flaming, Hut almost leaped to his feet. "I am amazed!" he cried vehemently. "Nobody has asked what I meant! It is an outrage to condemn a man without allowing him to defend himself. It is a violation of Natural Law to pass judgment upon another as Rhu has done. I have always loved him as a brother, and even though he has gone too far now, I still love him because I know he will realize his error in time.

"I want him to go because he can do more than anybody else

in influencing Nohr and the Tama Yans. I am not trying to be your leader in the sense of being your ruler. I merely have the ability, as Murdo says, to plan far into the future, always leaving it to Rhu to carry out my plans, and you all know how good he is at that."

Dorg Mauk interrupted without rising. "Rhu's plans good as Hut's. Dorg not trust Hut's plans. Hut plan get Rhu away and seize rule while Rhu gone."

"Let Hut finish," Rhu interposed. "I am sure he plans only for our good."

"Thank you, Brother Rhu," Hut said, and although he tried to smile at his friend, the cold sweat was beading his forehead and his eyes refused to meet Rhu's. "Dorg assumes I am suggesting this merely to get rid of Rhu so I can assume rulership. This is only his guess. I have no such idea. As for Ord and Dargh, I merely requested that they leave the Council because they interrupted me which is against our rules of procedure as established by the Elders. I did not mean they were to be removed from the Council. They are so blinded by their feelings for Rhu that they will not listen to reason. I am surprised at Murdo. I thought he was my friend and would see things as Harco does. Harco does not think I seek to rule."

"Yes, Harco does!" Murdo snapped. "He said so before Murdo came here. Murdo willing as Murdo thought Hut was wonderful man after listening to Harco's praises. Hut *is* remarkable man, but Murdo think as Murdo like. Harco not yet rule Murdo's clan. Murdo want to be good citizen. Elders say think of group first and self afterwards. Murdo do. Murdo think Hut fine man, but think Rhu better. Rhu DO things. Hut talk, talk. Do little."

"I would be the last to deny that Rhu is a better man than I am," Hut answered smoothly. "It is just that the gods have given me the ability to plan better. That is all. I still think Rhu should go to the Tama Yan Valley for Nohr. If I had planned as Ku Kut says, would I have wanted Rhu to go?" Hut was rapidly regaining his self-confidence, and already he fancied he could see that the force of his logic was having its effect upon the Council.

"No, I did not plan upon getting Rhu away in order to take

advantage of his absence. In my earnestness, I am afraid I was not careful in the words I chose. I did not mean to *order* him to go. I merely meant to convey how anxious I am to have him do it. I still think my idea is best but am willing to leave it to the Council to decide. Has anyone anything to say?"

Mai Dan rose. "Mai opposed to Rhu's going," he said. "Mai opposed to Hut's going. Mai opposed to any plan in which Rhu has no part. Hut my son. Rhu Sol's son. What Sol do, Mai do. If fathers do, why not sons do? Mai make no plans without Sol. Sol make no plans without Mai. Why Hut think can plan without Rhu? Unless Rhu say plan good, Mai want no such plan. What good plans of men who cannot make plans work? If Rhu make plans, plans work. I move Rhu stay here."

"Sol second motion," Rhu's father agreed.

"All in favor of the motion hold up their hands," said Rhu, and it was unanimously carried.

"Does anybody want to make a motion that Hut shall go?" Rhu asked.

There was no response.

Now Dargh got to his feet and looked at each member of the Council in turn, and Rhu felt uneasy. There was never any telling what Dargh might do or say. Hut frowned as he invariably did when thinking deeply or when annoyed.

"Hut order Dargh and Ord leave Council," the Muson began. "Hut say he meant only for this meeting. Dargh not know which he meant. Dargh not care. Dargh prefer Council say whether Ord and Dargh remain or leave."

"I move Ord and Dargh stay," Ku Kut replied, almost instantly seconded by Dorg Mauk, and the motion was carried unanimously.

Notwithstanding this action of the Council, it was clearly evident that Dargh had not yet finished with what was on his mind for he promptly asked for permission to speak further, and upon being granted this continued. "Hut always try take credit for all new ideas," he stated. "Hut say he made laws Elders gave us. Lord Lithargos, not Hut, made laws."

Unwilling that Hut should be so completely discredited, Rhu quickly defended his friend. "Oh, Hut probably meant that he was trying to work out some of the details," he said.

"Thank you, Rhu. That was what I meant. I am sorry Dargh wants to believe the worst of me."

"Dargh want only truth. Dargh believe nothing he does not know all about. Rhu say wheel *Dargh's* idea, yet *Rhu* tell Dargh how make strong. Rhu say Dargh make stone arrowhead, yet *Rhu* give Dargh plan."

"Hut designed that arrowhead," Rhu commented quietly.

Dargh's only reply was a broad smile directed to the appreciative Council members.

"Hut always talk about seeing far ahead," he continued. "Hut always say Rhu only able to do after told plans. Yet, Sol Ku say plan for coming here Rhu's idea. Mai Dan say same thing. Rhu plan arrowhead. Hut just draw. Rhu put feathers on arrow. Rhu suggest glider. Rhu suggest log rollers for stone carriers. Rhu make wheels possible. Dargh think Rhu better planner and everybody know who *does* things. Rhu claim no credit. Hut always claim credit. Hut have dream, Rhu make dream work. Hut try be leader. Rhu *leads!*" With this last emphatic statement, Dargh sat down, evidently well satisfied at putting over his point and clearly determined to settle in the minds of all who, in *his* estimation, was their real leader.

For several days after the meeting, no one saw Hut. Taking some simple food, he hid himself away while nursing his sorely injured pride. All that he had learned from the Elders was as nothing in this situation, for Hut had always felt that as a leader, Natural Laws did not apply to him, and now he did not even consider them and thus reason out what had occurred.

Like so many whose thirst for power has led them into serious error, he attributed his discomfiture to another. Bitterly, he figured that it was Rhu's failure to abet him which had caused the present situation. That his most serious setbacks came from the Council itself did not mitigate the fact that Rhu had actually questioned his judgment and motives. That Rhu had stood ready at all times to defend him seemed to have no significance, and Rhu's efforts to make things as easy for him as possible were forgotten. Yet, upon his return, try as he might, Hut could find nothing in Rhu's behavior or attitude to indicate that he was any different from what he had always been.

Chapter Thirty-two

QUE JOINS THE COUNCIL

B Y NOW, many, many families were becoming trained citizens and arriving constantly so that as far as eye could reach, the Rhu Hut Plains were dotted with homes. For the most part, these people occupied themselves with the raising of cattle and in farming, according to the nature of the land on which they found themselves. It was not long before they discovered that certain sections were better suited to grazing than for agriculture, and that while some crops flourished in one locality, they did not thrive so well in others, due to variations in soil and climatic conditions. Wheat flourished in some places better than in others. The same was true of maize, so that it was found practical to concentrate on a particular crop in a particular locality, or engage in cattle raising.

Industrial activities became ever more defined. Bows and arrows, shields, and such other implements as the army required were made by the Forest Dwellers, who now numbered more than a thousand. Many of the Musons, whose numbers were always growing, engaged in the production of carts and the construction of homes. The crude lathes were always in the process of improvement and were soon at the point where it was possible to make almost perfect wheels. With the new copper axes, adzes, and greatly improved saws, wood came into greater and greater use while the craftsmanship became increasingly fine.

Dargh made a discovery which eventually revolutionized their work with metal. He found that charcoal made a much hotter fire than wood, and by having relays of leather-lunged Forest Dwellers blow upon it, succeeded in melting the gold. Accidentally, some of this molten metal was spilled into one of the shells in which Pflugh had carved the design of some of their shell money. To his and Dargh's amazement, this design appeared in reverse on the gold when it was removed. Then began the casting of coins.

From this start came the invention of the first crude bellows, and experiments which led to the melting of copper in specially prepared clay pots over charcoal fires. It was decided to locate the copper-working shops at the place where the metal was mined, so that metal work also became a distinct industry. Following Pflugh's discovery of castings for the shaping of their money, the process was expanded to the casting of many of the tools they had formerly hammered out so laboriously. Stone tools and weapons were slowly replaced with the metal ones which were so superior and more easily produced.

Up to this point, the charcoal, being but the charred ends of incompletely burned wood, had been carefully garnered from the many family fires. With the discovery of its value in melting metal, the demand for ever increasing quantities became pressing, and they finally found that by burning certain hard woods in closed clay ovens, it would char. Soon the production of charcoal became still another of their vital industries.

In making a large copper sheet, Pflugh discovered as he hammered away at its center that it began to assume a cup shape. Always alert to find anything which would enhance their way of living, he persisted, eventually hammering out the first copper kettle. This he proudly gave to Haitee who found it much better than the earthen ones which were so easily broken. This was the start of another industry engaging in the production of copper cooking vessels.

Although stated so briefly, all these innovations were the end products of long and slow development, and the resulting specialization led to a complication never before known, presenting a problem whose solution was to be of monumental importance to the growing civilization. The consequent plan of economic procedure which gradually evolved became one of the major factors contributing to the future success of this civilization which was destined to become the greatest and most marvelous the world has ever known, and existing over fifty thousand years—something never since even approximated.

The various sections engaging in agriculture and the raising of cattle were producing more than the populace of these sections could possibly consume. The fabrication of tools and equipment was also definitely localized and the need of all in the immediate vicinity easily supplied. However, while each section had an over-abundance of its own products, those at a distance suffered for the lack of these essentials which could have been supplied were there some practical method of distribution.

For example, grain was becoming an increasingly essential commodity. The people were using it more and more extensively as a food, while its use for the fattening of cattle was steadily growing more common. However, there was no way to transport any such quantities as were necessary from the sections where grain raising was the major occupation to those sections engaged in cattle raising or industrial production. As a consequence, great quantities went to waste because those raising it could not possibly use it all and their neighbors for many miles around them were engaged in the same pursuit and so had no use for it either.

The art of threshing was not then known, so that grain was sold as it was cut—straw and all. This was both heavy and bulky, and the carts of that day were still crude and unsuited for its transportation over any great distances. Small amounts could be carried and exchanged for such commodities as tools or cooking vessels, et cetera, in those localities where they were made, but in most cases this meant traveling great distances with much inconvenience so that even trade of this kind was very limited indeed.

The same problem pertained to the distribution of the cattle, although, of course, herds of these could be driven to destinations not too far distant. However, other difficulties presented themselves, resulting in losses and disappointments, so that these sections, too, were glutted with their own surpluses.

Much the same situation existed in those sections engaged
in industrial production. Everyone in the locality was adequately supplied with such needs and to continue in their
production meant the amassing of goods of which those in
distant localities could not avail themselves.

To us, the solution probably seems very simple, but people
of that time did not have the foundation of economic and industrial experience our forebears have given us and from
which we have profited. Nevertheless, these simple, primitive
folk eventually evolved a way of life far superior to ours because they had implicit faith in the Great Ones who were guiding them and were ever willing to follow Their advice.

Therefore, though the solution to the problem may appear
comparatively easy to us, we of today have not incorporated
into *our* economic program those spiritual principles given
these first builders of civilization by the Great and Wise Ones
who were, and still are, ready to guide our faltering steps if
we will but seek to cooperate with Them. As a result of our
stubborn adherence to the belief that man is sufficient unto
himself and our neglect of spiritual values, nation after nation
has disintegrated and we today live in an uncertain, unhappy
world.

Realizing that the enormous surpluses accumulating in the
various sections could easily prove a stalemate to the progress
of the civilization, and unable to devise a practical solution
themselves, the Council referred their problem to the Elders,
who, in turn, sought the advice of the Lords Hiroto and
Lithargos. At Their suggestion, a number of centralized re-
positories were established in various localities where the
people from nearby sections could bring their products to sell
or trade for what they, in turn, required. These crude trading
posts or stores were established and controlled by the Council
purely for the benefit of the populace or commonwealth and
without thought of profit.

Before this time, and also at the suggestion of Lords Hiroto
and Lithargos, the principle of tithing had been established,
and each citizen gave one-tenth of his produce to the Council
for the support of those engaged in public projects. At first, the
tithes took the form of cattle, fowl, grain, tools, tanned hides,

pottery, and such other items as the people produced. Since the army and the Musons (builders) were engaged in public works, they were compensated from these supplies, and with the setting up of the trading centers, those operating them were also compensated from the tithe goods given the Council.

To the people of the Rhu Hut Plains, tithing was an expression of gratitude to God for the good which was theirs, and in using it for the good of all, the Council was using it to further God's work in helping man make the most of his environment.

Naturally, the living standards at that time were simple so that in being compensated with goods, those engaged in public projects received everything essential to their support, and later, as money was used more extensively, it replaced more and more the goods previously tithed.

Recalling the original conditions set forth in the earlier chapters of this book, it is little less than amazing that these first stores should have been inaugurated when the Plains had been occupied only about twenty years, and certainly demonstrates the character of the guidance that was being received. Without the cooperation of the Elders and the Lords of Venus and Mercury, it would not have been possible, as illustrated by the fact that for eight hundred years, the Ku and Dan families had successfully worked together as a unit without being emulated by any of the other Plains Dweller families.

During this period of growth on the Plains, the Elders had developed a new species of cattle by cross-breeding with some of the larger deer abounding in that portion of the Mu Valley lying close to the forests. Many of these creatures could run as swiftly as the modern horse so that it was necessary to design lighter, yet stronger types of carts. The improved method of transportation made it possible to stock the stores or Marts, as they were coming to be called, with all the products of all the now rapidly growing enterprises. Farm produce as well as all types of merchandise were taken to these places for marketing. Cattle pens were erected nearby, and with the passing of time, the killing and dressing of beef for human consumption was undertaken in buildings erected for this purpose.

It required years before they were functioning properly, but as time passed and the civilization expanded, the Marts grew in size and number until they were widespread throughout the Plains and were stocked with everything produced in the country.

The government continued to be the central control of the entire System of Distribution, all those engaged in its operation being government employed, carefully selected and trained for the places they were to fill. As a result the system was a perfectly coordinated and smoothly operating unit, while at the same time, there were no middlemen, wholesalers, manufacturers' agents, or others to add to the cost of the product sold. Under the wise guidance of the Lords of Venus and Mercury, an economic system based upon universally ethical principles was evolved whereby no few could prosper at the expense of the people as a whole. This resulted in such universal prosperity and satisfaction that no change was ever suggested, let alone contemplated.

Long before this time, each industrial enterprise paid what was called a Commerce Tithe which eventually was found to more than cover the cost of maintaining all the divisions of the entire Mart System of Distribution. The personal tithe which had been used originally for the establishment and maintenance of the first Marts was now diverted to maintain the government which soon began to grow rather complex.

The ten basic laws for correct and untroubled living were strictly adhered to, and as a result, the population on the Rhu Hut Plains enjoyed the happiness and peace which always emanates from a sense of security and right action. Ever mindful of the progress already made since being trained by the Elders and coming to the Plains from their tribal valleys, they were conscious that the future held even greater wonders for them just as long as they were determined to make the most of everything by being alert to learn and improve themselves and their way of life.

(The economic organization as it affected the commerce of the Great Empire which eventuated is a subject quite beyond the confines of this book, so we can give it but the barest mention here. At this time, we are concerned merely with the first steps taken by a slow-thinking and inexperienced people in the solution of their economic problem amidst elementary conditions. The many factors involved in the successful conduct of the economic arrangement which finally resulted will be fully discussed and explained in *THE SUN AT ZENITH,* the sequel to this book.

Lest the reader gain any erroneous impressions before he has the opportunity to study the entire procedure, however, it should be made clear that every man filling a governmental position, from the Emperor to the lowliest clerk, was especially educated and trained by the Elders for his particular position. Governmental positions could not be obtained through "political pull" or favoritism, for each was employed because of *what* he knew, and *not whom* he knew.

Each employee was an expert, highly trained in the performance of his duties. This was his life work and he could hold his position as long as he upheld the standards required, while unusual ability and satisfactory service were rewarded by commensurate advancement.

The required training, in addition to all the technicalities necessarily involved, included a comprehensive education in spiritual values and the importance of the individual to the success of the civilization. Each and every individual was afforded every opportunity for the expression of his abilities and initiative, there being no trace of regimentation or dictatorial management in the governing of the Empire.)

HUT took naturally to the supervision of the Marts and to establishing the citizenry in locations best suited to their tastes and needs, while Rhu handled the affairs of the army and industries, the normal outcome of the close association between him, Ord, and Dargh.

- As new families came in, Hut sought to weld them closely to him, for the passing years never changed his determination to become the supreme leader or ruler of the citizenry. As the older Council members passed on, he supervised the selection of new members with infinite care. With the transition of Mai Dan, he refused to limit his activities by assuming the leadership of the family, causing Yaug to take over that function and with it, membership in the Council. When Murdo passed on, Harco took his place on the Council, and of the twelve members who now made up the Council, eight were of Hut's selection. When this had been accomplished, he felt that at last he was in position to assert his claim to the rulership of the entire citizenry.

(With the great numbers of families now on the Plains and more arriving constantly, the earlier plan of making the patriarch of each sept a member of the Council was no longer feasible. The Elders had limited the number to twelve, exclusive of Rhu and Hut, and gradually a system whereby eventually each of the twelve tribes would elect its own representative was being worked out. This was still in its initial formative stage, however, so that Hut was able to use his influence to good advantage as indicated.

Whether he actually realized the full implications of what his great decision was to mean, no one may say. Like many since, he apparently was so blinded by his great ambition to rule that he gave little thought to anything beyond his personal desires. Otherwise, it is almost inconceivable that he would knowingly have taken the great risks he assumed by his decision. He seemed to consider nothing beyond becoming the undisputed ruler.

Although the Elders must have known that Hut still held ambitious plans for assuming control of the inhabitants of the Plains, they did nothing to indicate it, evidently depending upon the Council and Rhu to handle any situation that might arise. Furthermore, Hut had been admonished by Those greater than they. Beyond this, the Elders would not go, for every individual has the right of self-determination, and no one may interfere. By this time, also, they were fully occupied with training aspirants for citizenship on the Plains, encountering many new and perplexing situations. The Lords of Venus and Mercury helped them with only those they could not possibly solve, allowing them to work out all others so that they might gain the experience necessary to meet still greater difficulties and thus further their own personal advancement.

In addition to their other duties, Rhu was bringing them models of everything made on the Plains, explaining how each had been fashioned. The Elders had not yet learned to write so that records concerning the construction were kept by means of rude pictographs. As new discoveries were made, these models with their pictographs were placed in special archives. When the Elders learned to write, a record was kept of the progress of the civilization, a work continued even when the Empire was at the height of its glory. In fact, these records have been kept through the ages for every nation since, always playing an important role in the advancement of humanity.)

On the morning of the day Hut had selected to make his great attempt at taking over the reins of government, Que arrived on the Plains. His first move was to seek out Rhu whom he found sitting in the Council chamber studying intently a new type of cutting instrument he was devising. Their meeting was both cordial and enthusiastic, and Que listened avidly as Rhu complied with his request to tell him all that had occurred during the years the Chi Yan had been with the Elders.

Que then told Rhu that he intended to remain on the Plains except for a possible trip later to interest other Chi Yans. "The Elders desire that I be given the next vacancy on the Council. One of the Hata Yan patriarchs is soon to pass on, if indeed, he has not already done so," he explained to Rhu. "Nothing could please me more than to help you in every possible way."

Throughout the conversation, Que eyed with interest the two flat pieces of metal with which Rhu was experimenting. Now he referred to them. "May I ask what that is upon which you are working?"

Rhu explained that the women were having great difficulty cutting cloth which the weavers were now supplying in goodly amount. "It seems to me that two knives operating in this manner should make cutting such things much easier. What do you think, Que?"

Before Que could answer, however, Dargh approached hurriedly, stopping short and grinning his pleasure at seeing Que. "Ard Moro of the Hata Yans was just killed by a bull," he announced, then greeted Que with more enthusiasm than was his usual custom.

"He was one of the Hata Yan patriarchs on the Council," Rhu explained to Que. "I suppose he is the one to whom the Elders referred." Turning to Dargh, he said, "Que is to be made our Chi Yan member of the Council, Dargh. Will you suggest this at the meeting? He will replace Ard."

AS THE Council meeting came to order, Hut looked about for Ard, asking Harco concerning him. Hut wanted all his supporters to be present and Ard was among the first group whom Harco had brought.

"Ard was killed by one of his bulls just a short time ago," Dargh explained. "I move that Que, who has just arrived from the Elders, be made our Chi Yan member."

"I second the motion," boomed Ord.

"But he is not to remain here," Hut objected uneasily.

"Yes, he has returned to stay," Rhu asserted. "The Elders asked that this be done. All in favor hold up their hands."

So quickly was it done that even Harco agreed without hesitation, and Que was called in and seated.

Frowning, Hut got to his feet. He suddenly realized that if he were going to make his carefully planned move, he must do so at once. He dreaded what Rhu might say or do, but after all, did not he, Hut, still have the majority of the Council on his side? And if the Elders were going to begin suggesting new members, he must move fast. He threw a swift glance at Rhu who was smiling his welcome to Que and did not observe it. Hut drew a long breath.

"Fellow Councilmen," he began, "I have a most important plan to suggest this morning. It is one I have long considered, so please pay close attention to what I have to say as it concerns us all."

Chapter Thirty-three

THE FLIGHT OF HUT

THERE WAS a general stirring among the Council members, then they leaned forward, intent upon missing no word of what Hut was saying. Rhu's eyes narrowed, and instantly, both Dargh and Ord were on their guard.

"As we all know, our bodies are made up of several parts," Hut began. "Every time we walk, shoot an arrow, eat, or do anything, our body works as a unit. It works as one. Why? Because our head directs the various parts so they work that way. Suppose each part of our body had a head of its own. If one of our legs wanted to go east and the other west, we would never get anywhere. They must work together, and to do this properly, there must be a single, definite control, such as our head.

"In our head we make plans. When we are ready to carry out one of those plans, our head causes each part of our body to work with all the others. Suppose we had two heads. One might decide to go east and the other one west, just as I said about our feet, and we would never get anywhere.

"All of you know that no two people think alike. Each one has a head of his own. If each of us followed his own desires about considering what is best for all of us, we would be like a body with one eye looking up and the other down; one arm might reach forward and the other backward, just as one foot might start east and the other west. But our head causes them all to work together for a common purpose. Imagine your mouth being hungry, but your hands, wanting to do something else, refusing to put food into your mouth!"

Here several of the members chuckled as this ludicrous picture took form in their minds. Thus encouraged, Hut smiled into their not unfriendly faces and resumed the thread of his discourse.

"Dimly, we have all known these things, for each family has a single head or patriarch who directs all members of his family to work together for their common good. He is the leader of his family, and in times past, if any member refused to do his bidding, he was either forced to do so or was sent away from the family circle.

"We all know that no family can prosper with a divided rulership. Each has to have a head with final authority to direct the family. Even the Elders tell us that we must work together for a single purpose or we cannot hope to prosper. In other words, our many families here on the plains are like the many members of a single family. Therefore, we should have a single head to make plans for us and direct our work so that we shall all work together to accomplish our common purpose. Isn't that right?"

Several shaggy heads nodded as they slowly comprehended Hut's logic. Que, however, was quick to see the flaw in Hut's reasoning.

"What about the Ku and Dan families?" he asked softly. "Did they have a single head, and if so, who was he?"

Hut had thought of this when thinking through what he would say, but like many another ambitious man, had discounted the discernment of his listeners, depending upon the flow of his words and the basic logic of much of what he would say to keep them too busy to think of this weak spot in his argument. Rhu was the only one on the Council he really respected or feared, and he felt sure Rhu would not let him down or ask awkward questions. He never did. Of course, he had not known that Que was to be present, but even so, he thought he could handle the situation.

"My father and Sol Ku were exceptional men," he declared. "They invariably worked together. Whatever one wanted to do, the other always agreed. Each governed his own sept as he chose, but when it came to anything affecting their common interests, they always worked as one." Hut believed this answer should satisfy Que.

He underestimated the shrewd Chi Yan, however, for Que was quick to ask, "Then what is the purpose of all this talk? You and Rhu are their sons. Do you not always work together?"

Ord grinned at Dargh, but Dargh's eyes were frosty.

"That is just the trouble," objected Hut. "With our fathers, each ruled his own family, but their other interests were in common. In a general way, Rhu's and mine are too, but . . . ." He hesitated, hunting exactly the right words and inwardly regretting his failure to have cultivated Que more assiduously, "here, our work is very unlike that of the two families. True, I handle certain portions of the work while Rhu conducts the industries and the army. Our main point of contact is the Marts which I handle, but I am compelled to handle through them many things I think should be marketed otherwise, if at all."

"For instance?" Que persisted.

"W-el-l, I do not think copper knives should be handled by the Marts because they can be used in fights." Hut heaved a sigh of relief at being able to answer Que specifically.

"How many fights with knives have you had here on the Plains?" Que asked.

"Not one!" Ord boomed, unable to keep silent any longer without exploding from pent-up emotion. Only too well did the mighty Mu Yan know what Hut was leading up to.

Nettled beyond control by the unforeseen turn things were taking, Hut plunged into his main topic. "It is not alone that, but Rhu has refused to accede to my wishes here in the Council, influencing the members against me and leading them adroitly into moves which are against my desires and what I know to be best for all."

Dargh was on his feet, eyes blazing. "That is not true. I have been present at every Council meeting since it was organized, and never once has Rhu gone contrary to Hut's wishes, except the time when, without authority of the Council, he attempted to exclude Ord and me from the Council. Hut tried to excuse himself by claiming that he merely wanted us to leave for the remainder of that meeting because Ord and I refused to agree with him. Rhu only defended us.

"On the other hand, Hut has made repeated attempts to do exactly what he is trying to do today—to assume complete control of what is being done here on the Plains. He is next going to say that he is a better planner than Rhu. He is *not* and never will be. Every older member of the Council knows this!" Dargh sat down, seemingly as astonished at his sudden fluency as were both Rhu and Hut.

His face scarlet with the rage he could no longer restrain, Hut turned to Que. "There! You can see for yourself the sort of problems which face me every time I want to make a suggestion. Dargh," he said sharply, now turning to the lowering Muson, "this time, you have gone too far. Council or no Council, Rhu or no Rhu, as the undisputed ruler of this group, I order you and Ord off the Council and do not return at any time!"

For a brief moment, only the dead silence bespoke the amazement of those who heard him. Then Que was on his feet, and for once, Rhu saw him jarred out of his habitual calm.

"Hut Mai Dan, by your own words you have proved yourself unworthy of any trust or respect as a proposed leader of men!" he declared sternly. "I move that Hut be dismissed from the Council for unwarranted and unlawful assumption of power not vested in him by either the Council or the Elders."

"I second the motion!" Ord, Dargh, and Yaug shouted in unison.

"Before I put this momentous question to a vote, have I the permission of the Council to speak?" asked Rhu.

"Rhu speak," the Council roared as one.

"I regret beyond words the necessity for this vote and the conditions which have led to it. I cannot believe that Hut meant all he has said, but having said it, it cannot be withdrawn unless he is willing to ask the pardon of the Council and its permission to withdraw his words which were spoken in anger. Hut, do you desire to withdraw all you have said?"

His face white with anger, Hut stubbornly refused. "Not alone do I refuse to withdraw what I have said, but as befits my position as the originator of this plan and the one who has brought it to its present state, I instruct the Council to cast aside Que's motion by a unanimous vote. Then I move that all who are unwilling to accept my clear right to my position be voted off the Council. Any who refuse to vote against Que's motion shall be considered as the ones to be voted off."

Very quietly, Rhu ordered the vote upon Que's motion, and only Harco voted "No."

"Because Hut's motion has not been seconded as well as because I question the legality of asking for a vote on a motion from one thus discharged from its membership by the Council, I now ask Harco if he desires to repeat the motion made by Hut."

Harco, tears streaming down his face and head bowed, simply arose from his seat and left the Council chamber rather than stay to witness Hut's further abasement.

Rhu then again addressed the Council.

"It is now almost twenty Great Suns, twenty years, as the Elders call them," he began, "since Hut and I led the first of you people to the Plains and established the beginning of what you now see about you. As our fathers before us, together we planned and together we worked without thought or desire for anything but the success of this Great Work. Then came a temptation beyond Hut's strength to resist, and the desire to be your leader became the ambition of his life—one for which I had hoped he would qualify. I have no desire to rule, and at our very first Council meeting, I asked that he be made Chief of this Council which amounts to almost the same thing as being your leader."

Here Rhu paused and, stepping to the side of the now stunned and drooping Hut, laid his hand gently upon his shaking shoulder. He then continued. "To all of us, the unreasoning effects of an aroused temper are only too well known. None of us can say what we would have done in Hut's place for the stress was great. Even Dargh was swayed by anger, largely, I fear, through his loving loyalty to me and in the belief that he was fighting for my sake. He did only what I probably would have done under like circumstances, and by his act has fully discharged any small debt of gratitude he may feel he owes me."

Rhu stopped and drew a long breath, then made his concluding statement. "My friends of the Council, I move that our vote regarding Hut be rescinded and forgotten and that by so doing, he be reinstated as he was." He sat down, and there followed a silence so complete that the buzzing of a fly was plainly audible.

Then Que spoke. "You have all heard Rhu's motion," he announced. "Does anyone second it?"

Slowly and very deliberately the only Upa Yan member of the Council and one who had been exceptionally friendly to Hut, one Yort Pauto, hairy, grizzled, and uncouth, but of stately bearing, rose to his feet. "Yort listen close," he said gravely. "Yort like Hut. Hut good to Yort. Yort not know Rhu well, but Yort admire Rhu. Rhu make noble talk for Hut. Yort would do what Rhu ask, but Yort think Hut wrong. Yort move Rhu be made ruler."

Crude in so many respects, childlike in their faith, and slow in thought and speech, a certain rugged courage and independence motivated the laborious thinking of the people at that time. The very nature of their lives in the tribal valleys had developed in them the power to arrive at their own conclusions and make their own decisions. And once a decision was made, it was adhered to with all the tenacity of their sturdy natures.

Hut, who had come to feel he was their superior, did not understand them as did Rhu who was accustomed to meeting them on their own ground, man to man. This difference in attitude they were quick to sense and react to. Also, they loved fair play and undaunted courage, qualities which they had always found in Rhu. From the time when he had fearlessly faced the mighty Gurd—and bluffed him—he was their hero, and no one could have persuaded them to think otherwise.

"We must first act upon Rhu's motion," stated Que quietly. "Does anyone second the motion that our vote be rescinded and that Hut be reinstated?"

Yaug arose and faced Rhu. "Rhu, Yaug speak for Dargh, and Ord, too, Yaug know. Gladly will Yaug die for Rhu, fight for Rhu, do anything for Rhu but what you just ask. Hut my brother. Rhu more than brother, and Hut lose all right to more chance to plot behind Rhu's back!"

"Rhu, I am afraid your motion is lost," commented Que,

smiling blandly. "I hear no seconds. Yort, will you repeat your motion?"

"Yort move Rhu be made *supreme* ruler," the Upa Yan repeated, adding one more word to his original motion so that his meaning be made clear beyond all question.

"Ord second motion!" Ord boomed so loud that the several other seconds were completely drowned out, and Que smiled into his glowing face.

"All in favor hold up their hands," Que then directed, and the usually stoical Chi Yan was hard pressed to restrain a chuckle when every man on the Council raised both hands instead of the customary one.

His face ablaze with embarrassment, Rhu got to his feet. He tried to speak, but his voice choked and the tears streamed down his face.

Almost instantly, the Council broke up with a concerted roar, its members swarming around Rhu without the usual formalities. Only Ord's sharp eyes, shining above the heads of all the others, saw Hut slip away, forgotten and crushed by his utter defeat.

PREY to mixed emotions, Rhu escaped his friends as soon as possible to hasten to the sanctuary and comfort of his home. Overwhelmed at the trust and loyal faith of the Council in appointing him their Chief, still, he was sorely saddened and almost heartbroken that Hut should have been so blinded by his ambition as to act contrary to the teachings and wishes of the Elders.

Already the news had spread from the Council chamber to the farthest reaches of the Plains. Grut had sped to Haitee with the tidings, so that she was radiant as she ran to meet Rhu. But Rhu's mind was filled only with thoughts of Hut.

"Poor Hut," he mourned into her, for once, inattentive ears. "Poor, poor Hut! What under the sun shall I do now? Whom can I possibly get to replace him until I can get him reinstated?"

"Pooh!" Haitee snorted. "Que can do Hut's work much better, and he will not be everlastingly trying to be what he is not. I think Hut got only what was his due!"

"Quiet!" Rhu snapped. Only then did Haitee realize how great this blow was to him, in whose heart love was more than a mere word.

Upon reaching the house, he suddenly exclaimed, "I must find Hut and let him know that I am already making plans." He almost ran across to Hut's home, but all was silent. Already the little place had taken on an air of desertion, and a cold chill shot up Rhu's spine. "Could he . . . . would he . . . . !" The vision of Grut as he stood with the dripping, lifeless body of Marda in his arms came before him, and he fled for the river, at whose edge he met Grut.

"Nord say Hut pass through great stone door with bow and arrows and run up trail," Grut explained. "Grut think go to Cari Yans and Wardu." Grinning boldly, he asked, "Must Grut bow to new ruler?"

Before the raging Rhu could reach him, he fled, his almost boyish laughter echoing through the timber until, in spite of himself, Rhu had to smile. A great load seemed to lift from his heart.

A much more normal Rhu returned to the steaming supper the half tearful Haitee was waiting to serve him. Taking her trembling form into his arms, he gave her such a squeeze as to leave her breathless and tingling. "Let's eat!" he almost shouted, and she flew to set out their evening meal.

"What happened to change your feelings?" Haitee finally ventured, still more than half afraid of him, and when he told her about Grut, she joined in his laughter.

There was no repressing Grut who, a few minutes later, peered in their door and with a wide grin upon his bewhiskered face, thumbed his nose impudently at Rhu, then disappeared into the gloom.

After a restless night, Rhu rose early to seek out Nord and Ord whom he found at the big door discussing Hut's flight from the Plains. Nothing else could describe the manner in which he had sped up the trail, they told him. Ord, like Grut, was positive that Hut had fled to Wardu, except that Ord was adamant in his belief that Hut fully intended to try the use of force to accomplish his purpose.

To this, Rhu would not agree, and hurried back to the Council chamber in the hope of finding Que there. Not finding him, he hastened to Dargh's workshop, and there found them both in deep conference, their welcoming smiles showing how glad they were to see him.

Hurriedly, Rhu told of Hut's flight after the Council meeting, and of Ord's stubborn insistence that he was planning the use of force against them.

"There is no telling to what ends a desperate man will go," Que mused, much to Rhu's amazement. "Hut cannot help realizing that by his unwarranted actions of yesterday, he has tossed away his life's greatest opportunity. That is sufficient to inspire him to the most desperate of actions.

"Personally, I do not believe he will be any too well received by Wardu. Not that Wardu will do anything to hurt Hut, but when I talked with him before I left to be with the Elders, I had the feeling that he would prove undependable in times of stress. From what Dargh has told me, Hut tried to get Wardu to do as Harco has done and bring in a goodly number of Cari Yans who would be loyal to both him and Hut, thus forming a nucleus with which to further his ambition to rule.

"It is very sad that Hut, who is a remarkable man in many ways, should allow his personal ambition and lust for power to defeat the very ends for which he seeks. The words of the Elders before I left caused me to feel that something of this nature was about to occur. They have given him every opportunity, and he now has only himself to blame, although he will probably feel otherwise.

"That the Elders have done nothing beyond suggesting my return to help you if need be shows plainly the entire confidence which they repose in you and in your ability to meet just such a situation as obtained yesterday. Your efforts to save Hut were admirable and noble, Rhu, and no matter how great my esteem before, it is even greater today. Proud must the Elders be at your able defense of one who, in the final analysis, sought to repress and belittle you. Well have you learned the many lessons they have sought to give you both, and nobly have you repaid them for their trouble.

"It is my privilege and pleasure to be able to tell you that you have justified to the fullest extent their confidence in you.

Also, I, too, feel as does the Council, that you have well earned the great distinction bestowed upon you, and you may count upon my most earnest and sincere cooperation at any and all times."

Rhu was a rather shy and diffident fellow where he personally was concerned and if anything, too much inclined to minimize his own accomplishments. This was a rather rare trait in an age when too many were prone to accept another upon the basis of his claims to great deeds. Only of his skill in archery was Rhu inclined to pride, and this was amply justified by his ability. Therefore, all this commendation from Que's lips made him feel awkward and uncomfortable, and though he wanted to stop him, the Chi Yan's compelling eyes deterred him. His face flushed to what Grut would have said was the color of "fresh bird blood."

As Que finished, Dargh smiled warmly at Rhu. "Grut was here a short while ago and dared me to call you 'Your Bigness.' He seemed so happy about something that I am wondering just what he had in mind."

To the great amusement of both Dargh and Que, Rhu repeated the tale of Grut's actions the evening before. "I'll have to teach him a lesson," he growled, but his dancing eyes belied his tone.

"Grut impresses me as well able to take good care of himself," declared Que. "In fact, I would not want to be the man who sought to bring hurt to you with Grut around."

"Tell His Bigness Ord has word of Hut," came Grut's voice from behind a clump of bushes back of Rhu. But quick as he was, Rhu was not able to catch sight of the fleeing and happy Grut.

"Let no man seek to do as Grut does," growled Dargh.

"Grut is like Nord and Ord in his assurance that Hut has fled to the Cari Yans," Que stated. "I only hope that the repercussions of Hut's unfaithfulness to the Elders in his attempt to take for himself powers they have never granted him do not overtake him on his trip. I would see him come to no serious harm," he concluded.

A sense of dire premonition settled upon Rhu.

"Dargh, will you send word to Haitee that I shall be gone

for a few days?" he said quickly. "I am going to trail Hut. I have the feeling that he is about to encounter impossible odds. Que, will you take my place until my return?"

"Indeed, I shall try to do so," Que assured him, "but do not run unnecessary risks. You must not forget that from this day on, your life and well-being belong to all of us and not to yourself alone. If you are going, why not take several Forest Dwellers with you? The Cari Yans are known for their ill-treatment of strangers."

"No," Rhu replied as he hurried along with Que at his side. "I would ask no man to take such risks. Besides, one man may slip through where several would surely be detected and trapped. I shall use every care and take with me two extra quivers of arrows. Here comes Dargh," he remarked as his keen ears caught the soft padding of Dargh's bare feet in the dust.

"With your alert ears," Que remarked, smiling, "it will be a clever man who is able to slip up on you undetected." His confidence in the successful outcome of Rhu's venture was rapidly rising. Dimly he recalled some of the feats of daring he had heard attributed to Rhu, but Rhu was now in his early forties, while he had been but a lad when those other adventures had occurred.

Glancing quickly at Que, Rhu observed that his expression had suddenly become very complacent. "What idea have you in mind, Que?" he asked. "You look as innocent as a newly born lamb, so I know you are up to something."

"It was but a passing thought," Que said, avoiding a direct answer, his face even more expressionless than usual, and Rhu chuckled. What had been but a surmise before was now an absolute certainty in Rhu's mind, but he did not press the question. Had he done so, he might well have been spared many anxious moments within the ensuing twenty-four hours, for he was to be forever thankful for that idea crystallizing in the mind of his friend.

Chapter Thirty-four

THE FINAL ATONEMENT

DISAPPOINTMENT, chagrin, rage, and a tumultuous desire for revenge tore at Hut's heartstrings as he fled up the pass from the Plains. His first impulse was to ascribe his discomfiture to Rhu, but as his first wild anger subsided, he had to admit that Rhu was blameless. Unable to fasten the blame upon any single individual, a keen desire to wreak vengeance upon everybody concerned overwhelmed him. After a bit, he ceased to run and began plodding ahead. His temper cooled and he started to think.

His first thought upon fleeing had been to escape his humiliation. Now he began to realize how utterly fruitless such an attempt was . . . . he was but adding to his trouble. Too late, he recalled that the Elders always had said one cannot run away from his problems. They invariably accompany one and, sooner or later, manifest in some even more serious form. He could readily see that if he should turn back now, he would face not only the original humiliation of his defeat, but the pity and perhaps scorn with which the others might regard his running away.

Still, he was not swayed from his objective. He was determined that he should become sole leader on the Rhu Hut Plains. He must think of something to save his self-respect and reinstate his claims to the right to rule. Bitterness overcame him at the thought of the injustice done him in misunderstanding his motives, and with it came self-pity. Everyone was against him. Even Harco had deserted him.

With the thought of Harco came the recollection of Wardu

from whom nothing had been heard since his departure from the Plains. Like the proverbial drowning man, Hut clutched at this straw. Perhaps, with Wardu's cooperation, he would be able to work out some satisfactory plan. If he could do nothing more than take Wardu and a goodly group of Cari Yans to the Elders for training, he could easily claim that this was his sole purpose in leaving at this time. The more he thought about it, the more feasible the plan appeared. So distracted was Hut that he forgot the Elders' greatest problem at this time was not in securing more aspirants, but in caring for the great and steadily increasing numbers of them they already had!

By now, he had reached the point where the trail to the Mu Valley branched off, so he sat down upon a stone to think over this new idea. If he could secure the support of the Elders, he knew his cause was not lost. But that was the fly in the ointment. Could he persuade them to his view of the situation? Could he get them to see it was *his* plan that he and Rhu should bring the Mu Yans on to the Plains in the first place? Of course, this was not altogether true, because he knew Rhu had had a part in it, but as Marda had said, the original idea was his. And Rhu—good old Rhu—would never dispute this. He could always be depended upon to back him up. The thought heartened him.

The more he pondered the situation, the surer he became that the best way to convince the Elders of his sincerity was to show his anxiety to help in the building of the civilization. The best way of accomplishing this, he reasoned, would be by taking in a goodly number of Cari Yans for training. By doing this, they would be sure to consider his cause favorably.

Evening was approaching, so Hut hurried toward the Cari Valley although he realized he would not find Wardu until some time the following day. Fortunately for him, the Wardu family, like the Kus and Dans, occupied the end of their valley nearest to the Plains, making it more readily possible for Hut to find Wardu. The exact location of the family huts he did not know, of course, and he must approach cautiously in order to escape detection by any wandering Cari Yans, who were prone to kill first and ask questions later.

Near noon the next day, he discovered the family huts, and

with all the craft at his command, managed to get within easy
bowshot of the place. He considered it a good omen that the
very first person he should see was Wardu who was sitting
watching a band of sheep. Hut hailed him and hurried forward.

At Hut's shout, Wardu reached for his bow, which, even at
that distance, Hut recognized as either the one given the Cari
Yan by Rhu, or one exactly like it. It was already strung and
an arrow notched as Wardu wheeled to face the stranger.
Recognizing Hut, he lowered his weapon and smiled, although
reservedly.

"I thought I knew that voice," he announced, but made no
move to come forward to greet Hut.

Hut observed these signs with some misgivings. "It has been
so long since we have had word from you," he declared as he
neared Wardu. "Thought I would come over to see you and
find how you are making out."

Wardu shifted uneasily. "When Wardu leave Plains, Wardu
begin see he taking sides between Hut and Rhu. Wardu not
want be in such position. Wardu take no sides. Wardu interested only in seeing plan successful," he stated. "Now, Wardu
lose interest. Do well here. Peaceful and quiet. No taking sides.
Wardu decide wait till Rhu and Hut agree. Hut come eat with
Wardu?" he invited, his entire demeanor showing the relief he
felt at having thus settled the matter. He had always liked Hut
personally, and now he could be more natural.

All that afternoon and well into the evening, Hut strove to
reawaken Wardu's earlier enthusiasm by telling him of all that
had taken place on the Plains since his departure, but Wardu
remained indifferent. Rather discouraged at the outlook, Hut
accepted his invitation to stay there for the night, but hardly
had he fallen asleep when he was awakened by excited voices,
one of which was Wardu's. Grasping his bow and arrows and
making sure his copper knife was in its sheath and handy, Hut
arose and rejoined Wardu who was talking excitedly with several men whom Hut guessed were his brothers.

Seeing him, the newcomers scowled until Wardu introduced
him, and although they then accepted him, Hut observed that
they cast many a suspicious glance in his direction.

"What is wrong?" he asked Wardu.

Wardu hesitated as if trying to find the proper words to make his meaning clear. At last he spoke. "Odd this happen after all these years, and just when you here, Hut. Clan of one of Thedo's sons with three others want pass through Wardu's land to attack Plains. Many men. Want Wardu agree. Wardu not let pass through valley, but must let pass through hills. Wardu not help, but not fight them. Wardu sorry."

Hut stared at him, apprehension tugging at his heart. His thoughts flew back to the peaceful life on the Plains. Nothing must interfere with that. "What about your father?" he asked excitedly.

"Wardu now head of clan. Father dead five Great Suns."

"Won't you send a swift runner to warn my people?" Hut cried.

"No. Wardu not help either side. Hut hurry, Hut maybe reach Plains first. Force pass through narrow place in hills west of here. Wardu show Hut way."

Hurriedly, Hut secured the extra quiver of arrows he had brought with him, and accompanied by Wardu, headed for the pass. Completely forgotten were resentment and desire for revenge. Forgotten, also, was the fact that his people were far better prepared to resist attack than when what must have been a still larger force under the leadership of Marda's father had been defeated. All he could think of was to reach home in time to warn Ord and Rhu of the approaching danger. He hurried the panting Wardu in his desperation. If only Rhu were here! Rhu, he was sure, would be able to devise some means for delaying this attack until he could get word to Ord.

"There is entrance to pass," Wardu gasped. "Wardu go no farther. Hut hurry may beat them into pass," and he turned back to his own clan.

Just inside the pass, an arrow whizzed past Hut's ear, and he flung himself into the shelter of some boulders. The bright moonlight revealed that for more than a hundred yards, the narrow gorge ran perfectly straight with no cover. Since the enemy were already so close, Hut knew he would not be likely to reach the turn before he was overtaken.

Well, if he could not get through in time to escape, he could at least delay them, though what good this would do, he was not sure. Hastily, he emptied one of his quivers so his arrows would be ready for instant use, and notching an arrow, peered back toward the entrance of the pass. As he launched his first shaft at the approaching men, he inwardly thanked Rhu for the many hours of patient coaching in the use of his bow. A second later, the screech of his stricken target reached him just as he shot again, while arrows of all sorts began to drop around him.

AS HE sped along the trail, Rhu wrapped his two extra quivers of arrows so they could not spill, then thrust them inside his hoogwarskin clothing. Just as he had reached the stone door, Dargh had overtaken him and thrust into his hand a beautifully made, wide-bladed copper war axe, and Rhu now fastened its rawhide thong around his wrist. Not that he felt its use would be necessary, but one never knew what he might encounter on these trails ouside the Plains.

Despite all he had been told, even yet Rhu placed no confidence in the idea that Hut would try to enlist help to attack their own people. He knew Hut too well for that. Angry he unquestionably was, and bitter over the defeat of his plans, but there was no treachery in Hut.

Even as Rhu ran, his keen eyes picked up Hut's trail, the imprints of his feet still clear in the dust. Then he reached the rock where Hut had sat to think things over, after which he saw where Hut had gone ahead toward the Cari Valley. Unlike Hut, however, Rhu did not once slacken his pace with the result that he covered the same distance in less than half the time consumed by Hut whose progress had been somewhat leisurely.

Then, just as the light dimmed, Rhu discovered where the trail branched, the one to the right leading along the base of the mountains, while Hut had taken the left branch. Rhu's first impulse was to follow Hut, but, taking advantage of one of the many lessons he had learned from Dargh, he climbed to a high pinnacle of rock in order to get a good view of the surrounding country. His sharp eyes told the trail-wise Rhu that by following the path to the right, he could shorten appreciably the distance between him and the Wardu clan which he knew occupied the end of the valley nearest him.

Scrambling down, he headed into what quickly became a narrow gorge, but this he expected, having observed it from his lofty perch, as well as the fact that there were no side canyons to confuse him. The almost full moon was now above the horizon, enabling him to make nearly as good time as during the day, and he sped along.

He had covered perhaps half a mile when the faint screech of the first man killed by Hut's arrow reached his keen ears, and for a moment, he hesitated. Something was wrong along this trail, and he was half tempted to turn back, but some force seemed to impel him to continue.

"It is a fight," he growled, hearing more screeches. He paused long enough to untie the axe from his wrist so that his arms were unimpeded, swinging it behind him by the simple expedient of thrusting its handle through his belt. At the same time, he made sure his long-bladed knife was safe and free, then strung his bow and extracted an arrow from his quiver.

By now, the screeches were increasing in volume. Then he heard Hut's war cry. Trotting around a corner in the gorge, he saw the clear hundred yards of open trail and Hut as he crouched behind some boulders, speeding arrow after arrow in the other direction. The keen-bladed, copper-headed arrows were taking a deadly toll, every shot bringing screeches from stricken men.

About to give vent to an encouraging shout to Hut, the cry died on Rhu's lips, for Hut, an arrow transfixing his chest, staggered back and dropped to the ground, even as he struggled to withdraw the shaft. Heedless of the arrows now dropping all about him, Rhu dashed ahead along the trail, his only thought to reach his wounded friend.

Then he was at Hut's side, and his own arrows began to take an even more deadly toll from the approaching mass of howling Cari Yans, until, unable to face this deadly and withering hail, they stopped and sought cover. His first quiver of arrows exhausted, Rhu tore open the other two, dumping the contents of one upon the few left by Hut, and methodically picked off every man in sight.

Then he turned to Hut. Drawing forth the arrow Hut's weakening hands could not extract, Rhu choked as he saw the blood spurting from the hole in his friend's chest and come in a bubbling froth from his white lips. "Hut! Hut! Oh, Hut!" he moaned.

Hut's slowly glazing eyes brightened. "Rhu," he gasped. "Rhu! I knew, somehow, you would come. The Cari Yans are going to attack us. Wardu is not—not with—not with . . . ." He coughed up a crimson froth, and went limp.

No need to tell the experienced Rhu that Hut was beyond all help. He had known it the moment he saw where the arrow had penetrated Hut's chest. Dashing the streaming tears from his face, he turned to the business in hand. He determined grimly that, once and for all, he would teach these Cari Yans how a Mu Yan can fight, and his glistening arrows again started searching out every man who showed so much as an inch of his body. Unlike in the old times, the arrows were now barbed, and once having entered a body, could be withdrawn only by breaking the shaft or pulling it on through.

An arrow grazed Rhu's head, staggering him momentarily. Another tore at his leg, although not crippling him. If only they used no poisoned ones! Hastily, Rhu dumped the arrows from his last quiver beside the fast diminishing ones still remaining from his and Hut's supply. Minutes passed during which not a single Cari Yan had shown even a hair. Aside from the moans of the wounded who lay where they had fallen, there was no sound from them. Rhu waited uneasily. Hut was now dead, but even had he not been so, there was nothing he could have done beyond telling him he was forgiven, but Rhu had the feeling that Hut already knew this.

His bow twanged as a Cari Yan, intent upon dragging a wounded comrade under cover, exposed himself. He died with Rhu's arrow through his brain.

Rhu could not know that in the rocks across the trail, another daring Cari Yan was silently edging himself into a position where he could reach Rhu with his arrow. At last, slowly, lest his movement catch Rhu's alert eye, this man raised himself, drew his bow into position, arrow notched, and prepared to launch the deadly shaft.

The Death of Hut

Meanwhile, Rhu cautiously drew forth his war axe and laid it handy to his hand, placing the long and razor sharp knife beside it. Only too well did he know what the long silence portended. They were trying to sneak up on him and surround him. Then it would be man to man, and Rhu was determined to sell his life dearly.

He knew there could be but one end to this unequal fight, but he smiled grimly as he thought of the terrible cost of their victory. At least thirty bodies lay in sight even now, and he knew many more were hidden among the rocks, either dead or seriously wounded. It had been a good fight. These people would think long and seriously before they again summoned up sufficient courage to attack a Mu Yan. (Despite the other tribes joining them, to Rhu, the Plains were a Mu Yan commonwealth.)

As the Cari Yan in the rocks across the trail drew his arrow to its head preparatory to launching it, a shadowy and towering figure rose silently behind him. Ere he could loose his bolt, Ord's wide axe flashed as it described an arc, shearing both head and arm from the archer whose shaft rattled harmlessly on the rocks near Rhu.

Wheeling, Rhu's deadly bow swung toward Ord, only to drop quickly as he recognized his friend. With a sob of relief, he sank to the ground, suddenly weak from loss of blood. He was only faintly aware of Mu Yan war cries as forty of Ord's best men swung into action and began to slay.

The rout of the Cari Yans was utter and complete, and for many, many years the stories told by the survivors held their audiences spellbound. Not one of the men of Ord was killed, and while all bore wounds, none was seriously injured.

Ord had only one thought in mind—to reach Rhu. He greatly feared he had struck too late to save the one person in all the world who meant more to him than life itself. Tenderly, he gathered the almost unconscious Rhu into his mighty arms, his experienced hands traveling swiftly over his bloody body until, with inexpressible relief, he knew this was not the end and that Rhu was safe.

His men, who had definite orders not to pursue the fleeing enemy very far lest they fall into some trap or encounter fresh reserves of which they knew nothing, began to return. By now Rhu was able to explain as much as he knew. Sorrowfully, one of the big men gathered up Hut's body, wrapped it in a skin, and with it over his shoulder, started back to the Plains. Ord followed carrying Rhu as if he were a child.

Before the other Mu Yans left the scene of the battle, they garnered all the undamaged arrows and counted the slain. Rhu and Hut had accounted for forty-eight, while the men of Ord had killed at least fifty more. They could not be sure of this as they did not want to take the time to search carefully, but Wardu later told Rhu that of three hundred in the attacking body, only a hundred and seventy-five finally made their way home. No doubt, many of the missing ones were only wounded, but, abandoned by their fleeing companions, they probably perished from their wounds or under the ravening jaws and tearing claws of wild beasts.

"How did you come to get there?" Rhu asked weakly as Ord carried him along.

"Que told us to follow you but not to let you know of our presence unless necessary. Huh! I had already picked out my men and we were just ready to leave when Que came to me." Here the big fellow chuckled. "Que said his chief fear was that he would reach me too late and that I would be gone despite your orders. He just wanted us to be sure you did not know we were following."

As they neared the entrance to the Plains, Rhu would have walked, but found himself too weak to stand, so Ord, who had carried him all the way, again picked him up. It was thus that the streaming thousands of citizens saw them emerge from the building, and a mighty cry went up. Never could Rhu remember anything even approaching such a demonstration as then ensued. He may well have felt his inadequacy as a leader, but it was clear that of all upon the Plains, he was the only one entertaining any such idea.

The care with which he was treated by Que and Haitee was all the most modern man could possibly desire so that the following day, he was sufficiently recovered to conduct Hut's funeral and place his ashes beside those of his child and Marda.

Within a week, Rhu was able to be around, and then it was that the Elders arrived in a body, accompanied by Lords Lithargos and Hiroto. Formally, he was made the leader with Their full sanction.

For Hut, no word of blame was ever uttered. His thirst for power and ambition to rule were far more than offset by the many great services he had rendered his people. Only his many good qualities were ever mentioned by the citizenry, and the last painful episode in his life was referred to only as the trip he made to enlist the Cari Yans.

THUS it was that civilization originated.

EPILOGUE

THE STORY you have just read is true. It chronicles pre-historic times — 78,000 years ago — when an ignorant and primitive people took the beginning steps toward building what was to result in the first and most magnificent civilization ever to come into being on this planet Earth. Because they had complete faith in the Lords of Venus and Mercury — those Divine Beings who wisely guided them — and because they adhered to the natural laws governing human conduct, these simple folk succeeded in building a life far superior to the insecure discontented existence we lead today.

By complying with the instruction given them, these once rugged individualists came to reap the benefits of cooperative living. They no longer lived from day to day— merely eating, sleeping, mating, and quarreling among themselves. Their efforts were now directed toward the greater good of those with whom they were associated. And though, judging by today's material standards, their accomplishments were nothing spectacular, life was very worthwhile for them. Their days were filled with purpose, their activities were meaningful, and their goals embodied vision.

Today, we live in a world far different from that portrayed in THE SUN RISES. Discerning intelligence is no longer a mark of distinction; sophistication is the goal and the symbol of status. Many enjoy comforts, conveniences and pleasures hitherto unknown in recorded history, and certainly beyond the imagination of the early people whose lives are portrayed in this book. And yet, the peace of mind and contentment experienced by those on the Rhu Hut Plains are lacking. Dissatisfied with the established order, young people long to find something that will give purpose to their lives — something that will answer the age-old questions: Who am I? Why am I here? Where am I going? Surely man was not born to lead such an aimless, futile existence as do so many at the present time!

Probably seeing more deeply than any generation before them, thinking youth of today are painfully aware that the future depends upon them. To follow the pattern set by their parents and most other adults holds little promise.

But what to do that a satisfying world may come into being — a world in which people will live more purposeful lives than is true today? To whom does the younger generation look for intelligent guidance? Where does it turn for an understanding of what human conduct should be, or for a plan helpful to them and others in facing life and building such secure and satisfying conditions as they believe should exist?

The information found in the book, THE SUN RISES, was released for a purpose other than entertainment. Through its reading, one comes to know there *is* a plan, and that guidance *is* provided those who will avail themselves of it. Just as the Lords of Venus and Mercury helped the people on the Continent of Mu to build a new and better way of life, so do other Great Beings stand ready to help us today.

They do this by releasing instruction helpful to those who would dedicate themselves to building a new world order based upon natural laws and helpful in the improvement of one's personal life and affairs. Studying this information, one also finds that all human beings are here to work toward fulfilling a very definite and all-encompassing purpose — a purpose that transcends purely material gain — a purpose that makes life decidedly worthwhile.

Those who would like to learn more about this great and wonderful program are invited to send for the 34-page booklet, INTO THE SUN. It is free upon request.

Write:

Lemurian Fellowship
P O Box 397
Ramona, CA 92065
U S A

UIGHUR
(ASIA)

CHI

THIBI

Mud Flats

Padapa

NEW GUINEA

UPA

AUSTRALIA

LEVI

Tasmania

New Zealand

Marsh
Forests
Mountains
Present Islands
And
Continents

CONTINE